ITALIAN AND SPANISH PAINTINGS
IN THE
NATIONAL GALLERY OF SCOTLAND

RAPHAEL
The Bridgewater Madonna [Loan]
after cleaning

Italian and Spanish Paintings
in the
National Gallery of Scotland

CATALOGUED BY HUGH BRIGSTOCKE

SECOND EDITION

THE TRUSTEES OF THE NATIONAL GALLERIES OF SCOTLAND

EDINBURGH 1993

© The Trustees of the National Galleries of Scotland, 1993
Published by the Trustees of the National Galleries of Scotland

Designed by Cinamon and Kitzinger, London
Typeset by Koinonia Ltd, Bury, Lancashire
Printed by BAS Printers Ltd, Over Wallop, Hampshire

Cover illustrations –
front: *The Three Ages of Man* (detail) by Titian;
back: *An Old Woman Cooking Eggs* (detail) by Velázquez

CONTENTS

FOREWORD

When the first edition of Hugh Brigstocke's catalogue of Italian and Spanish paintings in the collection was published in 1978 it was the stated intention of the Board of Trustees that this should be the first of a series of detailed critical catalogues of European works in the National Gallery. For various reasons further volumes have not yet appeared, though work on the French catalogue is in progress. We are therefore especially grateful, in the meantime, to Dr Brigstocke who left the Gallery in 1983 and is now at Sotheby's, London, for having undertaken this revision of his original text. This second edition substantially retains the format of its predecessor with the welcome addition that all catalogued works are illustrated. The author's Introduction has been revised where necessary in order to bring it up to date. Sculpture has been excluded and will be included in a separate volume.

We continue to be deeply grateful to the Duke of Sutherland for allowing us to include detailed catalogue entries on the pictures that have been on loan to the Gallery from his collection since 1946. In particular, we thank him for the kind agreement of the Ellesmere Trustees to the cleaning of the three Raphaels. This work has been expertly carried out by John Dick, Keeper of Conservation. The Sutherland pictures, and a picture from the National Gallery, London, are the only loan works included in this catalogue. A note on the history of the Bridgewater House collection is given on page 11.

MICHAEL CLARKE   TIMOTHY CLIFFORD
Keeper   *Director*

INTRODUCTION

The first complete catalogue of the Gallery's collection was written by W. B. Johnstone R. S. A., the first curator, and was published in 1859. Fifty-one editions were issued; the last revised edition, which appeared in 1957, has been unavailable since 1968. In 1970 the Gallery published a new *Shorter Catalogue* with a complete list of the collection and concise details of 356 principal works and works on extended loan; a revised edition appeared in 1978. For the history of the Gallery and the formation of its collections, reference should be made to the Gallery's publication: *Pictures for Scotland. The National Gallery of Scotland and its collection: a study of the changing attitude to painting since the 1820s*, Edinburgh 1972.

Most entries in the present catalogue have been revised. The condition of the pictures has been carefully examined, in close consultation with the Gallery's Keeper of Conservation, John Dick. Our condition notes are based on close visual inspection, assisted in some cases by X-ray and infra-red photographs, but without the assistance of other scientific aids or technical analysis, except when otherwise stated. I am deeply indebted to John Dick, not only for the patient manner in which he collaborated on this task, but also for opening my eyes to many problems which I might otherwise have overlooked.

My research on the Italian and Spanish pictures in the collection began in 1968. The detailed preparation of the first edition of this catalogue began in 1973 and was finished in June 1977; revision of the second edition was completed in 1992. In compiling the entries, I have, of course, relied extensively on the work of those who investigated the pictures before me, particularly the late Sir Ellis Waterhouse, Director of the Gallery from 1949–52, and Colin Thompson, Keeper 1967–77 and Director 1977–84. Sir Ellis began the serious study of the pre-nineteenth-century pictures in the collection, and was responsible for most of the new material published in the 1957 *Catalogue*. Colin Thompson initiated the X-ray photography of many of the most important pictures, and I owe him a particular debt for teaching me how to make the best possible use of this material. I must also acknowledge the assistance of my colleague, the late Keith Andrews, former Keeper of the Department of Prints and Drawings, who, with characteristic generosity, was always willing to discuss any art historical problem as soon as it arose, and who guided me at many difficult moments. The late Giles Robertson, a former Trustee of the Gallery, kindly agreed to read the final draft of my manuscript for the first edition and made a number of stimulating comments, especially on the entries for the Venetian pictures.

For the revised, second edition I am grateful for the collaboration of Michael Clarke, present Keeper of the National Gallery of Scotland who, with his colleague Aidan Weston-Lewis, has spent a considerable amount of time checking proofs and references, and to Hugh Macandrew, former Keeper of Prints and Drawings. The revised draft of this text was typed by Sheila Scott with her customary thoroughness and good humour, and the catalogue has been designed by Gerald Cinamon.

HUGH BRIGSTOCKE 1992

THE BEGINNINGS OF THE PERMANENT COLLECTION

The Royal Institution, Edinburgh, began in 1819 as the Institution for the Encouragement of the Fine Arts in Scotland. By 1827, or before, they were buying pictures from living Scottish artists. In 1830/1, using an accumulation of funds recently released for the purpose, they bought 38 'ancient pictures' in Italy, and these formed the nucleus of their collection of old paintings. At much the same time the Royal Scottish Academy, founded in 1826, began a collection of British art with its purchase of some large paintings by Etty in 1829/31. With the notable exception of Bassano's *Adoration of the Kings*, they bought virtually no old masters. These two collections, enriched by gifts from private individuals, which included Tiepolo's *Finding of Moses*, formed the permanent exhibition when the present gallery was opened in 1859, together with the collection of Sir James Erskine of Torrie (1772-1825), which was deposited on loan by Edinburgh University in 1845.

THE DUKE OF SUTHERLAND LOAN

Most of the twenty-six pictures on loan from the Bridgewater House collection were acquired by the 3rd Duke of Bridgewater (1736–1803). Sixteen of them came from the collection of the Duc d'Orléans, and three of these had belonged to Queen Christina of Sweden (sold by her heir in 1692 to Prince Livio Odescalchi, and by his heir in 1721 to the Duc d'Orléans). In 1791 Louis Philippe Joseph, Duc d'Orléans (Philippe Egalité), sold his Italian and French pictures to Viscount Walchiers of Brussels. They were bought from him by François de Laborde de Méréville, who hoped to save them for the French nation but was forced to send them to England. They were sold in London in 1797–8 to Mr Bryan, who was acting for the Earl of Carlisle, the Duke of Bridgewater and his nephew Earl Gower. All the pictures were exhibited for sale at Bryan's Gallery and the Lyceum Gallery from 26 December 1798, but the majority were reserved for this syndicate of three.

At his death in 1803 the Duke of Bridgewater bequeathed most of his pictures, including his share of the Orléans collection, and Bridgewater House where most of them hung, to Earl Gower who then became Marquess of Stafford and later Duke of Sutherland. Both the Bridgewater and Stafford collections were housed in the Stafford Gallery until his death in 1833. The second son, Lord Francis Egerton, who became Earl of Ellesmere in 1846, then inherited a great part of the collection, including the Bridgewater pictures which were entailed to him. The pictures passed by descent to the 5th Earl, the present Duke of Sutherland, by whose generosity the present loan was arranged with the Gallery in 1946.

Ten pictures from the Duke of Sutherland's collection qualify for inclusion in this volume of the Gallery catalogue:

RAPHAEL	*Holy Family with a Palm Tree*
RAPHAEL	*The Bridgewater Madonna*
RAPHAEL	*Madonna del Passeggio*
after RAPHAEL	*Madonna with the Veil*
TINTORETTO	*Portrait of a Venetian*
TITIAN	*The Holy Family with S. John the Baptist*
TITIAN	*The Three Ages of Man*
TITIAN	*Venus Anadyomene*
TITIAN	*Diana and Actaeon*
TITIAN	*Diana and Callisto*

In 1984 the Gallery purchased four paintings by Private Treaty from the Ellesmere Trustees with a grant from the National Heritage Memorial Fund. Two of these paintings, the Lotto (2418) and the Tintoretto (2419), are included in this catalogue.

EXPLANATIONS

Measurements are given in centimetres, height preceding width. The size of the support is recorded where necessary, followed by the measurements of the painted surface. If only one set of measurements is recorded they represent the dimensions of the original painted surface.

The date of the cleaning is given for paintings wherever it is known. *X-rays* existing at the time of going to press are noted and some are reproduced among the comparative plates at the back of the catalogue. These and other photographic records are normally available for study on request.

Literary references given in abbreviated form will be found in full under *Abbreviated references* on pp. 13–14. No attempt has been made to give complete bibliographies or to cite exhibitions unless useful information, including previous ownership, is given in the catalogue.

A brief biography of each artist represented in the collection is provided. In the case of a well known artist, for whom biographical information is readily available elsewhere, this has been kept to a minimum. More extended biographical information is provided for lesser known artists where the relevant information is widely scattered or difficult to locate.

ABBREVIATED REFERENCES

Bartsch	A. Bartsch *Le Peintre Graveur* Vienna 1803–21.
Berenson	B. Berenson
1894	*The VenetianPainters of the Renaissance* New York 1894.
1896	*The Florentine Painters of the Renaissance* New York 1896.
1907	*The North Italian Painters of the Renaissance* London 1907.
1909	*The Florentine Painters of the Renaissance* 3rd edn. London 1909.
1909 *(Central Italian Painters)*	*The Central Italian Painters of the Renaissance* 2nd edn. London 1909.
1932	*Italian Pictures of the Renaissance* Oxford 1932.
1936	*Pitture italiane del Rinascimento* Milan 1936.
1957	*Italian Pictures of the Renaissance: Venetian School* London 1957.
1963	*Italian Pictures of the Renaissance: Florentine School* London 1963.
1968	*Italian Pictures of the Renaissance: Central Italian and North Italian Schools* London 1968.
B.F.A.C.	The Burlington Fine Arts Club, London.
B.I.	British Institution, London.
Britton 1808	J. Britton *Catalogue Raisonné of the Pictures belonging to the most honourable the Marquis of Stafford in the Gallery of Cleveland House* London 1808 .
Buchanan 1824	W. Buchanan *Memoirs of Painting with a chronological history of the Importation of Pictures by the Great Masters into England since the French Revolution* London 1824.
Catalogue of the Bridgewater Collection	*Catalogue of the Bridgewater Collection of Pictures belonging to the Earl of Ellesmere at Bridgewater House, Cleveland Square, St James's* London 1851.
Catalogue of Bridgewater House, 1926	*Catalogue of the Collection of Pictures and Statuary of the Right Honourable John Francis Granville Scrope Earl of Ellesmere at Bridge-water House, Cleveland Square, St James's* London 1926.
The 1859/1957 Catalogue	*National Gallery of Scotland Catalogue of Paintings and Sculpture* 1st edn. Edinburgh 1859; 51st and final edn. Edinburgh 1957.
Cust and Bourke 1903	L. Cust and W. L. Bourke *The Bridgewater Gallery* London 1903.
Jameson 1844	Mrs Jameson *Companion to the most celebrated private galleries of art in London* London 1844.
Lugt	F. Lugt *Répertoire des Catalogues de Ventes Publiques* The Hague 1938–64.
N.A.C.F.	National Art Collections Fund.
Nagler	G. K. Nagler *Neues allgemeines Künstler-Lexicon* Leipzig 1835–52.
N.G. London	National Gallery, London.
N.P.G. London	National Portrait Gallery, London.
Ottley and Tomkins 1818	W. Y. Ottley and P. W. Tomkins *Engravings of the Most Noble the Marquis of Stafford's Collection of Pictures in London arranged according to schools and in chronological order, with remarks on each picture* London 1818.

Passavant 1836	J. D. Passavant *Tour of a German Artist in England with notices of private galleries and remarks on the state of art* London 1836.
Pictures for Scotland	C. Thompson, with contributions by H. Brigstocke and D. Thomson *Pictures for Scotland. The National Gallery of Scotland and its collection: a study of the changing attitude to painting since the 1820s* Edinburgh 1972.
R.A.	Royal Academy.
R.I.	Royal Institution.
R.I. 1826	*Royal Institution for the Encouragement of the Fine Arts in Scotland. Third Exhibition of Ancient Pictures* Edinburgh 1826.
R.I. 1830	*Royal Institution for the Encouragement of the Fine Arts in Scotland. Fourth Exhibition of Ancient Pictures* Edinburgh 1830.
R.I. 1831	*Royal Institution for the Encouragement of the Fine Arts in Scotland. Fifth Exhibition of Ancient Pictures* Edinburgh 1831.
R.I. 1832	*Royal Institution for the Encouragement of the Fine Arts in Scotland. Sixth Exhibition of Ancient Pictures* Edinburgh 1832.
R.S.A.	Royal Scottish Academy.
Shorter Catalogue 1970	C. Thompson and H. Brigstocke *National Gallery of Scotland. Shorter Catalogue* (A complete list of the collection and concise details of 356 principal works and works on extended loan) Edinburgh 1970.
S.N.P.G.	Scottish National Portrait Gallery.
Thieme-Becker	*Allgemeines Lexikon der bildenden Künstler von der Antike bis zur Gegenwart* ed. U. Thieme and F. Becker, Leipzig 1907–50.
V. and A., London	Victoria and Albert Museum, London.
Vasari (ed. Milanesi)	G. Vasari *Le Vite de' più eccellenti pittori scultori ed architettori* 1568 (ed. G. Milanesi, Florence 1878–85).
Waagen 1838	G. F. Waagen *Works of Art and Artists in England* London 1838.
Waagen 1854	G. F. Waagen *Treasures of Art in Great Britain* London 1854.
Waagen 1857	G. F. Waagen *Supplemental Volume to the Treasures of Art in Great Britain* London 1857.

THE CATALOGUE OF PAINTINGS

Giuliano AMEDEI *active in the second half of the fifteenth century; died 1496*

In the Badia at Tifi, near Caprese (not far from Sansepolcro and Arezzo) there is a triptych of the *Virgin and Child between two angels, and flanked by four saints* which is inscribed: TPR DNI MICHAELIS DE VVLTERRIS ABBATIS [IVLI] ANVS MONARCHVS CAMALDVLENSIS ORDINIS PINXIT ... Salmi has argued, on the evidence of this inscription, that the artist might have been a Camaldolese monk, Giuliano Amedei, who is first recorded in Florence in 1446 in the monastery of S. Benedetto fuori di Porta a Pinti, and who was later Abbot of S. Maria di Agnano in the diocese of Arezzo. Amedei is also known to have worked as an artist in Rome *c.* 1467–72, and he was apparently there again in 1495. He died in Lucca in 1496.[1] Salmi's attribution of the Tifi altarpiece was later accepted by Levi d'Ancona.[2] Salmi has further argued, on stylistic evidence, that the predella of Piero della Francesca's *Misericordia Altarpiece* at Borgo San Sepolcro may be by the same hand as the Tifi altarpiece, working under Piero's supervision.

Attributed to Giuliano AMEDEI

1528   The Death of S. Ephraim

Wood, irregular fragment, made up; maximum dimensions of the original panel 34 × 43.5
Cleaned 1960. In very good condition for a work of its age, except for a damage in the rock at the top left.

One of the 20 fragments from a large dismembered mid-fifteenth-century panel depicting the lives of the hermits and the death of S. Ephraim of Syria in A.D. 373. The other fragments are at Christ Church, Oxford, at Yale, and in Zurich. The original appearance of the complete panel, before it was cut up in Italy before 1836, is reconstructed by Callmann.[3]

In our panel hermits and anchorites are shown assembling round the body of the Saint before his burial. The earliest surviving painting showing the *Death of S. Ephraim* in this way is the central panel of a thirteenth-century tabernacle of Tuscan origin, acquired by Lord Lindsay in the mid-nineteenth century, and now in a private collection. Martin has suggested that it is probably based on a lost Byzantine prototype of the *Death of S. Ephraim*, although the earliest surviving Byzantine examples with the same iconography date from as late as the sixteenth century.[4] Isolated scenes from the complete *Death of S. Ephraim* composition can however be traced, individually, to eleventh-century Byzantine MS of the *Heavenly Ladder* by John Climacus and in particular to Vatican MS gr. 394 and the Princeton Climax manuscript. As Martin suggests, these scenes were then probably fused by a Byzantine artist into a single and presumably famous composition, centred round the *Death of S. Ephraim*, on which subsequent Byzantine versions were then always based.

In later Italian examples, of horizontal format, and dating from the fourteenth and fifteenth centuries, the Byzantine composition of the focal scene showing the *Death of S. Ephraim*, with the procession of mourning monks to the bier, was still retained with only slight iconographical variations; this scene, invariably placed at the left hand of the picture, remained the principal and unchanging feature of each composition. But, in the

remaining part of the picture, additional scenes were introduced, which originated in a
quite different, Tuscan, iconographical tradition; these scenes are elaborations of the
frescoes in the Campo Santo at Pisa, now attributed to Francesco Traini and assistants.
This fusion of two different iconographical traditions is first seen in a late fourteenth-
century panel, perhaps from the circle of Mariotto di Nardo, now cut up and divided
between the Keresztény Museum at Esztergom,[5] and a British private collection (offered for sale Christie's 28 June 1974 (47)[6] and previously in the Davenport-Bromley
collection sale at Christie's 12 and 13 June 1863 (130)). The fifteenth-century panel in
the Uffizi, Florence, by an artist close to Fra Angelico, was directly copied from this
composition.[7] However later fifteenth-century examples, such as the dismembered
panel (including our fragment) and two horizontal panels acquired by Lord Lindsay in
Italy in the mid-nineteenth century, and now in a private collection,[8] do not directly
follow the composition and iconography of the fourteenth-century panel formerly in
the Davenport-Bromley collection, except in the principal scene of the *Death of S.
Ephraim* where the traditional Byzantine form is still retained.

Berenson (1932 and 1963) places our panel and the connected fragments in Oxford,
Zurich and Yale among the 'Unidentified Florentines *c*. 1420–65', and includes in the
same category the two horizontal panels formerly in Lord Lindsay's collection.
Berenson further characterises both the dismembered panel (including our fragment)
and the larger ex. Lindsay collection panel as 'between Giovanni di Francesco and Neri
di Bicci'; Byam Shaw has subsequently made a tentative and not altogether convincing
suggestion that these two pictures might well have been painted by the same hand, on
the evidence of similarities in their composition and the resemblances in the figures and
in the convention for rocks, trees, plants, and buildings.[9] Byam Shaw further suggests,
again on the evidence of similar treatment of plants and stones, that the dismembered
panel (including our fragment) might be by the same hand as the predella of Piero della
Francesca's *Misericordia Altarpiece* at Sansepolcro, and that the painter was the young
Neri di Bicci. The suggested connection with the predella of the *Misericordia Altarpiece*
is convincing and has also been accepted by Zeri; but Zeri draws attention to Salmi's
attribution of this predella to the artist who painted the altarpiece at Tifi, who was
probably Giuliano Amedei, and proposes this as an alternative to Byam Shaw's suggestion of Neri di Bicci.[10] The Tifi altarpiece depicts no rocks or plants to assist stylistic
comparison with either the Sansepolcro predella or the dismembered panel (including
our fragment), and the figures are much larger in scale; but there is a definite similarity
between all three works in the facial types, in the rather staring eyes, and in the
handling of hair and beards. On this basis, it seems reasonable to relate the three
pictures and to place them, tentatively, under the name of Giuliano Amedei.

Our panel cannot be dated with any precision. The *Misericordia Altarpiece* at
Sansepolcro was commissioned in 1445, but was not completed until some fifteen years
later.[11] There is some evidence that the Tifi altarpiece was painted *c*. 1480.[12] Our picture
is closer to the predella of the *Misericordia Altarpiece* than to the picture at Tifi, and
may therefore date from relatively early in the second half of the fifteenth century.

Coll: The original panel to which the Edinburgh fragment belonged must have been cut up in Italy[13]
and sold piecemeal before 1836, since Walter Savage Landor, who owned both our fragment and the
nine panels now at Christ Church, Oxford, offered nine of them for sale at Christie's on 25 June 1836

(105).[14] These 9 panels were bought in at £3 and they are presumably the same nine fragments which formed part of the Landor-Duke gift to Christ Church in 1897; the tenth fragment, now in Edinburgh, was sold by Landor (died 1864) to William Bell Scott (1811–90).[15]

Bought from James R. Saunders 1921.

1. M. Salmi in *Rivista d'Arte* XXIV 1942 pp. 26. ff. See also Thieme-Becker I p. 367 where this artist is listed under Giuliano Amadei (sic).

2. M. Levi d'Ancona *Miniatura e Miniatori a Firenze dal XIV al XVI secolo* Florence 1962 p. 158. For further discussion of the Tifi altarpiece see *Arte nell'Aretino* Exhibition Catalogue, San Francesco, Arezzo 1974/75 pp. 94 ff. no. 34 tav. 127 and 128.

3. E. Callmann in the *Burlington Magazine* XCIX 1957 pp. 149 ff.

4. J. R. Martin in the *Art Bulletin* XXXIII 1951 pp. 217 ff. fig. 5.

5. For the Esztergom fragment see M. Boskovits in *Antichità Viva* VII 1968 5 pp. 6 ff. fig. 4; but Boskovits was not aware of its connection with the panel later sold at Christie's in 1974. For this connection see H. Brigstocke in the *Burlington Magazine* CXVIII 1976 pp. 585 ff. figs. 44 and 45 where both panels are reproduced. See also E. Callmann in *Antichità Viva* XIV 1975 3 pp. 3–22 notes 27 and 28.

6. The Christie's sale catalogue, following E. Callmann in the *Burlington Magazine* XCIX 1957 p. 150, describes this panel unacceptably as Florentine fifteenth-century. It also states wrongly that a fragmentary panel in the Budapest Museum of Fine Arts (Inv. 18d.) might originally have belonged to the same picture as the panel at Christie's and the fragment in Esztergom (for which see note 5 above). Although the Christie's panel and the Esztergom panel do join together almost exactly, the Budapest panel is a later copy (early fifteenth century) of part of this composition. For the Budapest picture, and another fragment in a private collection, Florence, which originally may have been joined to it, see E. Callmann in the *Burlington Magazine* XCIX 1957 p. 150 note 7, M. Boskovits *Tuscan Paintings of the early Renaissance in Hungarian Museums* Budapest 1969 no. 4, E. Callmann *Apollonio di Giovanni* Oxford 1974 p. 18 note 64, and in *Antichità Viva* XIV 1975 3 p. 7 ff., and Brigstocke *op. cit.* pp. 585 ff. fig. 47.

7. The attribution to Fra Angelico was first suggested by R. Longhi in *Critica d'Arte* V 1940 II pp. 173 ff. See also J. Pope Hennessy *Fra Angelico* London 1974 p. 239. For an earlier attribution to Starnina see U. Procacci in *Rivista d'Arte* XVII 1935 pp. 360 ff.

8. Both panels are reproduced by P. Schubring *Cassoni, Truhen und Truhenbilder der Italienischen Frührenaissance* Leipzig 1915 nos. 36 and 37 pl. VI. See further E. Callmann in the *Burlington Magazine* XCIX 1957 pp. 149 ff. fig. 13.

9. J. Byam Shaw *Paintings by Old Masters at Christ Church, Oxford* London 1967 pp. 40 ff. nos. 21–29 under Tuscan school *c.* 1440–50.

10. Federico Zeri's opinion is quoted by Byam Shaw *loc. cit.* and has been confirmed in a letter (in the Gallery files) dated 14 March 1989. For Salmi's view of the predella of the *Misericordia Altarpiece* see note 1 above. But Salmi did not himself notice any connection between the dismembered panel (including our fragment) which he attributed to the circle of Uccello (see *Commentari* I 1950 p. 28) and the predella of the *Misericordia Altarpiece*.

11. For the evidence concerning the commissioning of the *Misericordia Altarpiece* see K. Clark *Piero della Francesca* London 1951 p. 203.

12. The evidence for this date, based on both an inscription which has since been damaged, and also on a recorded date of the office of Abbot Michele da Volterra, is summarised by Salmi (see note 1 above).

13. The fragments in Zurich were not exported from Italy until 1912; see Byam Shaw *loc. cit.*

14. In the sale catalogue these were attributed to Laurati and were described as follows: 'A set of nine subjects from the Old Testament and from monkish legends; *highly curious specimens of the early Siennese School*'.

15. According to an undated note written by William Bell Scott, formerly on the back of the picture and now in the Gallery files.

APOLLONIO DI GIOVANNI

Florentine. He kept a joint workshop with Marco del Buono Giamberti (1403–89). A complete list of the work put out by this busy workshop between 1446–63 has survived,[1] and this enabled Stechow to identify a panel at the Allen Memorial Art Museum, Oberlin, Ohio, representing *Xerxes' Invasion of Greece* as one of its products from the year 1463.[2] The Oberlin panel clearly belongs, stylistically, with the illustrations of a Virgil manuscript in the Biblioteca Riccardiana, Florence (Cod. 492), and with a group of *cassone* fronts, including two panels with scenes from Virgil's *Aeneid*, now in the Jarves Collection at the Yale University Art Gallery, New Haven. The hand responsible for the design of the panels in Yale had been called the Dido Master by Schubring (whose stylistic groupings are not satisfactory),[3] the Virgil Master by Offner,[4] and the Master of the Jarves *Cassoni* by Berenson in 1932. Although there is some evidence that Apollonio di Giovanni personally illustrated the Virgil manuscript in Florence, there is no other satisfactory basis for defining the individual style of the two partners. The workshop was a very active one; numerous works survive which must have been executed by assistants, as well as later derivations.

1940   **Triumphs of Love and Chastity**

Wood: 44 × 143; painted surface 40.3 × 141.7

Part of the front panel of a *cassone*. The position of the keyhole, which would normally have been in the centre, is now 84.5 cm. from the left edge of the painted surface and 57.2 cm. from the right. It can be assumed, therefore, that a piece of the panel around 26.7 cm. wide has been cut from the right-hand side. There are traces of an original gold border on all except the right-hand side; this has been obscured by a brown painted border which also continues along the right-hand edge. There is an edge of wood, beyond the gesso preparation, on the top, bottom and left-hand sides of the panel. The paint surface has suffered from numerous minor damages and general wear of a kind usually found on *cassone* panels, but there are no large areas of missing paint, except in the foliage which is heavily repainted. The pigment of the brown horizontal band in the landscape background, in front of the distant row of mountains, which probably represents water, has discoloured and was originally green.

The subject is taken from Petrarch's *Trionfi*. The figure at the front of the procession, carrying a palm, is Chastity. The figure of Love, bound by cords, is shown behind her. On the second car Love is again represented, as a naked winged boy, standing on a golden globe.

The *Triumphs of Love and Chastity* were usually followed by the *Triumph of Death*. On the basis of comparison with a panel showing this succession of subjects, now in the Gardner Museum, Boston, and attributed to Pesellino,[5] and a similar panel in the Victoria and Albert Museum, London, attributed to the Cassone Master,[6] it seems likely that the missing section of our panel also represented the *Triumph of Death*.

Our panel was attributed to Dello Delli while in the Lothian collection, and after its acquisition by the Gallery was again catalogued under this name in 1946. In 1957 it was described as a mid-fifteenth-century Florentine work and in 1968 it was catalogued as by a follower of Apollonio di Giovanni. In 1915 Schubring,[7] followed by Van Marle in 1928,[8] had associated it with a number of other *cassone* panels under the name of the Cassone Master. Although Schubring's definition of the Cassone Master as an artistic personality no longer seems coherent, some of the works in this group, including our picture, show obvious stylistic links with what are now identified as products of Apollonio di Giovanni and his workshop. Although Callmann observed that only a few of the figures in our picture find close counterparts in works which definitely originate from Apollonio di Giovanni's workshop, and classified it as the work of a painter who had, at some earlier date, been an assistant in Apollonio di Giovanni's shop, but who had already left it,[9] Fahy believes it to be a fairly early work by Apollonio himself.[10]

Coll: Bought in Florence by the 8th Marquess of Lothian, in 1861, possibly from William Blundell Spence, as by Dello Delli.[11] Lent by Lord Lothian to the *Exhibition of Early Italian Art* New Gallery, London, 1893–4 (36) as Dello Delli.

11th Marquess of Lothian bequest 1941.

1. First published by P. Schubring *Cassoni, Truhen and Truhenbilder der Italienischen Früh- renaissance* Leipzig 1915 pp. 430–37. A revised transcription made by G. Corti is printed in E. Callmann *Apollonio di Giovanni* Oxford 1974 pp. 76 ff.

2. W. Stechow in *Bulletin of the Allen Memorial Art Museum* Oberlin I 1944 pp. 5ff.

3. *Op. cit.* nos. 218–54.

4. R. Offner *Italian Primitives at Yale University* New Haven 1927 pp. 27–30.

5. See Schubring *op. cit.* no. 266 pl. LX.

6. Schubring *op. cit.* no. 207 pl. XLV.

7. *Op. cit.* no. 204 pl. XLV.

8. R. Van Marle *The Development of the Italian Schools of Painting* The Hague 1928 x p. 563.

9. E. Callmann *Apollonio di Giovanni* Oxford 1974 p. 60 no. 17 pl. III.

10. Letter in Gallery files dated 24 August 1990.

11. The date of acquisition is given in a MS inventory of the collection (copy in S.N.P.G. files) where it is listed as no. 581. The possibility that the panel had previously belonged to Spence is suggested by a letter from William Blundell Spence to his son William Campbell Spence, dated Florence 8 February 1861 (private archive Florence), in which he wrote that he was 'now in treaty with Lord Lothian for several pictures'. I am indebted to John Fleming for this reference. See further *Pictures for Scotland* pp. 111 ff. For W. B. Spence see J. Fleming in the *Burlington Magazine* CXV 1973 pp. 4 ff.

Workshop of APOLLONIO DI GIOVANNI

1974   **The Rape of the Sabines**

Wood: 39.3 × 61.5

Probably part of the front panel of a *cassone*. Since all the edges of our panel appear to have been trimmed, it is difficult to establish whether the missing section would have been joined to the left or right-hand edge. The panel is made up from two pieces of wood; the join runs horizontally, 3 cm. from the bottom left, 2.5 cm from the bottom right. The paint surface which goes up to the edges on all four sides, is affected by numerous minor paint losses.

After Romulus had invited the Sabines to Rome to celebrate the Consualia, a festival in honour of Neptune, the women are raped by the Romans during the entertainment. See Livy *Ab Urbe Condita* I.9.

Gombrich, who first identified the subject of our picture,[1] suggested that a panel in the Ashmolean Museum, Oxford, representing an acrobat and wrestlers performing, might have originally formed part of the same *cassone* panel.[2] Although the juxta-position of these two scenes could be justified so far as the subject matter is concerned, inasmuch as a *cassone* panel at Harewood House, Yorkshire (attributed by Fahy to the Master of Marradi,[3] and by Callmann to the workshop of Apollonio di Giovanni[4]) also shows the same scenes in sequence together, technical examination of the Edinburgh and Oxford panels does not suggest that they were originally joined together. Since our panel is made up from two pieces of wood, it seems reasonable to suppose that any extension of its length in the horizontal sense would also have been constructed in the same way, and that the line of the join in our panel would have run along the entire length of the *cassone* front. However the Oxford panel is made from a single piece of wood. The force of this argument against acceptance of the reconstruction proposed by Gombrich was accepted by Anderson in 1970,[5] by Callmann in 1974,[6] and by Lloyd in 1977.[7]

Our panel was catalogued in 1946, shortly after its acquisition, as Sienese school. It was first associated with the name of Apollonio di Giovanni by Gombrich in 1955.[8]

Coll: First recorded in a MS Catalogue of pictures belonging to Lord Southesk at Kinnaird Castle in 1904.[9] It is there said to have been bought in Florence, in 1865, from the dealer, William Blundell Spence.[10]

Bought from the 10th Earl of Southesk 1942.

---

1. E. Gombrich in *Journal of the Warburg and Courtauld Institutes* XVIII 1955 pp. 16–37 pl. 114b. See also Callmann *op. cit.* p. 41 note 14 and pp. 71 ff. no. 46 pl. 196.

2. The Oxford panel is reproduced by Gombrich *op. cit.* pl. 14c. and by Callmann *op. cit.* pl. 197. It measures 38.2 × 60.3 cm.

3. E. Fahy in the *Burlington Magazine* CIX 1967 p.134.

4. E. Callmann *Apollonio di Giovanni* Oxford 1974 p. 60 no. 17.

5. B. Anderson in *Museum Studies* Art Institute of Chicago V 1970 pp. 29–30 note 15. Anderson went on to suggest what appears to me an even less probable reconstruction, based on an idea which was not supported by any evidence, that the Edinburgh and Oxford panels might have been *testate* or side panels in a *cassone*, in which the central scene would have been a panel now in the Art Institute of Chicago. Here she interpreted and quoted my observation, communicated by letter in 1969, that the Edinburgh and Oxford panels 'could never have originally been part of the same panel' as corroboration of *her* hypothesis that 'the two panels cannot be fragments'. In my view there is still every reason to suppose that each of these two panels is a fragment from a *cassone* front.

6. *Op. cit.* p. 71 no. 46 and p. 72 no. 47.

7. C. Lloyd *Catalogue of The Earlier Italian Paintings in the Ashmolean Museum* Oxford 1977 pp. 10–11 no. A92. pl. 12.

8. *Op. cit.* p. 27.

9. There is a transcription of this catalogue in the Gallery files.

10. For W. B. Spence see J. Fleming in the *Burlington Magazine* CXV 1973 pp. 4 ff.

Francesco Ubertini called BACCHIACCA *1494–1557*

Born 1 March 1494.[1] Francesco d'Ubertino, son of Ubertino di Bartolommeo, a gold-smith from S. Lorenzo, in the Mugello valley near Florence. According to Vasari, he was a friend of Perugino and a pupil of Andrea del Sarto.[2] He was probably in Rome around 1523–24, to judge from the evidence of Benvenuto Cellini's *Autobiography*.[3] Among

Bacchiacca's paintings which may be identified from Vasari's account are a series of *Scenes from the Life of Joseph*, now in the National Gallery, London, and the Borghese Gallery, Rome; a predella, now in the Uffizi, Florence, from an altarpiece by Sogliani (dated 1521) painted for S. Salvatore di Camaldoli; and the *Baptism of Christ* (Berlin) and the *Legend of the Dead King* (Dresden) which may probably be identified as panels commissioned for Giovanni Maria Benintendi's house in Florence. None of these works can be firmly dated but they are all thought to be relatively early, before *c.* 1525.[4] According to Vasari, Bacchiacca was a skilful animal painter and he was employed in this capacity by Cosimo I in Florence. He was also commissioned by the Ducal government in Florence to design tapestry cartoons representing the *Months of the Year*. The tapestries, which are now in the Uffizi, must have been made after 20 October 1546 when the contract with the weavers was signed.[5]

2291 ## Moses Striking the Rock

Wood: 100 × 80
Cleaned shortly before acquisition. In very good condition, apart from some paint losses along the lines of a series of vertical cracks running from the top edge.

Moses strikes the rock in the desert, causing water to flow from it. In the top right, the Israelites are seen complaining to Moses prior to his miracle. See *Exodus* XVII, 27, and *Numbers* XX, 7–13,

Acquired as by Bacchiacca. The attribution, which is now beyond dispute, was first proposed by Morelli in 1890, when the picture was still in the Giovanelli collection, Venice, under an attribution to Dürer,[6] which had apparently replaced an earlier attribution to Andrea del Sarto in a 1723 inventory.[7] Morelli's attribution was followed by Berenson in 1896.

The difficulties which surrounded the attribution of our picture during the eighteenth and nineteenth centuries were probably aggravated by the extraordinary eclecticism of Bacchiacca's design, with its numerous quotations from the works of earlier artists. For instance, the man lying in the right foreground, so as to drink water from the stream, is freely derived from Filippino Lippi's picture of *Moses Striking the Rock*, in the National Gallery, London (Inv. 4904).[8] The pose of the young mother and child at the extreme right of the picture is based on Marcantonio Raimondi's engraving of *God Appearing to Noah* (Bartsch XIV 3). The old woman, crouching in the extreme left foreground, is based on a figure in Lucas van Leyden's engraving of *Beggars* (Bartsch VII 143). The man seated immediately behind Moses, and the man standing above him, just behind the shepherd holding a lamb, are both taken from Lucas van Leyden's engraving *Esther before Ahasuerus* (Bartsch VII 31). The structure of the rock in the centre of the picture is based on the background of Lucas van Leyden's engraving of the *Conversion of S. Paul* (Bartsch VII 107). In style and subject matter our picture is closely connected with Bacchiacca's *Gathering of Manna* (Fig. 1), now in the National Gallery, Washington (K. 1362),[9] but they were clearly not intended as a pair. This is evident both from the fact that they are different in size, and from the almost exact repetition in both pictures of certain motifs, such as the grovelling man seen in the right foreground. Yet they might well originate from a common prototype, and it is tempting to regard them both as elaborated versions, on a more intimate scale, of the series of scenes from the Old Testament, mainly representing the life of Moses, which, according to Vasari, were painted for a Triumphal arch which had been designed by Jacone in Florence for the *Festa di San Felice in Piazza* in 1525.[10] The *Compagnia dell'Orciuolo* (Jug Society) sponsored this festival which might possibly account for the obsessive emphasis on metal and glass jugs, seen both in our picture and the *Gathering of Manna* in Washington.[11]

The elaborate designs of many of the jugs may be somewhat fanciful; but several of the exotic animals, which are another notable feature of our picture (there is a serval in the foreground, and a genet and a West African grey parrot on the rock in the centre), might well be based on direct observation especially if, as seems probable, Bacchiacca had had access to Leo X's zoo in Rome.[12] On the other hand the giraffe, which is not anatomically convincing, was probably derived from an earlier Florentine painting, such as Piero di Cosimo's *Vulcan and Aeolus* now in Ottawa (Inv. 4287).[13] Such representations of giraffes occur quite frequently in Florentine art after 1487, the year when Lorenzo il Magnifico received one as a present from the Sultan of Egypt.[14]

There is no firm evidence on which to date our picture. It appears to be more advanced in style than the Benintendi panels representing the *Baptism of Christ* (Berlin) and the *Legend of the Dead King* (Dresden), which are still reminiscent of Franciabigio, especially in the heavy use of local colour, and of blue in particular. In contrast our picture, together with the *Gathering of Manna* in Washington, appears to mark what was probably a later development in Bacchiacca's style, when his handling became harder and more polished, his colouring brighter, sharper and more harmonious, and when he began to make use of two presentation drawings which, according to Vasari, Michelangelo had given to Gherardo Perini in *c.* 1525 and which are now in the Uffizi, Florence.[15] In our picture Bacchiacca used one of these, a study of three heads, Uffizi Inv. 599 E *recto* (Fig. 2), for the elderly female figure standing with her hand on her chest on the left, for the young woman holding a child on the right, and for the young female figure drinking from a jug and kneeling in the right foreground. He may also have used the *verso* of Uffizi Inv. 599 E for the head of the female figure seated in the left foreground of our picture. Some of the heads also occur in the Washington picture, where Bacchiacca used Uffizi Inv. 598 E *recto* for the elaborate head-dress of the female in the right foreground.[16] These two sheets of drawings by Michelangelo were copied and adapted in many other pictures by Bacchiacca, including the *Beheading of S. John the Baptist* in Berlin,[17] but they do not all necessarily date from the same moment.

It should not even be assumed that the Edinburgh and Washington pictures are necessarily of the same date, simply on the strength of their closely related subject matter and their dependence on the same drawings and prints. The evidence of costume, although arguably unreliable in such self-consciously eclectic works, suggests that there might have been an interval of nearly a decade between them. For although many features of the dress indicate that Bacchiacca was deliberately attempting to represent historical Jewish costume, seen, for instance, in our picture, in the belt worn by Moses and in several of the men's hats, Newton has drawn attention to a number of unconscious references to current Italian fashions. She points out that whereas the long hair worn by Moses in the Edinburgh picture suggests a date before *c.* 1532, after which it might have appeared unacceptably unfashionable in Florence, the tight sleeved dress, worn by the woman standing on the right of the Washington picture, suggests a date for it no earlier than the very late 1530s.[18] There still appears to be no other more reliable method of dating our picture. The various views on the chronology of Bacchiacca's work propounded by Morelli, McComb, Marcucci and Nikolenko, are all based on an arbitrary view of his stylistic development. Thus Morelli dated our picture *c.* 1518–36,[19] McComb dated it *c.* 1530[20] but placed the Washington picture as late as *c.* 1545–55,[21] Marcucci dated our picture *c.* 1545 and the Washington picture *c.* 1540,[22] and Nikolenko dated both works *c.* 1545–55.[23]

Coll: Prince Giovanelli collection, Venice, since at least 1723 when it is recorded in an inventory under an attribution to Andrea del Sarto.[24] It was apparently still in the Giovanelli collection when McComb saw it, prior to publishing his article on Bacchiacca in 1926.[25] But by 1939, when Salvini referred to it in Thieme-Becker, it had been sold,[26] and its whereabouts remained unknown until 1967 when it was exhibited by Colnaghi's, London.

Bought from Colnaghi's 1967.

1. See F. Abbate in *Paragone* 189 1965 p. 31 and p. 46 note 24.

2. Although Vasari did not devote a special chapter of the *Vite* to Bacchiacca, his book contains numerous useful references to him. See Vasari (ed. Milanesi III p. 592 and VI pp. 454–56).

3. For Bacchiacca's journey to Rome see Abbate *op. cit.* pp. 42–3.

4. The best account of Bacchiacca's stylistic development with reference to all these pictures is still the article by A. McComb in the *Art Bulletin* VIII 1926 pp. 141–67. See further L. Marcucci in *Bolletino d'Arte* XLIII 1958 pp. 26–39, Abbate *op. cit* pp. 26–49, and L. Nikolenko *Francesco Ubertini called Il Bacchiacca* New York 1966.

5. See M .Tinti in *Dedalo* III 1920 pp. 803ff. and McComb *op. cit.* p. 149.

6. See I. Lermolieff [Morelli] *Kunstkritische Studien über italienische Malerei: die Galerien Borghese und Doria Panfili in Rom* Leipzig 1890 pp. 135–6. Dr J. Anderson (letter in Gallery files, 7 May 1989) has drawn attention to a letter from Morelli to his cousin Giovanni Melli, dated Venice 9 January 1872, which tells of his visit to the Giovanelli residence where he recognised our picture. The letter is in the private archive of the Zavaritti family in Bergamo and will be published by Anderson in her forthcoming edition of Morelli's letters. The relevant passage reads: *Fra gli altri quadri egli mi presentò, 'pour la bonne bouche', una Tavoletta circa della grandezza del tuo 'Abele e Caino', in cui è rappresentato Moise che fa scaturire le acque della roccia. Questo quadro, mi disse il Principe, è reputato dagli intelligenti una delle belle opere di Alberto Durero. Io, che vi riconobbi subito la mano dell'autore, non potei a meno di chiedergli il permesso di essere anche questa volta di opinione diversa, e lo assicurai essere quella sua tavola anzi che di autore tedesco opera di pittore toscano, è null'altro che un'altra di quelle rare tavolette con soggetti biblici del nostro caro Bacchiacca. Ebbene, questa tavoletta col Moisè, il Principe la dovette pagare 15,000 lire! Essa è più pallida di colore della tua.*

7. For the 1723 inventory see N. Barbantini in *Emporium* XXVII 1908 pp. 183–5, where our picture is also reproduced.

8. This derivation was first pointed out by Philip Pouncey; see M. Davies *National Gallery Catalogue, The Earlier Italian Schools* London 1961 p. 289 note 3.

9. See F. Rusk Shapley *Paintings from the Samuel H. Kress Collection, Italian Schools XVI–XVIII century* London 1973 pp. 8–9 figs. 13–14. The sources from which Bacchiacca borrowed for the design of the Washington picture have been identified by H. Merritt *Bacchiacca and his Friends* Exhibition Catalogue, Baltimore Museum of Art 1961 p. 32.

10. Vasari (ed. Milanesi VI pp. 451–52).

11. It is not altogether clear whether the *Compagnia dell'Orciuolo* was a fraternity of jug makers or jug vendors or else a social 'jug and bottle' club.

12. For the identification of many of the animals in our picture and the related picture in Washington see H. Friedmann in *Gazette des Beaux-Arts* XXXII 1947 pp. 156–8.

13. Reproduced by R. H. Hubbard *National Gallery of Canada, Catalogue of Paintings and Sculpture* Ottawa/Toronto 1957 p. 33.

14. Cf. for instance Andrea del Sarto's fresco of the *Tribute to Caesar* at Poggio a Caiano and dating from *c.* 1521 which is discussed and reproduced by J. Shearman *Andrea del Sarto* Oxford 1965 I p. 85 and pl. 74. For representations of the giraffe in Florentine art see further J. B. Lloyd *African Animals in Renaissance Literature and Art* Oxford 1971 pp. 49ff.

15. Vasari (ed. Milanesi VII pp. 276ff.). For the probable identification of the Perini presentation drawings see A. E. Popham and J. Wilde *The Italian Drawings of the XV and XVI Centuries in the collection of His Majesty the King at Windsor Castle* London 1949 p. 264.

16. For a detailed discussion of these two drawings of *teste divine* and the history of their attribution see P. Barocchi *Michelangelo e la sua scuola. I disegni di Casa Buonarroti e degli Uffizi* Florence 1962 pp. 233 ff. nos. 185 and 186 tav. ccxc, ccxciv, ccxcviii. But Barocchi's decision to catalogue the drawings under the name of Bacchiacca, following the attribution of Morelli *loc. cit.*, is not convincing; see M. Hirst in the *Burlington Magazine* CV 1963 p. 171 note 17.

17. Reproduced by McComb *op. cit* fig. 25 and by Nikolenko *op. cit.* fig. 69.

18. I am indebted to Stella Newton of the Courtauld Institute, London, for her helpful advice on this question, which was communicated to me in 1976.

19. *Loc. cit.*

20. *Op. cit. p.* 162.

21. *Op. cit. p.* 154.

22. *Op. cit.* pp. 33 and 39 note 6.

23. *Op. cit.* pp. 59.

24. See note 7 above. The Giovanelli family was ennobled in 1668. For the collection see F. Haskell *Patrons and Painters* London 1963 p. 262 note 6.

25. *Op. cit. p.* 162.

26. Roberto Salvini in Thieme-Becker XXXIII pp. 522–3.

Jacopo BASSANO *c. 1510/18–92*

Jacopo dal Ponte, called Bassano after the name of his birthplace. He was the son of the painter Francesco dal Ponte. There is no evidence of Jacopo's precise birthdate, but it was probably between *c.* 1510 and 1518. His artistic activity appears to have begun *c.* 1535 and his early work suggests he was influenced by Bonifazio Veronese, with whom he might have studied in Venice. His later work, which is more mannerist in style, reveals the impact of Francesco Parmigianino's paintings or prints. Jacopo's artistic achievement has been obscured by the activity of his sons, in particular Francesco and Leandro, who began as his studio assistants and whose own work was closely modelled on their father's late style.

100 Adoration of the Kings

Canvas: 183 × 235
Cleaned 1964. The paint surface is worn, especially in the areas of shadow, but it nevertheless retains a remarkably fresh appearance. The best preserved area is in the landscape, above an old horizontal seam running along a line from just above Joseph's head. The sides and the bottom edge of the canvas are badly damaged. A small local damage affects the right eye of the Virgin; and another more substantial damage affects the right shoulder of the man standing below the banner, on the extreme right of the picture.

The attribution to Jacopo Bassano was first proposed by Crowe and Cavalcaselle in 1871 when the picture was in the collection of the R.S.A.,[1] and it has never been questioned since,[2] although it had previously been attributed both to Titian[3] and to Pordenone.[4]

Our picture, like so many of Bassano's works, cannot be firmly dated, but on stylistic evidence it is usually placed *c*. 1540,[5] just after the altarpiece of the *Madonna with S. Zeno and John the Baptist* in Borso del Grappa which dates from 1538,[6] and the *Adoration of the Kings* in the Marquess of Exeter's collection at Burghley House, Stamford.[7] It may also date from about the same time as *The Journey to Calvary* in the Fitzwilliam Museum, Cambridge.[8] For in each of these works, as in our picture, Jacopo Bassano's early debt to Bonifazio Veronese is combined with fresh stylistic influences derived from Pordenone. There are, for instance, clear stylistic links between our picture and Pordenone's fresco of the *Adoration of the Kings* in the Duomo at Treviso. On the other hand, the influence of Parmigianino, which strongly affected Bassano's later style, is not apparent in our picture.

Some features in the distant landscape of our picture, particularly the thatched cottages, recur in other pictures by Jacopo Bassano which are usually thought to date from the 1540s, including the *Trinity* in the church of SS. Trinità at Angarano,[9] the *Flight into Egypt* now in the Toledo (Ohio) Museum of Art (Inv. 1977.41),[10] and the *Flight into Egypt* formerly at Prinknash and now in the Norton Simon Collection in the U.S.A.[11] Such topographical features might well be an idealised rendering of Bassano and Monte Grappa. The ruined building on the extreme left, however, is derived from Dürer's woodcut *Sojourn of the Holy Family in Egypt* (Bartsch VII 90).

Coll: Giacomo Balbi collection, Genoa, by 1758 when it was noted by Cochin under an attribution to Titian;[12] noted in the Francesco Maria Balbi collection, Genoa, by both Ratti in 1766[13] and by Brusco in 1788,[14] in each case again as by Titian; bought by Andrew Wilson from the Balbi collection, Genoa, in 1805;[15] Andrew Wilson sale, Peter Coxe, London, 6 May 1807 (28) as from the Balbi Palace and as by Titian, when it was probably bought by Lord Eldin;[16] exhibited R.I. Edinburgh 1826 (74) as by Titian and lent by Lord Eldin; Lord Eldin sale, Winstanley, Edinburgh, 15 March 1833 (113) as Titian, bought Neil.

Bought by the Royal Scottish Academy from Mr Neil 1856; transferred 1910.

---

1. J. A. Crowe and G. B. Cavalcaselle *A History of Painting in North Italy* 1871 (ed. T. Borenius, London 1912 III p. 183) and J. A. Crowe and G. B. Cavalcaselle *The Life and Times of Titian* London 1877 II p. 468.

2. See E. Arslan *I Bassano* Milan 1960 I pp. 62–3 and p. 167.

3. See C. G. Ratti *Istruzione di quanto può vedersi di più bello in Genova* 1766 (Genoa 1780 ed. p. 186) and G. Brusco *Description des beautés de Gênes* Genoa 1788 (2nd ed. p. 129). Our picture continued to be attributed to Titian until after 1833 (see under *Coll*)

4. By Waagen 1857 p. 429.

5. See S. Bettini *L'Arte di Jacopo Bassano* Bologna 1933 pp. 39–40; R. Longhi in *Arte Veneta* II 1948 II p. 46; and Arslan *loc. cit.* See further Magagnato in *The Genius of Venice 1500–1600* Exhibition Catalogue ed. J. Martineau and C. Hope, R.A., London 1983 p. 146.

6. See Arslan *op. cit.* I p. 164 and II pl. 29.

7. See W. R. Rearick in *Arte Veneta* XII 1958 pp. 197–200. Rearick convincingly identifies this picture as the Jacopo Bassano described by C. Ridolfi *Le Maraviglie dell'Arte* 1648 (ed. von Hadeln, Berlin 1914–24 I p. 400) as in the Widmann collection, Venice. An earlier suggestion put forward by G. Lorenzetti in *L'Arte* XIV 1911 pp. 248–9 that our picture might be the ex. Widmann collection picture was thus shown to be mistaken.

8. See J. Goodison and G. Robertson *Fitzwilliam Museum Cambridge, Catalogue of Paintings, Italian Schools* Cambridge 1967 pp. 11 ff. no. M. 6 pl. 23.

9. See Arslan *op. cit.* I p. 161 and II pl. 57.

10. See L. Herrmann in the *Burlington Magazine* CIII 1961 pp. 465–6 and fig. I.

11. See *Italian Art and Britain* Exhibition Catalogue, R.A., London 1960 (86); B. Nicolson in the *Burlington Magazine* CII 1960 p. 76 fig. 39; and Herrmann *op. cit.* p. 465.

12. M.Cochin *Voyage d'Italie* Paris 1758 III p. 279. Cochin had lost his own notes and therefore quotes from the owner's catalogue.

13. See note 3 above.

14. See note 3 above.

15. According to his Discharge (MS. in National Library of Scotland, Edinburgh), Andrew Wilson bought fifteen pictures from the Balbi collection on 13 November 1805. H. Wethey *Titian, The Religious Paintings* London 1969 p. 67 states that the ex. Balbi collection picture may be identified as Titian's *Adoration of the Kings* in the Cleveland Museum of Art, Ohio, but this is almost certainly incorrect.

16. See Buchanan 1824 II p. 200.

Traditionally attributed to Jacopo BASSANO

3   Portrait of a Gentleman

Canvas: 127 × 98
Cleaned 1959. In good condition.

Acquired as by Jacopo Bassano and hitherto catalogued under this name; the attribution has also been accepted on stylistic evidence by Berenson (1907, 1932, 1936 and 1957), Arslan in 1931,[1] Frölich-Bume in 1932,[2] Bettini in 1933,[3] and Zampetti in 1957.[4] The only portrait which can be securely attributed to Jacopo Bassano is the signed picture of a *Bearded Man with Open Book and Letter* (Fig. 3) which first came to light when it was acquired for the Kress collection, New York, in 1950 and which is now in Memphis; but it is quite different in style from our picture and from most of the other portraits which by 1959 had been attributed to Jacopo Bassano.[5] If, therefore, the traditional attribution of our picture were to be accepted, it would first have to be agreed, as Suida has indeed suggested,[6] that the Kress collection portrait is an early work; and it would then have to be argued that Jacopo Bassano's style as a portrait painter subsequently developed towards much closer proximity with Tintoretto's manner, in spite of the fact that his securely attributed late subject pictures show no such marked degree of dependence on Tintoretto. As an alternative to such a hypothetical and speculative line of argument, the possibility, first raised by Longhi and Pallucchini in 1957 after the Bassano exhibition, that our picture might in fact be by Tintoretto also deserves serious consideration.[7] Yet there is no signed or documented portrait by Tintoretto which provides a sufficiently close stylistic comparison with our picture to justify outright rejection of the traditional attribution.

Coll: Said to have been inherited by the Marchesa Pallavicini from the Grimaldi family, Genoa.[8] Brusco notes a *Portrait d'un Vieillard du Tintoret* in the Palazzo Grimaldi which might conceivably be this picture.[9] Bought from the Marchesa Pallavicini, Genoa, by Andrew Wilson, on behalf of the R.I., Edinburgh, in 1830.[10] Exhibited R.I. 1831 and 1832 (12). Recorded by Waagen in the collection of the R.I. in 1854.[11]

Royal Institution 1830.

---

1. W. Arslan *I Bassano* Bologna 1931 pp. 120–121. He suggests a date in the late 1560s. But cf. note 7 below.

2. L. Frölich-Bume in the *Burlington Magazine* LX 1932 p. 88.

3. S. Bettini *L'Arte di Jacopo Bassano* Bologna 1933 p. 173.

4. P. Zampetti *Jacopo Bassano* Exhibition Catalogue, Palazzo Ducale, Venice 1957 p. 222 no. 6 illus.

5. See W. E. Suida *Paintings and Sculpture from the Kress Collection* Washington 1951 p. 124 no. 52 illus. See also F. Rusk Shapley *Paintings from the Samuel H. Kress Collection, Italian Schools XVI–XVIII century* London 1973 p. 45 no. K1793 fig. 82. The picture, now in the Brooks Memorial Art Gallery, Memphis, is on canvas 76.2 x 65.4 cm. It is signed *Jac. a Ponte Bassanensis F. In Venitiis.* John Shearman has made the interesting suggestion (verbally in April 1977) that a male portrait at the Museum of Fine Arts, Boston, reproduced by P. Rossi *Jacopo Tintoretto, I Ritratti* Venice 1973 p. 139 Fig. 242 as Domenico Tintoretto, might turn out to be an example of Jacopo Bassano's portraiture at a somewhat later date. It is inscribed lower left . . COB (letter from L. Giese dated 11 May 1977 in Gallery files).

6. See note 5 above.

7. R. Pallucchini in *Arte Veneta* XI 1957 p. 116 and quoting Longhi's verbal suggestion. Roberto Longhi has subsequently confirmed his belief that our picture might be by Tintoretto (letter in Gallery files dated 16 July 1969). E. Arslan *I Bassano* Milan 1960 p. 167 also suggests there is room for doubt regarding the traditional attribution to Bassano.

8. See *Catalogue of the Fifth Exhibition of Ancient Pictures* R.I., Edinburgh 1831 (12). Duchessa Teresa Grimaldi married the Marchese Alessandro Pallavicini; their son was the Marchese Francesco Pallavicini, Duca Grimaldi (b. 1809 d. 1878).

9. G. Brusco *Description des beautés de Gênes* Genoa 1788 ed. p. 61.

10. See further *Pictures for Scotland* pp. 27ff.

11. Waagen 1854 III p. 269.

Studio of Jacopo BASSANO

4   Christ Driving the Moneychangers from the Temple

Canvas: 168 × 230.5

Cleaned 1977. There are some paint losses along the line of a horizontal seam *c.* 55cm. from the top; there is also a tear and a patch at the end of the seam, on the right-hand side. A large tear runs horizontally from below the shoulder of the seated man in the left foreground across to the chin of the kneeling woman with the basket. There are damages along the bottom edge, a small tear in the bottom right corner, a further damage to the centre of the top edge. The paint surface is badly worn.

Acquired as by Jacopo Bassano and hitherto catalogued under his name. However, even allowing for its condition, it does not appear to be sufficiently well executed to be acceptable as an autograph work by Jacopo, and Arslan's suggestion, made in 1960, that it is a studio work is entirely convincing.[1] The cow and the sheep in the foreground of our picture are derived from a picture of the same subject, attributed to Jacopo Bassano, in the National Gallery, London (Inv. 228).[2]

Coll: Probably the picture of this subject, attributed to Jacopo Bassano, which was bought in Leghorn by Andrew Wilson in 1805 and subsequently sold at the Andrew Wilson sale, by Peter Coxe, London, 6 May 1807(22);[3] bought by the R.I. Edinburgh from Mr Berry of Glasgow in 1826 on the recommendation of Andrew Wilson.[4] Recorded by Waagen in the collection of the R.I. in 1854.[5]

Royal Institution 1826.

1. E. Arslan *I Bassano* Milan 1960 I p. 338.

2. C. Gould *National Gallery Catalogue, The Sixteenth-Century Italian Schools* London 1975 pp. 19–20. Canvas 158.7 × 265cm.

3. See Buchanan 1824 II p. 200. But cf. also Gould *loc. cit.* who points out that, according to the 1859 National Gallery London *Catalogue*, the ex. Andrew Wilson collection picture should perhaps be identified as the *Purification of the Temple* by Jacopo Bassano in London (Inv. 228).

4. Recorded in the R.I. Minute Book (R.I. MSS deposited in the Scottish Record Office) 11 May 1826. See further *Pictures for Scotland* p. 27.

5. Waagen 1854 III p. 270.

Studio of Jacopo BASSANO

1511 **Adoration of the Shepherds**

Canvas: 97.5 × 126

The paint surface is obscured by discoloured varnish, but appears to be in good condition.

In the background, towards the left, the Annunciation to the Shepherds is also represented.

Acquired in Rome by William Hamilton Nisbet in 1802, with an attribution to Jacopo Bassano; Nisbet also acquired a companion picture of *Dives and Lazarus* which is now in a private collection.[1] In 1907, when the two pictures were both still in the Nisbet Hamilton Ogilvy collection at Biel, Berenson described them as late works by Jacopo Bassano;[2] and our picture has always been catalogued under this name since it was acquired by the Gallery in 1921. In 1931 Arslan described it as a good quality picture from Jacopo's workshop, by a hand close to Francesco Bassano,[3] but in 1960 he described it as close to Gerolamo and Leandro Bassano, and pointed out that its composition is similar to that of a picture in the Museo Civico at Padua which he believed to be by a hand close to Leandro.[4] There is no real basis, apart from very inconclusive stylistic comparisons, on which positively to identify the artist in Jacopo Bassano's workshop who painted our picture, but it must certainly have been executed by one of the more competent assistants.

Coll: Bought by William Hamilton Nisbet from the Palazzo Mattei, Rome, in 1802.[5] By inheritance to Mrs Nisbet Hamilton Ogilvy of Biel.

Mrs Nisbet Hamilton Ogilvy of Biel bequest 1921.

1. A receipt, dated 27 January 1802, and a certificate, dated 1 February 1802 which were issued to William Hamilton Nisbet by Giuseppe Duca Mattei in Rome, are both preserved in the Ogilvy MSS. in the Scottish Record Office (GD 205 Portfolio 18). A transcription from a copy of the certificate is also published by G. Panofsky-Soergel in *Römisches Jahrbuch für Kunstgeschichte der Bibliotheca Hertziana* XI 1967–68 p. 188. In this document our picture and its pendant are described as *due Quadri di Giacomo Bassano, uno rappresentante Lazzaro alla tavola dell'uomo ricco, l'altro l'Adorazione dei Pastori.* See further *Pictures for Scotland* pp. 109 ff.

2. But Berenson does not include the picture in his *Lists* of 1932 and 1957.

3. W. Arslan *I Bassano* Bologna 1931 p. 343.

4. E. Arslan *I Bassano* Milan 1960 I p. 338. The picture in Padua (Inv. 1054) measures 77 × 94cm.; this information kindly provided by the Director of the Museo Civico. An almost identical version of the same composition is in the collection of Sir Joseph Weld at Lulworth Manor; see *Pictures from Ince Blundell Hall* Exhibition Catalogue, Walker Art Gallery, Liverpool 1960 (16).

5. See note 1 above.

Studio of Jacopo BASSANO

35 Madonna and Child with S. John and a Donor

Canvas: 76.2 × 77
The paint surface is badly worn, especially in the shadows and the dark areas. There are damages on S. John's head and on his left shoulder.

Acquired as by Jacopo Bassano and catalogued under this name until 1957, when, following Arslan (1931),[1] it was ascribed to Gerolamo Bassano. Later, in 1957, Berenson placed it under the name of Jacopo, but as assisted by Gerolamo. The design is based on a signed picture, of horizontal format, by Jacopo Bassano, now in the Art Institute of Chicago (Inv. 68.320),[2] and another signed version by Jacopo Bassano, also of horizontal format, in the Contini Bonacossi collection, Florence,[3] but in our version the figure of a donor has been added. Although Arslan's attribution of our picture to Gerolamo is not at all implausible, there is no very strong basis for it, apart from Gerolamo's reputation as a faithful imitator of Jacopo's style. It is, therefore, less speculative to describe it as simply a good quality studio repetition of a design by Jacopo.

Sir Claude Phillips bequest 1924.

1. W. Arslan *I Bassano* Bologna 1931 p. 304. See also E. Arslan *I Bassano* Milan 1960 I p. 288 where he repeats the same view.
2. This picture was formerly in the Castle Howard sale, Christie's 18 February 1944 (3); Archibald Werner collection; Archibald Werner sale Sotheby's 27 March 1968 (27). See E. Arslan *op. cit.* Milan 1960 I p. 167 and reproduced II pl. 136.
3. E. Arslan *op. cit.* Milan 1960 I p. 168 and reproduced II pl. 138.

After Jacopo BASSANO

36 S. Francis Kneeling before the Virgin and Child

Canvas: 35.5 × 30.2
In good condition.

The design of the Virgin and Child is based directly on Jacopo Bassano's *Podestà Moro before the Madonna* in the Bassano museum.[1] Our picture was acquired as by Leandro Bassano, and was catalogued under this name until 1957 when it was recognised as a feeble imitation of Jacopo Bassano's style.

Coll: Presumably once in the possession of a Miss Cresswell, whose name is on the back.

Sir Claude Phillips bequest 1924.

1. See E. Arslan *I Bassano* Milan 1960 I p. 163 and II pl. 172.

Pompeo BATONI *1708–87*

He was born in Lucca but lived in Rome from 1727. He became the most celebrated artist in the city and enjoyed particular success as a portrait painter among the British Grand Tourists who accounted for more than three-quarters of his commissions in this genre. In Italy, however, Batoni's reputation was based far more on his history paintings, including the *Sacrifice of Iphigenia*, at present on loan to the Gallery from the Earl of Wemyss and March, which is the masterpiece of his early style.

2369   Portrait of Princess Cecilia Mahony Giustiniani (1741–89)

Canvas: 73.7 × 60.7
Signed and dated lower left: POMPEO DE BATONI / PINX. ROM. / 1785.
Cleaned 1978. In good condition, apart from the background which has suffered during unsuccessful cleaning in the past. An old eighteenth-century label attached to the stretcher is inscribed: *[Princess]Giustiniani [daughter] of Lady Ann/Clifford Countess of [Mahony] married to Prince Giustiniani*

Princess Giustiniani was the daughter of the Italian, Count James Joseph Mahony and Lady Anne Clifford. She married Prince Benedetto Giustiniani and lived in Rome. Her portrait, together with a companion portrait of her husband (now in the Andrea Busiri Vici collection, Rome) was commissioned for Sir William Constable (1729-91) whose father had inherited Burton Constable Hall in Yorkshire.[1] Through his mother, Constable was first cousin to Lady Ann Clifford (1715–93).

The portrait was commissioned from Batoni on Constable's behalf by James Byres who had earlier helped him buy pictures in Rome during his second Grand Tour of 1769–71. The circumstances of the commission which also included a copy of a portrait of Countess Mahony by Pierre Subleyras (now in the Musée des Beaux-Arts at Caen) are all documented in a letter from Byres to Constable dated 11 June 1785: 'I waited on Princess Giustiniani and communicated your letter. She explained in the warmest terms her sense of your friendship and the honour you did her and the Prince and said that as soon as her daughter the Duchess of Ciri [sic.] was recovered as she was daily expecting her lying in she would sit for her portrait and that she would prevail on the Prince to sit that his portrait had never been done although often wished for and in the meantime she would send her mother's portrait to whoever I should prevail upon to do it. I said, if agreeable to her, as Pompeo Battoni is reckon'd the best Artist and had painted Her Excellency when a child I believed it would be more agreeable to you that he should do it than any other. She approved of the choice and sent Countess Mahony's portrait to his house the next day and about a month after began sitting herself when I had the honour of attending there, at which time she told me she would have the honour of writing you to thank you for your kind attention to her. The Princess's portrait and that of the Countess Mahony are fine but the Prince had only time to give two sittings before they went into the country. They return in about a fortnight when it will be finished, as soon as thoroughly dry I shall forward them to Leghorn directed as you desire to be sent by the first ship for London and shall forward the Bills of Lading to Mr Bell drawing on him for the expense. I have agreed to pay Sig.[r]. Battoni one hundred Zuchins for the two originals and thirty Zuchins for a copy of the Countess ... The commission is most pleasing to me. I have always had the greatest respect for the Princess Giustiniani.'[2]

The pictures were completed in early July and despatched from Leghorn on 30 July. In a further letter to Constable on 10 August 1785 Byres reveals that the portraits were intended to hang in Constable's gallery 'with those of your other Relations'. And he adds: 'they are very like, were seen for eight days at Giustiniany (sic.) Palace and much approved of by the connexions of the Family, the Roman nobility and Artists.'[3]

Clark and Bowron have pointed out that our picture shows the sitter in one of the earliest and most beautifully executed examples of the *chemise* dress which startled many when it first became fashionable in the 1780s, because of its connotations of *déshabillé*.[4]

The vivid characterisation of the sitter, who had lost a daughter in childbirth in 1783 and suffered a still-birth in 1785, is in marked contrast to the flattering idealised imagery of Batoni's portraits of fashionable English tourists. Brinsley Ford has noted 'the cruel truthfulness about the head of the Princess',[5] and Busiri Vici has compared its pictorial construction with the work of Goya.[6] Painted only two years before the artist died, our picture (and its companion) reveal a psychological intimacy not generally associated with Batoni's portraiture.

Coll: Commissioned by James Byres in Rome and despatched to William Constable at Burton Constable in July 1785; by family descent until 1953; sold Christie's, London 6 February 1953 (lot 38) with pendant of Prince Giustiniani; bought Dent, London; Morandotti, Rome; Anthony M. Clark, Minneapolis and New York, USA 1964–76; his sale Christie's London 6 July 1978 (lot 7).

Bought with the aid of a contribution from the N.A.C.F. 1978.

---

1. A. M. Clark (ed. E. P. Bowron) *Pompeo Batoni. A Complete Catalogue of his Works* Oxford 1985 pp.362–4 no. 456 (Princess Giustiniani) and no. 457 (Prince Giustiniani). See also E. P. Bowron *Pompeo Batoni and his British Patrons* Exhibition Catalogue, Iveagh Bequest, Kenwood 1982 pp. 70–1 no. 39 (Princess Giustiniani).
2. See Clark *loc. cit.* The original letter is in East Riding County Record Office, Beverley, Yorkshire DD/CC/145/6.
3. See note 2 above.
4. See note 1 above.
5. B. Ford in *Apollo* XCIX June 1974 p. 414 pl. IV.
6. A. Busiri Vici in *L'Urbe* 5 September-October 1969 pp. 1–5 fig. 2. Cf also J. Maxon in *Art News* LXVI 1967 p. 46 fig. 5 where he compares our picture to David's *Marquise de Pastoret* (Art Institute, Chicago).

After Giovanni BELLINI *active c. 1459 died 1516*

He was the son of Jacopo and brother of Gentile. He lived and worked in Venice. His early work shows the influence of Mantegna, and by the end of his life he had developed a style close to that of Giorgione and the young Titian.

458   ### The Feast of the Gods

Oil on canvas: 174 × 192.4
The cartellino in the bottom right corner is inscribed: *Johannes bellinus venetus/No. 204.MDXIII.*
Blanching of the paint surface, otherwise in good condition, was treated in 1986.

Mercury, Jupiter, Ceres and Neptune sit in the centre, with Bacchus. At the left, Silenus tries to prevent the ass from braying, a sound which would disturb Priapus, who is about to surprise the sleeping Vesta at the right.

Our picture is a full-size replica of the original painting, signed and dated by Bellini in 1514 and later completed by Titian, which is now in the National Gallery of Art, Washington.[1] It had been commissioned by Alfonso d'Este of Ferrara and was subsequently displayed at the Castello at Ferrara together with three paintings of similar format by Titian (*Bacchus and Ariadne* in the National Gallery, London, and two further *Bacchanals* in the Prado, Madrid). The Bellini was in the hands of the Aldobrandini from 1598 and remained in Rome until the nineteenth century. The number 204 inscribed on the cartellino in our picture corresponds with the number assigned to Bellini's original in the 1603 inventory of the Aldobrandini collection which was compiled by Agucchi.[2] Recently the present picture was exhibited in Washington[3] alongside Bellini's newly cleaned and restored original.

Our picture is generally agreed to be a copy of exceptionally high quality dating from the seventeenth century. The loose weave canvas and the use of a pinkish brown ground suggest it is of Italian origin. It has been associated with Nicolas Poussin since at least 1849 when in the Coningham collection; and most recently by Alfassa in 1925,[4] Bertin-Mourot in 1948,[5] Clark in 1949,[6] Walker in 1956[7] and by Blunt in 1960 and in 1966, although he subsequently changed his mind.[8] Poussin's early interest in the Aldobrandini *Bacchanals* is recorded by Bellori,[9] and his particular study of Bellini's picture is readily apparent in early works such as the *Bacchanal with Lute Player* in the Louvre[10] and the *Triumph of Pan* (National Gallery, London, from the Richelieu series of *Bacchanals*).[11] On the other hand, there is no record of Poussin ever having made such a copy, and a full-scale literal copy of this kind would not have been necessary simply to absorb the spirit of Bellini's design. The attribution to Poussin was questioned by Davies who claimed to have found little evidence in Poussin's work that the French artist had ever particularly admired the Bellini figures![12] This argument now seems extremely perverse, and Davies' alternative attribution to Duquesnoy is not convincing (although Félibien did indeed commission a copy, or partial copy, of Bellini's picture from the Flemish artist[13]). However many other writers have shared Davies' scepticism about the attribution to Poussin; they include Wild,[14] Kauffmann,[15] Mahon[16] and Thuillier.[17]

The possibility of an attribution to Poussin was again aired, in a speculative spirit, by Brigstocke in 1981, in the context of the Edinburgh exhibition, *Poussin: Sacraments and Bacchanals*.[18] Here our picture was displayed in close proximity to the Richelieu *Bacchanals* of 1635–6, where Poussin was consciously imitating the archaic style of Mantegna, and where the modelling of the female figures, the crisp treatment of the draperies and the use of a frieze of trees behind the figures all suggest careful study of Bellini's *Feast of the Gods*. Without documentary evidence, a specific attribution of the present picture to Poussin would clearly be most unwise. However it unquestionably reveals a profound understanding not only of Bellini but of the stylistic aspirations of Poussin and his friends in Rome (including Pietro Testa) during the 1630s.

Coll: William Coningham sale, Christie's, 9 June 1849, lot 4, as by Poussin;[19] bought by Sir Charles Eastlake, who gave it to the National Gallery of Scotland in 1862.

Presented by Sir Charles Eastlake 1862.

1. See E. Wind, *Bellini's Feast of the Gods*, Harvard 1948; G. Robertson, *Giovanni Bellini*, Oxford 1968 p. 152 and note 2; F. Rusk Shapley, *Catalogue of the Italian Paintings*, National Gallery of Art, Washington, 1979 I pp.38–47.

2. See C. d' Onofrio in *Palatino* 1964 p. 205.

3. D. Bull and J. Plesters *The Feast of the Gods. Conservation, Examination and Interpretation.* National Gallery of Art, Washington, 1990 p. 39 fig. 28.

4. P. Alfassa in *Gazette des Beaux-Arts* 1925 I pp.

5. T. Bertin-Mourot in *Bulletin de la Société Poussin*, Paris 1948 p. 54 no. XXXIX.

6. K. Clark, *Landscape into Art*, London 1949 p. 67

7. J. Walker *Bellini and Titian at Ferrara*, London 1956 pp. 106–8 fig. 32

8. A. Blunt in *Nicolas Poussin*, Exhibition Catalogue, Musée du Louvre, Paris 1960 no. 28; A. Blunt, *The Paintings of Nicolas Poussin. A Critical Catalogue*, London 1966 pp. 138–9 no. 201, as *c.* 1635. For Blunt's subsequent change of mind on the attribution see the *Burlington Magazine* CXVI 1974 p. 762.

9. G. P. Bellori, *Vite de pittori* ... Rome 1672 (ed. E. Borea and G. Previtali, Turin 1976 p. 426).

10. See Blunt *op. cit.* 1966 p. 99 no. 139.

11. See Blunt *op. cit.* 1966 p. 97 no. 136; see further H. Brigstocke in *Poussin: Sacraments and Bacchanals,* Exhibition Catalogue, National Gallery of Scotland, Edinburgh 1981 p. 44 no. 18.

12. M. Davies in *Burlington Magazine* XCIX 1957 p. 253.

13. See A. Félibien *Entretiens sur les vies et sur les ouvrages des plus excellens peintres anciens et modernes* Trevoux 1725 vol 4 p. 421

14. D. Wild in *Pantheon* XVIII no. 3 1960 p. 159.

15. G. Kauffmann in *Kunstchronik* XIV 1961 p. 97.

16. D. Mahon in *Gazette des Beaux-Arts* II 1962 pp. 1 ff.

17. J. Thuillier *L'opera completa di Poussin,* 1974 no. R.105.

18. See Brigstocke *op. cit.* p. 24 no. 6; also in the *Burlington Magazine* CXXIV April 1982 pp. 239–40. It should be noted that when Anthony Blunt accepted our picture as by Poussin, he also favoured a date around 1635.

19. Waagen 1854 II p. 266. On Coningham see F. Haskell in the *Burlington Magazine* CXXXIII 1991 pp. 676 ff.

BONIFAZIO VERONESE *1487–1553*

Bonifazio de' Pitati, also known as Bonifazio Veronese. He was born in Verona but settled in Venice and trained under Palma Vecchio. He ran an unusually large studio which accounts for the very uneven quality of the works associated with him.

Studio of BONIFAZIO VERONESE

9   **The Last Supper**

Canvas: 144.5 × 278.5
Surface cleaned in 1949.
A seam runs horizontally across the centre of the canvas. The background is rubbed and restored. Otherwise the paint surface is in good condition, apart from losses around two old tears which have been repaired and which affect the leg of the apostle in the centre foreground and the shoulder and neck of the third figure from the right.

Acquired as Bonifazio Veronese's picture from the Certosa of Venice (i.e. the Carthusian Monastery of S. Andrea del Lido) which had been described by Lanzi in 1795.[1] It is closely related in design to a picture deposited by the Brera Gallery, Milan in the Seminario Vescovile in Venegono which is also attributed to Bonifazio Veronese, and which has also been associated with S. Andrea del Lido.[2] The main variation in the composition of these two versions is found in the three figures at the extreme right. To judge from a photograph, the Brera version is greatly superior to ours and has been accepted as an autograph work of Bonifazio Veronese by Westphal in 1931.[3] Westphal also rightly observed that our picture is only of studio quality.[4] Another variant version of the Brera picture is in the church of S. Alvise, Venice.[5]

Coll: Bought by the R.I. Edinburgh from the Venetian dealer Natale Schiavoni in 1849.[6] Recorded by Waagen in the collection of the R.I. in 1854.[7]

Royal Institution 1849.

1. See the R.I. *Annual Report* 1850 p. 489. See also L. Lanzi *La Storia Pittorica della Italia ...* Bassano 1795–96 II p. 89.

2. See R. Gironi *Pinacoteca del Palazzo Reale ... di Milano* Milan 1812 I no. XXVII with reproductive engraving by Giberti. See also D. Westphal *Bonifazio Veronese* Munich 1931 p. 103 no. 71. Dr Matalon of the Brera Museum has kindly confirmed that this provenance is secure (letter dated 10 March 1976 in Gallery files).

3. *Loc. cit.*

4. *Op. cit.* p. 92 no. 35.

5. See Westphal *op. cit.* p. 111 no. 96.

6. See R. I. Minute 20 December 1849 (MS. in Scottish Record Office). See further *Pictures for Scotland* p. 33.

7. Waagen 1854 III p. 271.

Paris BORDON *1500–71*

Born in Treviso, but already living in Venice by 1518. According to Vasari, he was a pupil of Titian. He worked mainly in Venice, and also apparently visited Augsburg and Paris.

10   A Venetian Woman at her Toilet

Canvas: 97 × 141
Signed bottom left: /RIS B.
Cleaned 1990, revealing tattoos on the face of the older woman to the left. The incomplete signature indicates the canvas has been trimmed, but the reduction is probably very slight to judge from the clearly accentuated swagging threads in the canvas, pulled towards the nails along the edges. The paint surface is in good condition, apart from minor tears in the canvas, which affect the dress, left arm, and the right pigtail of the central figure.

In 1831 it was suggested that our picture might represent *Judith preparing to go to the Tent of Holofernes*,[1] but this is too specific, and the picture might more reasonably be interpreted as an allusion to the theme of Vanitas.[2] It was correctly attributed to Paris Bordon at the time of acquisition but without any reference to the signature. Bordon's works cannot be dated easily on the basis of style, but Canova believes our picture may be relatively late, from the mid-1540s.[3] Canova has also suggested that it might be identified as a picture by Paris Bordon from the collection of Count Widmann in Venice, which Ridolfi described in 1648.[4]

Coll: Bought in 1830 by Andrew Wilson, on behalf of the R.I., Edinburgh,[5] from the Marchesa Pallavicini, Genoa, who claimed to have inherited it, a little earlier, from the Grimaldi family in Genoa.[6] Exhibited R.I. 1831 and 1832 (4). Recorded by Waagen in the collection of the R.I. 1854.[7]

Royal Institution 1830.

1. See *Catalogue of the Fifth Exhibition of Ancient Pictures*, R.I., Edinburgh 1831 (4).

2. G. Canova in *Paris Bordon* Exhibition Catalogue, Palazzo dei Trecento, Treviso 1984 p. 78 no. 16.

3. *Loc. cit.* See also G. Canova *Paris Bordon* Venice 1964 pp. 77–8 fig. 93.

4. See notes 2 and 3 above. See also C. Ridolfi *Le Maraviglie dell'Arte* 1648 (ed. von Hadeln, Berlin 1914–24 I p. 234) who described it as: *una femina col seno scoperto, che si mira in ispecchio, tenutole da una vecchia con una bella giovine à canto.*

5. See *Pictures for Scotland* pp. 27 ff.

6. For the Genoese provenance see note 1 above. If the Marchesa Pallavicini's evidence is correct, our picture might well be the *Tableau de Femmes de Paris Bourdon* noted in the Grimaldi Palace, Genoa, by Brusco in 1788; see G. Brusco *Description des Beautés de Gênes* Genoa 1788 ed. p. 61. Duchessa Teresa Grimaldi married the Marchese Alessandro Pallavicini; their son was the Marchese Francesco Pallavicini, Duca Grimaldi (b. 1809 d. 1878).

7. Waagen 1854 III p. 269 who writes: 'This picture … has all the animation and luminous flesh tones of the master. It belongs, however, to his somewhat gaudy works.'

Orazio BORGIANNI *c. 1578–1616*

He was born in Rome *c.* 1578.[1] His earliest known painting, signed and dated 1593, is to be found in Catania, and this suggests that he may have been in Sicily in his youth. There is firm evidence that he was in Rome in 1603–4, in Madrid in 1605, and that he had returned to Rome by 1607. It has also been suggested that he may have made an earlier visit to Spain around the turn of the century. His chronology after 1607 is difficult to establish, except for a picture at Sezze Romano which is dated 1608. Some of Borgianni's late work shows the influence of Caravaggio; this is evident, for instance, in the *Holy Family with S. Anne* in the Corsini Gallery, Rome, the *Holy Family* in the Longhi collection, Florence (and another good version in a Swiss private collection), and the *David and Goliath* in the Prado Museum, Madrid.

48   S. Christopher

Canvas: 104 × 78
Cleaned 1957. In good condition.

The composition probably depends on a painting of *S. Christopher* by Elsheimer.[2] Three versions of Elsheimer's composition are known, two at Windsor, and another in Leningrad which may be the original. Andrews dates Elsheimer's composition no later than *c.* 1598–1600, i.e. from the period when he was in Germany and Venice.[3] It remains uncertain how Borgianni could have known the picture, unless Elsheimer took it with him to Rome in *c.* 1600.

The position is complicated by a Rubens drawing in the British Museum, London (Inv. Gg. 2.231), which is probably based on Elsheimer's picture. If the drawing by Rubens were to date from his years in Italy, it would provide further evidence that Elsheimer's picture might have been in Rome by 1608. However Held has argued that this drawing must be dated, on evidence of style, *c.* 1611–12 when Rubens was in Antwerp.[4] He therefore suggests that Rubens may also have made an earlier 'original' drawing in Italy which Elsheimer used for his composition, and which either directly, or indirectly through its realisation in Elsheimer's painting, may have exercised an influence on Borgianni. The London drawing is then seen as representing a return to his earlier preoccupation. However, Held's thesis ignores the fact that the lower of the two studies on the British Museum sheet follows the arrangement of Elsheimer's figures exactly and has all the characteristics of a copy.

Our picture was attributed to Giovanni Lanfranco until 1957 when it was catalogued by Waterhouse, with some reservation, as a possible original by Borgianni. It has since been cleaned and there can now be no doubt that it is an autograph work by Borgianni; it has also been accepted as such by Wethey in 1964,[5] and Moir in 1967.[6] Nicolson lists a further version in a private collection, England in 1978 as a 'certain original painting', and apparently regarded it as superior to our picture which he described as a 'possible original'.[7] Another apparently good version of our picture was formerly in the collection of Hermann Voss in Germany, but it disappeared during the Second World War.[8] There are copies after the composition in Edinburgh (no. 20), in the University of Würzburg, and in San Vicente, Seville.[9]

Borgianni also painted a quite different composition of the same subject which is signed and which is probably a much earlier work, perhaps painted during his supposed early visit to Spain; it is now in the Prado, Madrid (no. 7402).[10]

Four pictures of S. Christopher by Borgianni are recorded in Italy in the seventeenth century. Baglione notes two versions painted after Borgianni's return to Italy from Spain. One is described as very large (di grandissima forma); the other was bequeathed by Borgianni to the church of S. Lorenzo in Lucina, Rome.[11] A S. Christopher by Borgianni is also listed in the collection of Giovanni Vincenzo Imperiale of Genoa in 1661, among the pictures offered for sale to Charles II of England.[12] Finally, a signed etching by Borgianni (Bartsch XVII 53), dedicated to Giovanni de Lescano, the executor of Borgianni's will and the secretary to the Count de Castro, may reproduce a painting which Borgianni had already completed for him, to judge from the dedicatory inscription which reads Juxta originale quod Dominationi tue' pinxi ...[13]

The composition of our picture and of the version formerly in the H. Voss collection corresponds closely to the figure of S. Christopher in Borgianni's etching, and there is a prima facie case that they date from about the same time; indeed one of them might well be the picture referred to in the print's dedication. Wethey originally argued that the print must date c. 1605–6, but his conclusion was based on an incorrect interpretation of the inscription.[14] He subsequently revised his view and pointed out that the print must date from c. 1609–16 when Count de Castro was Spanish Ambassador to the Holy See.[15] The etching is extremely close in style and technique to another etching by Borgianni of a Lamentation (Bartsch XVII p. 321) which is dated 1615 and which is dedicated to Count de Castro. This print relates directly to an oil painting of the same composition, in the collection of the Longhi Foundation, Florence, which might also date from c. 1615.[16] In our picture the fluid treatment of the draperies and the modelling of S. Christopher's left thigh are very similar to the handling of the loin cloth and the modelling of the legs in the Lamentation, and both pictures have the same Caravaggesque light. These comparisons suggest that our picture might also be a very late work painted not long before the artist's death.

Presented to the Royal Scottish Academy by Sir John Watson Gordon PRSA in 1850; transferred 1910.

1. For the chronology of the artist's work see H. Wethey in the *Burlington Magazine* CVI 1964 pp. 147 ff. and also in *Dizionario Biografico degli Italiani* XII pp. 744 ff.

2. See H. Voss in *Berliner Museen, Berichte aus den Preussischen Kunstsammlungen* 1920 pp. 25 ff.

3. K. Andrews in *Münchner Jahrbuch der bildenden Kunst* XXIV 1973 pp. 172 ff. See further K. Andrews *Adam Elsheimer* London 1977, p. 140, pl. 23.

4. J. Held *Rubens, Selected Drawings* London 1959 p. 106 no. 30 pl. 26.

5. H. Wethey in the *Burlington Magazine* CVI 1964 p. 153 fig. 13.

6. A. Moir *The Italian Followers of Caravaggio* Harvard 1967 II pp. 48–9 fig. 49.

7. B. Nicolson *The International Caravaggesque Movement. List of Pictures by Caravaggio and his followers throughout Europe from 1590 to 1650* Oxford 1979, p. 25, pl. 7. See further B. Nicolson *Caravaggism in Europe*, second edition revised by L. Vertova, Turin, 1990 I p. 68.

8. See Voss *op. cit.* p. 25 fig. 6.

9. Wethey (see note 5 above) p. 153 note 38. See also R. Longhi in *Proporzioni* I 1943 p. 42 note 29. See further *The Age of Caravaggio* Exhibition Catalogue, Metropolitan Museum of Art, New York 1985 no. 21 for a further version in a village near Seville.

10. Wethey (see note 5 above) p. 151 fig. 4 as in the collection of E. Milicua, Barcelona. It was later with Manuel Gonzales, Madrid; Colnaghi's, London by 1976; Christie's, London 13 December 1985 (lot 24).

11. G. Baglione *Le Vite De' Pittori Scultori et Architetti* Rome 1642 p. 141.

12. Wethey (see note 5 above) p. 153 note 36.

13. However, the alternative possibility that Borgianni, in his use of the word *pinxi* is referring to the creation of the print and not to a painting of the same design cannot be excluded; certainly this word was frequently used in connection with drawings.

14. Wethey (see note 5 above) p. 153.

15. H. Wethey in *Dizionario Biografico degli Italiani* XII pp. 746–47. See also O. F. Osti *Il testamento di Orazio Borgianni* in *Quaderni di Emblema* II Bergamo 1973 pp. 98 ff.

16. A. Boschetto *La Collezione Roberto Longhi* Florence 1971 no. 56 illus. Another version, in the Palazzo Venezia, Rome, is reproduced by Wethey (see note 5 above) p. 156 fig. 14.

After Orazio BORGIANNI

20   S. Christopher

Canvas: 99 × 73.8

There is a damage over S. Christopher's right thigh. The paint surface in the area of the landscape at the right is badly worn.

Acquired as by Caravaggio, and catalogued as school of Caravaggio until 1957 when it was recognised as an interior copy of no. 48 *supra*.[1] Although Wethey has described it as a 'workshop replica', there is no good reason to suppose that the copyist was necessarily an immediate follower or assistant of Borgianni.[2]

Coll: Bought by Andrew Wilson in Italy (perhaps in Genoa) on behalf of the R.I. Edinburgh, 1830.[3] Exhibited R.I. 1831 and 1832 (28).[4]

Royal Institution 1830.

1. As early as the 1929 *Catalogue*, and again in the 1936 and 1946 editions, our picture had been identified as a copy of a design by Borgianni, yet its relationship to no. 48 *supra*, then attributed to Lanfranco, was not apparently recognised.

2. H. Wethey in the *Burlington Magazine* CVI 1964 p. 153 not 38.

3. See *Pictures for Scotland* pp. 27 ff.

4. It is not clear if the *S. Christopher* by Caravaggio recorded by Waagen 1854 III p. 270 as in the

collection of the R.I., and admired by him for its 'offhand power' notwithstanding its 'moral vulgarity' is this picture or no. 48 *supra*, which at that time was attributed to Giovanni Lanfranco, and was the property of the R.S.A., not the R.I.; there is a *prima facie* case for supposing he was referring to no. 20.

Sandro BOTTICELLI *c. 1445–1510*

Alessandro, son of Mariano Filipepi, called Botticelli. Born in Florence where, according to a tradition dating from before Vasari, he was a pupil of Filippo Lippi. A member of the Compagnia di San Luca in 1472. Visited Rome to work in the Sistine Chapel in 1481–2. Mainly active in Florence where he ran a busy workshop.

Workshop of Sandro BOTTICELLI

1536 **The Virgin and S. John Adoring the Infant Christ**

Wood: 46.6 × 41.6

Cleaned 1942. The panel was probably originally a tondo *c.* 71 cm. in diameter. The paint surface is in good condition, apart from some losses in the background and a damage in the top left corner.

Acquired as a Botticelli studio work, a view which had already been expressed by Crowe and Cavalcaselle in 1864 when the picture was in the Fuller Maitland collection,[1] and which was later endorsed by Mesnil in 1938.[2] Berenson (1932, 1936 and 1963), on the other hand, believed that much of it was executed by Botticelli himself, and this had also been the view of Venturi in 1924.[3] It is difficult to see which parts of our picture might have been painted by Botticelli himself, and it seems more likely that it is a relatively late workshop product, dating from the early years of the sixteenth century. Lightbown has catalogued it under workshop and school pictures.[4]

The design of our picture, especially so far as the figures of the Virgin and S. John and the architectural background are concerned, is very close to a tondo that was in the Seymour Maynard sale, Christie's 29 January 1954 (72), ascribed to Jacopo del Sellaio. The S. John in our picture also recurs in a tondo, attributed to Jacopo del Sellaio, in the Jacquemart-André Museum, Paris (Inv. I. 1827 D. 1039). The infant Christ recurs in a tondo, attributed to Botticelli, in the National Gallery, Washington (K. 1432). The ox and ass are apparently repetitions, in reverse, after the animals in Botticelli's *Mystic Nativity* in the National Gallery, London (Inv. 1034), which dates from 1500.[5]

Coll: Said to have been bought by W. Fuller Maitland from Smith's of Bond Street in 1851.[6] W. Fuller Maitland collection by June 1852 when he lent it to the B.I., London (96) as Botticelli; also exhibited *Art Treasures Exhibition* Manchester 1857 (100) as Botticelli;[7] *Exhibition of the Works of the Old Masters* R.A. London 1872 (232) as Botticelli; *Exhibition of Early Italian Art* The New Gallery, London 1893–4 (63) as Botticelli. Recorded in the catalogue of the W. Fuller Maitland collection at Stansted Hall in 1872 (p. 7) and again in the Stansted Hall Catalogue 1893 (12).

Bought from W. Fuller Maitland 1921.

1. J. A. Crowe and G. B. Cavalcaselle *A History of Painting in Italy* (ed. R. Langton Douglas, London 1911 IV p. 267). See also R. Van Marle *The Development of the Italian Schools of Painting* The Hague 1931 XII p. 234 fig. 143 where he attributes it unacceptably to an ill-defined artistic personality close to Botticelli.
2. J. Mesnil *Botticelli* Paris 1938 p. 223.

3. A. Venturi in *L'Arte* XXVII 1924 pp. 193–94 fig. 3.

4. R. Lightbown *Sandro Botticelli Complete Catalogue* London 1978, II, p. 135, no. C. 36.

5. See also R. Langton Douglas *Piero di Cosimo* Chicago 1946 p. 50 for an unconvincing suggestion that the figure of the Virgin both in our picture and in National Gallery, London (Inv. 1034) is derived from a common source, a drawing by Botticelli in the Uffizi (Inv. 209 E), reproduced by Van Marle *op. cit.* XII p. 201 fig. 120.

6. According to a MS note by W. Fuller Maitland in a copy of the *Stansted Hall Catalogue* 1872, in the library of the National Gallery, London.

7. The Catalogue of the *Art Treasures Exhibition* associates our picture with a picture described in Waagen 1854 II p. 3; but Waagen was probably referring to a picture attributed to Botticelli which is now in the National Museum of Wales, Cardiff (Inv. 747), and which was also formerly in the Fuller Maitland collection. Notwithstanding this misleading reference, there is no doubt that our picture was the one exhibited as no. 100 in Manchester: there is the evidence of an old Manchester label which was formerly on the back; and George Scharf's measurements of no. 100 in the exhibition are $18^1/_4 \times 16$ in. (his notes are in the archives of the National Portrait Gallery, London) which coincides with the present size of our picture.

Circle of Sandro BOTTICELLI

099 ## S. John the Baptist

Wood: 35 × 13.3

There are widespread paint losses, due both to flaking and to small cracks in the support along the vertical line of the grain. The best preserved areas are the saint's legs and arms, except that the outlines have been strengthened. The head has suffered from paint loss and restoration; the halo and the saint's red draperies have also been extensively repainted. The landscape is severely rubbed and restored.

Our picture, previously catalogued as circle of Filippino Lippi, is probably a fragment from a larger design, and shows the clear stylistic influence of Sandro Botticelli and Filippino Lippi, particularly in the expressive posture of the saint and the nervous articulation of his hands. Borenius[1] and Berenson (1936 and 1963) considered it to be an early autograph work by Filippino Lippi, but Fahy believes it is closer to Botticelli than to Filippino.[2] Although it is probably by an artist from Botticelli's circle, its condition precludes more precise identification.

Coll: A layer of walnut wood which has been attached to the back of the panel is inscribed *Acton/Villa/ Incontri/–/Bolognese*, which suggests that our picture was at one time in the possession of Arthur [Mario] Acton.

Lord Carmichael of Skirling bequest; received 1948.

1. T. Borenius in *Apollo* 1925 I pp. 67–8.

2. E. Fahy, letters in Gallery files, dated 24 August 1990 and 14 February 1991.

After Sandro BOTTICELLI

792 ## Portrait of Youth

Wood: 55 × 40.3

Technical examination by Ruheman at the National Gallery, London, in 1951 established the presence of artificial ultramarine under the black top layer of the tunic and cap; artificial ultra-marine was not invented until *c.* 1828.[1]

Acquired as an original work by Botticelli,[2] and published as such by Bodkin in 1933,[3] but rightly questioned by Scharf in 1935.[4] It is in fact a twentieth-century copy by M. Phillipot[5] of an original portrait in the Louvre, Paris (Inv. 1663), which has been attributed to Botticelli by Berenson (1932 and 1963) and by Mesnil.[6]

Bought from Knoedler's, London, 1933.

1. Report by H. Ruheman dated November 1951, in Gallery files.
2. See editions of the *Catalogue* up to 1946, but excluded from the 1957 *Catalogue*.
3. T. Bodkin in the *Burlington Magazine* LXII 1933 pp. 203–9 illus.
4. A. Scharf *Fillippino Lippi* Vienna 1935 p. 112.
5. Information in Gallery files, hitherto restricted, but revealed by E. K. Waterhouse in *Italian Studies* XXXV 1980, p. 100 (a review of the first edition of this catalogue).
6. J. Mesnil *Botticelli* Paris 1938 p. 227, where the size is given as 54 × 40 cm. For further discussion of the Louvre picture and the history of its attribution see Bodkin *loc. cit.*

Agnolo BRONZINO *1503–72*

Agnolo di Cosimo, called Bronzino. He was active in Florence, and his style was strongly influenced by Pontormo. His main artistic achievement was as a portrait painter.

After, or by a follower of, Agnolo BRONZINO

1943   **Portrait of Garzia or Giovanni de' Medici**

Canvas: 26.5 × 19.5
The paint surface is somewhat worn, but is otherwise in reasonably good condition.

A workshop repetition or an old copy of a portrait in the Palazzo Pitti, Florence (Inv. 279), of almost identical size, which is traditionally identified as a portrait by Bronzino of Garzia de' Medici, the third son of Cosimo I and Eleanora of Toledo.[1] In the light of recent research on the identification of Medici family portraits, published by Heikamp,[2] and on the basis of comparison with a drawing in the Uffizi showing four of the Medici children together, based on independent portraits painted by Bronzino,[3] the possibility that the Palazzo Pitti picture and our picture represent Giovanni de' Medici cannot be excluded. Our picture could well represent the same person as in portraits now in the Lansdowne collection at Bowood and in the Ashmolean Museum, Oxford, both of which are now identified as portraits of Giovanni, who was the second son of Cosimo I and Eleanora of Toledo.[4]

The attribution to Bronzino of the picture in the Palazzo Pitti, Florence, on which our picture is based, is also open to doubt. It can be traced back to the first catalogue of the Palazzo Pitti by Inghirami in 1834,[5] and since then has also been accepted by Schulze.[6] McComb, on the other hand, attributed it tentatively to Francesco Salviati.[7] In any case, the picture clearly originates from Bronzino's circle.

Our picture, which can be traced to the Alton Towers sale in 1857, was then attributed to Titian, and it reappears under this name in a nineteenth-century inventory of the Lothian collection. Then, shortly before its acquisition by the Gallery, it was exhibited on loan here as by Mabuse. It was first catalogued in 1946 as Italian school, and was catalogued under Bronzino's name in 1957.

Coll: 17th Earl of Shrewsbury (Alton Towers) sale Christie's 9 July 1857 (88) as Titian, bought King for the Marquess of Lothian. Recorded in a nineteenth-century inventory of the Lothian collection at Newbattle Abbey no. 568.[8]

11th Marquess of Lothian bequest 1941.

1. The Palazzo Pitti picture is painted on wood 23 × 19cm. See A. McComb *A. Bronzino His Life and Works* Cambridge (Mass.) 1928 p. 94. Reproduced by N. Cipriani *La Galleria Palatina nel Palazzo Pitti a Firenze* Florence 1966 p. 247.
2. D. Heikamp in *Mitteilungen des Kunsthistorischen Instituts in Florenz* VII 1953–6 pp. 133 ff.
3. Reproduced by Heikamp *op. cit.* p. 134 fig 1.
4. See C. Lloyd *Catalogue of The Earlier Italian Paintings in the Ashmolean Museum* Oxford 1977 pp. 39 ff. no. A. 105 pls. 30–2.
5. F. Inghirami *La Galleria dei quadri esistente nell'imperiale e Reale Palazzo Pitti* Badia Fiesolana 1834 p. 47 no. 279.
6. H. Schulze *Die Werke Angelo Bronzinos* Strasbourg 1911 p. XIII.
7. *Op. cit.* p. 94.
8. Copy of the inventory in the Gallery files.

Bernardino BUTINONE *active 1484–1507*

Born at Treviglio in Lombardy.[1] Influenced by Andrea Mantegna, Francesco Squarcione and Vincenzo Foppa. Active in Milan and Treviglio, often in collaboration with Bernardo Zenale, as in the case of the polyptych which was commissioned for the church of S. Martino at Treviglio in 1485. Two works signed by Butinone alone are also known: a triptych in the Brera Gallery, Milan, dated 1484; and a *Madonna and Child enthroned with S. John Baptist and S. Justina* in the Borromeo collection at Isola Bella.

Workshop of Bernardino BUTINONE

746   Christ Disputing with the Doctors

Wood: 25.1 × 22.3
Cleaned 1951. In quite good condition, apart from minor paint losses, mainly along the edges, and in the architectural background. A tree, once visible in the distance through the doorway at the back, had been painted over an old damage and was removed when the picture was cleaned.

Christ's throne is in the form of an oriental ziggurat, but reduced in scale and placed in a Renaissance room. The ziggurat, an oriental symbol of darkness and confusion, may be intended as an allusion to the tower of Babel which had a similar form. The disunity of language and understanding associated with the tower of Babel is conquered by the divine wisdom of Christ who sits astride it. A spider and spider's web on the left hand wall probably allude to God's divine providence, while the cracked structure of the walls suggests the crumbling of the old order.[2]

Fourteen other panels, similar in size and style and also representing scenes from the life of Christ, have been recorded. These are the *Adoration of the Shepherds* in the National Gallery, London (Inv. 3336);[3] the *Adoration of the Kings* in the Brooklyn Museum (Acc. 78. 151.6);[4] the *Circumcision* in the Carrara Gallery at Bergamo;[5] the *Flight into Egypt* in the Art Institute, Chicago;[6] the *Massacre of the Innocents* in the Detroit Institute of Arts (Acc. 64.81);[7] the *Baptism of Christ* formerly in the Stirling-

Maxwell collection at Keir, Scotland, and subsequently at the Hallsborough Gallery, London, in 1965;[8] the *Marriage at Cana* in the Borromeo Collection, Isola Bella;[9] *Christ in the House of Martha* in the Suida-Manning collection, New York;[10] *Christ before Caiaphas* in the Liechtenstein collection;[11] the *Descent from the Cross* in the Art Institute, Chicago;[12] the *Lamentation over the Dead Christ* and the *Resurrection* in the Crespi collection, Milan;[13] the *Incredulity of S. Thomas* in the Museo Civico, Pavia;[14] and the *Last Judgement* formerly at Knoedler's, New York, and now in a private collection.[15] In spite of some variation in style, it seems quite likely that these fourteen pictures originally belonged to a single series; if more than one series was involved one might reasonably have expected some duplication in the subjects represented.[16] If we are concerned with a single series, further panels probably still remain to be discovered, since certain important scenes from the life of Christ, including the *Crucifixion*, are missing.

Suida was the first to associate some of the panels in this group with the style of the predella paintings for the altarpiece in S. Martino at Treviglio which was executed by Butinone with the assistance of Zenale.[17] He also compared them to the small triptych, containing thirteen biblical subjects, in the civic museum at the Castello Sforzesco, Milan (Inv. 342), which Carotti and Malaguzzi Valeri had already attributed to Butinone.[18] These stylistic comparisons are extremely convincing and it seems very probable that the fourteen panels in the group to which ours appears to belong originated from Butinone's studio. However, to judge from the uneven quality of their execution, more than one hand may have been involved.[19] The attribution of our panel to Butinone was endorsed by Berenson in 1932, 1936 and 1963.

Bought from Knoedler's, London, 1930.

1. See *Arte Lombarda dai Visconti agli Sforza* Exhibition Catalogue, Palazzo Reale, Milan 1958 p. 147.

2. For the association of the ziggurat with the tower of Babel see H. Minkowski *Aus dem Nebel der Vergangenheit steigt der Turm zu Babel* Berlin n.d. p. 27 and H. Ost in *Zeitschrift für Kunstgeschichte* 30 1967 p. 133 pl. 29. For the spider see A. Henkel and A. Schöne *Emblemata Handbuch zur Sinnbildkunst des XVI und XVII Jahrhunderts* Stuttgart 1967 p. 939.

3. See M. Davies *National Gallery Catalogue, The Earlier Italian Schools* London 1961 pp. 132 ff.

4. See M. Salmi in *Dedalo* X 1929 pp. 344 ff. illus.

5. See Salmi *op. cit.* pp. 346 ff. illus.

6. See E. Siple in the *Burlington Magazine* LI 1927 pp. 240–41 fig. A. See also Salmi *op. cit.* pp. 347 ff. illus.

7. See *Detroit Institute of Arts Report* Detroit 1965 illus.

8. See *Arte Lombarda dai Visconti agli Sforza* Exhibition Catalogue, Palazzo Reale, Milan 1958 p. 148 no. 465 pl. CLXXXVIII.

9. See Salmi *op. cit.* pp. 349 ff. illus.

10. See Salmi *op. cit.* pp. 348 ff. illus.

11. See W. Suida in *Oesterreichische Kunstschätze* I 1911 pl. LX. Davies *op. cit.* p. 133 note 9 suggests that this item should probably be excluded from the group, and points out that Salmi had also questioned the attribution in *Dedalo* X, 1929 p. 426 note 21. On the other hand F. Zeri in the *Burlington Magazine* XCVII 1955 p. 77 note 4 appears to accept this panel as one of the series.

12. See Siple *op. cit.* p. 241 fig. B.

13. For both panels see Salmi *op. cit.* pp. 342 ff. illus.

14. See Salmi *op. cit.* pp. 350 ff. illus.

15. See Zeri *op. cit.* p. 77 fig. 20.

16. This was the view of Zeri *loc. cit.* On the other hand in *Arte Lombarda dai Visconti agli Sforza* Exhibition Catalogue, Palazzo Reale, Milan 1958 p. 149 it was suggested that more than one series were probably involved.

17. W. Suida *Repertorium für Kunstwissenschaft* XXV 1902 pp. 334 ff. See also *Arte Lombarda dai Visconti agli Sforza* Exhibition Catalogue, Palazzo Reale, Milan 1958 p. 153 no. 488 pl. CXCVI.

18. See *Arte Lombarda dai Visconti agli Sforza* Exhibition Catalogue, Palazzo Reale, Milan 1958 p. 149 no. 472 both for a full summary of the questions relating to the attribution of this triptych, and for the opinions of G. Carotti and F. Malaguzzi Valeri.

19. For an attempt to allocate the panels to a number of different hands see C. Baroni and S. Samek Ludovici *La pittura lombarda del Quattrocento* Messina/Florence 1952 pp. 235–9.

Luca CAMBIASO *1527–85*

Born in Moneglia, Liguria. Trained under his father, Giovanni, and already active as a painter in Genoa by 1544. His style shows the influence of numerous artists including Perino del Vaga, Domenico Beccafumi, Giovanni Antonio Pordenone, Giulio Romano, Correggio, Titian, and Paolo Veronese. His many paintings and frescoes in Genoa were to be a major formative influence in the development of the seventeenth-century Genoese school.[1]

18   Holy Family with the Young S. John

Canvas: 143 × 106.7
Cleaned and relined 1983. The paint surface is in quite good condition apart from relatively minor losses due to flaking. The Madonna's profile may have been strengthened, and her hair is somewhat worn.

Acquired as by Cambiaso which is certainly correct. It appears to be a mature work. Suida Manning and Suida suggest a date shortly before 1570.[2]

Coll: Bought from the Cambiaso family in Genoa by Andrew Wilson, on behalf of the R.I., Edinburgh, in 1830.[3] Exhibited R.I. 1831 and 1832 (19).

Royal Institution 1830.

1. See R. Soprani *Vite de' Pittori Scultori e Architetti Genovesi* 1674 (ed. C. G. Ratti, Genoa 1768 I pp. 76 ff.); B. Suida Manning and W. Suida *Luca Cambiaso, la vita e le opere* Milan 1958 pp. 13 ff.
2. *Op. cit.* p. 155 fig. 369.
3. See further *Pictures for Scotland* pp. 27 ff.

CANALETTO *1697–1768*

Giovanni Antonio Canal, called Canaletto. Born in Venice, the son of Bernardo Canal, a scene painter and stage designer. From *c.* 1725 he was mainly active as a view painter, influenced perhaps by Luca Carlevaris. Apart from his work in Venice, he also paid several visits to England, the first of which was from 1746–50. In Venice he had a busy studio, where assistants must sometimes have produced versions of his designs. It is not always easy to distinguish studio repetitions and variants from the work of imitators and followers who were active outside the studio.

Follower of CANALETTO

17   The Grand Canal, Venice

Canvas: 65 × 83.8
Cleaned and relined 1945. There is extensive restoration of the sky at the top right, and
there are numerous smaller damages.

Our picture shows a view of the Grand Canal, Venice, looking east from the Campo di S.
Vio: immediately to the right, the North façade of the Palazzo Barbarigo, and in the
distance the dome of S. Maria della Salute, and the Customs House; to the left of the
canal, the Palazzo Corner.

Acquired as by Canaletto and so catalogued until the 1957 edition where it was
described as a school work.[1] In 1962 Constable, in his *Catalogue Raisonné* of Canaletto,
also listed it as a school work.[2] Its composition is based on a picture by Canaletto in the
Brera Gallery, Milan,[3] but the viewpoint has been shifted slightly to the left so that in
our version the buildings to the left of the Palazzo Corner are not included, while the
dome of S. Maria della Salute on the right is more prominent than in the Brera picture.
The arrangement of the boat and figures has also been changed. Another variant of the
Brera picture is at Philadelphia; Constable attributed it to an imitator of Canaletto,
reminiscent of Marieschi.[4]

Coll: Bought by the R.I., Edinburgh, in 1831. Exhibited R.I. 1832 (39).

Royal Institution 1831.

1. For a discussion of the extent to which Canaletto used assistants, see W. G. Constable *Canaletto.
The Catalogue Raisonné* Oxford 1962 I pp. 163 ff.
2. Constable *op. cit.* 1962 II p. 264 no. 191b (also second edition revised by J. C. Links, Oxford 1976 II
pp. 278–9 no. 191b).
3. Constable *op. cit.* 1962 pp. 263 ff. no. 191. Canvas 53 × 70 cm.
4. Constable *op. cit.* 1962 p. 264 no. 191a. Canvas 63.5 × 98 cm.

Follower of CANALETTO

2014   Grand Canal: S. Lucia and the Church of the Scalzi, Venice

Canvas: 37.1 × 55.3
In good condition.

Acquired with an attribution to Canaletto and catalogued as such in 1946, but in the
1957 *Catalogue* it was described simply as eighteenth-century Venetian. Although our
picture is too routine in handling to be accepted as an autograph work by Canaletto, it
closely reflects his style and has been accepted by Constable as a school work.[1] It records
a view looking north across the Grand Canal from near S. Simeone Piccolo, of which no
example by Canaletto himself is known.

Margaret J. Leadbetter bequest 1944.

1. W. G. Constable *Canaletto. The Catalogue Raisonné* Oxford 1962 II p. 301 no. 265 (also second
edition revised by J. C. Links, Oxford 1976 II p. 321 no. 265).

Simone CANTARINI *1612–48*

Baptised in Pesaro on 21 April 1612.[1] Moved to Bologna *c.* 1635, and worked in Guido Reni's studio until this arrangement was disrupted by a quarrel *c.* 1637. By 1639 he was again in Pesaro, and he may have visited Rome soon afterwards before returning to Bologna *c.* 1642.

42   The Holy Trinity

Canvas: 190 × 126
Cleaned and relined 1988. There is a vertical seam in the canvas 7 to 8 cm. from the right-hand side. Unfinished; the dark red ground is clearly visible. There are small paint losses throughout. The cupid at the top left is heavily restored.

The seated figure of God the Father supporting the dead body of Christ on his knees is a symbol of divine redemption. An alternative interpretation of the subject, used, for instance, by Guido Reni in S. Trinità dei Pellegrini, Rome, was to depict Christ still nailed to the Cross. The iconography of each of these variants can be traced back to medieval times.

The figure of God in our picture has no right hand; and the dove, which would normally be shown flying around the heads of God the Father and Christ, is also omitted. The absence of these features is clearly due to the unfinished state of the picture. It was acquired as an unfinished work by Guido Reni and had been catalogued under his name until in 1971 Mahon, supported by Pepper, suggested that it might be by Cantarini, on the evidence of its style and handling.[2] The head of God the Father in our picture (Fig. 7) is almost identical to the head of Christ in another picture by Cantarini: a *Transfiguration* in the Palazzo della Cancelleria, Rome (see Figs. 4 and 6)[3] which is a version of the *Transfiguration* painted by Cantarini *c.* 1637 for the Chiesa del Forte, Castelfranco, and now in the Brera Gallery, Milan (see Fig. 5).[4] In the 1978 edition it was suggested that our picture might also date from around 1636–7, and this has since been supported by Colombo who compares it to a sketchily executed picture of *Lot and His Daughters* in the Neri Collection, Bologna.[5] Since then, however, the cleaning of our picture has shown it to be much closer than previously recognised to Guido Reni's late manner. The modelling of the figure of Christ prompts comparison with the *David with the Head of Goliath* (Sotheby's, 8 July 1992 lot 88) which Reni painted in the late 1620s, and which is documented in a letter from Cardinal Bernadino Spada, the papal legate in Bologna, to the Abate di San Luca, Queen Marie de Medici's agent in Italy, dated July 1631.[6] The free style of underpainting, the extensive pentimenti, and above all the treatment of the putto at the top left of the picture also prompt further comparison with Guido Reni's late work around 1640–2. The possibility that this picture is after all by Guido Reni should not be discounted, although Mahon and Pepper still stand by their attribution to Cantarini.

Coll: Presented to the R.I., Edinburgh, by Edward Cruickshank 1844.[7]

Royal Institution 1844.

1. For the best modern account of Cantarini's life see A. Emiliani in *Maestri della Pittura del Seicento Emiliano* Exhibition Catalogue, Bologna 1959 pp. 114 ff.

2. Oral communication by Denis Mahon and Stephen Pepper, in 1971.

3. The size has not been recorded and details are not readily forthcoming from the authorities at the Vatican.

4. Canvas 380 × 197 cm. See R. Gironi *Pinacoteca del Palazzo Reale ... di Milano* Milan 1833 II no. XXVII. For an earlier account of the picture, and the details of the commission, see C. Malvasia *Felsina Pittrice Vite de' Pittòri Bolognesi* 1678 (ed. M. Brascaglia, Bologna 1971 pp. 595 and 601 note 3).

5. A. F. Colombo in *Bolletino d'Arte* 13 LXVII 1982 p. 33 fig. 11. For the *Lot and His Daughters* see Colombo *op. cit.* p. 23 fig. 6.

6. See M. Dirani *Ricerche di Storia dell' Arte* 1952–3 p. 89

7. Recorded in the R.I. Minute Book (R.I. MS deposited in the Scottish Record Office) 10 April 1844. According to this minute, Mr Edward Cruickshank lived at 9 Lauriston Lane, Edinburgh; in 1842 he had offered to sell the picture to the Directors of the R.I. for one hundred guineas but now wished to present it to the R.I. for their gallery.

Vicente CARDUCHO 1576–1638

Born in Florence in 1576–8 and originally named Carducci, he is now usually known by the Spanish form of his name.[1] He was a pupil of his brother Bartolomeo whom he had accompanied to Spain in 1585. He was appointed Court painter in Madrid in 1609.

Dream of S. Hugh, Bishop of Grenoble

459

Canvas: 57 × 45.5

The paint surface is in fair condition except in the area of the sky which is badly worn, leaving the red-brown ground clearly visible.

Until 1957 the picture was catalogued as *An Incident from the Life of Pope Sixtus V*. The subject was correctly identified by Cuartero y Huerta in 1950.[2] In his dream S. Hugh saw seven stars of gold fall at his feet, rise up, cross the mountain and settle in a deserted place, within his diocese, called Chartreuse. Then, on God's orders, some heavenly spirits built a temple and some small houses. This incident immediately preceded the arrival of S. Bruno and his companions to ask for a site on which they might found what later became known as the Grande Chartreuse.

Acquired as by Velázquez and catalogued under his name until 1936. By 1930 Longhi had recognised it as Carducho's *modello* for his large painting now at the School of Fine Art at La Coruña in Spain.[3] This was originally one of a series of fifty-four canvases, illustrating the life of S. Bruno, which Carducho painted, between 1626–32, for the Claustro Grande of the Carthusian Monastery of El Paular near Segovia;[4] the paintings were removed from El Paular in 1836 and the series was dispersed in 1896.[5]

Coll: Sir John Pringle sale Christie's 18 June 1859 (82) as Velázquez *A pope sleeping with attendants watching.*[6]

Presented by Andrew Coventry of Edinburgh, 1863.[7]

1. See D. Angulo Iñiguez and A. Perez Sanchez *Historia de la Pintura Española, Escuela Madrileña del primer tercio del siglo XVII* Madrid 1969 pp. 86 ff.

2. See B. Cuartero y Huerta in *Boletín de la Real Academia de la Historia* CXXVI 1950 pp. 362–63. See further J. Baticle in *La Revue des Arts* 8 1958 I p. 19.

3. See R. Longhi '*Me Pinxit*' *e Quesiti Caravaggeschi* 1928–34 (*Opere Complete di Roberto Longhi* IV

Florence 1968 pp. 156 ff.). A. Braham *El Greco to Goya* Exhibition Catalogue, National Gallery, London 1981 p. 79 no. 36.

4. See Angulo Iñiguez and Perez Sanchez *op. cit.* pp. 122 ff. both for a list of the other paintings in the series and for twenty–two further *modelli*. Our sketch is no. 93 p. 123 pl. 70. The picture at La Coruña is no. 120 p. 128 pl. 95.

5. See J. A. Gaya Nuño *La Pintura española fuera de España* Madrid 1958 p. 127 no. 510.

6. Identifiable from a copy of the catalogue, annotated with sketches by George Scharf, in the archives of the National Portrait Gallery, London.

7. In earlier catalogues the date is incorrectly given as 1862. There is a letter in the Gallery files from Mr Coventry, dated 24 March 1863, offering the picture as a gift. The picture was accepted on 31 March 1863.

Giovanni Busi called CARIANI *c. 1485–1547*

He was probably born near Bergamo, but he trained in Venice and is recorded there from 1509. His early style reveals a debt to Giovanni Bellini, Giorgione, early Titian and Sebastiano del Piombo. By 1517 he was working in Bergamo and he was also active in Crema. He returned to Venice in 1523. His mature style reflects a Lombard sense of realism and an appreciation of the work of artists such as Romanino and Savoldo.

2494   S. Agatha

Canvas: 69 × 58

Cleaned and restored immediately prior to acquisition. The paint layer is very thin and the surface is somewhat abraded throughout revealing the weave of the canvas in places. The fine lines of the hair have been strengthened by retouching. The flesh paint and the yellow paint in the shawl are notably well preserved.

This picture first came to light at Sotheby's, London, in December 1986 where it was convincingly attributed to Cariani and dated, on stylistic evidence, *c.* 1517–23. It was subsequently published by Ballarin who confirmed the attribution to Cariani but proposed an earlier date soon after 1510.[1] Ballarin compares our picture to Cariani's *Judith with the Head of Holofernes*, formerly in the Neeld collection, and now in a private collection, which he interprets as 'an act of homage to Giorgione'.[2] He suggests that our picture represents 'an elusive moment in his [Cariani's] stylistic evolution when he reacted with precocious intensity to the late work of Giorgione, and that of his pupils Titian and Sebastiano del Piombo'. The design is closely modelled on Sebastiano del Piombo's *Salome* in the National Gallery, London (inv. 2493), which is dated 1510;[3] and in the treatment of the landscape, with its distant blue mountains, there are still echoes from Giorgione.

Coll: Anonymous sale, Sotheby's, London 10 December 1986, lot 22 bought Colnaghi.

Bought from Colnaghi's, London, 1989.

1. See A. Ballarin in *Gothic to Renaissance. European Painting 1300–1600* Exhibition Catalogue, Colnaghi, London and New York 1988–9 pp. 30–2 illus.

2. *Op. cit.* p. 31 fig. 1.

3. See C. Gould *National Gallery Catalogue. The Sixteenth-Century Venetian School* London 1959 p. 83.

Andrea del CASTAGNO *c. 1419–57*

Andrea di Bartolo di Simone, known as Andrea del Castagno from his place of birth. Born not later than 1419.[1] Mainly active in Florence, where he painted an important cycle of frescoes of the *Passion* in the Refectory of S. Apollonia.

Attributed to a close follower of Andrea del CASTAGNO

1210 **The Last Supper**

Wood: 29.9 × 36.2

Cleaned 1952. X-rayed. There is an original added strip on the left. There is a margin of wood, beyond the gesso preparation, on the left and bottom sides of the panel. The top and right edges are gilded. The paint surface is badly worn.

The composition, with three figures seated on the near side of the table, is unusual in fifteenth-century Florentine painting. It was more customary to isolate Judas on the near side, as seen, for instance, in Castagno's fresco of the subject in S. Apollonia, Florence.

A predella panel. It has been suggested that it is from the same predella as the *Crucifixion* in the National Gallery, London (Inv. 1138)[2] and the *Resurrection* (Fig. 10) in the Frick Collection, New York (Inv. 39.1.143),[3] although it is inferior in quality of execution to these two panels which themselves show a strong stylistic unity. The association between the London and Frick panels was first suggested by Van Marle,[4] and their connection has been accepted as certain by Davies.[5] The Edinburgh panel was associated with them in 1930,[6] and this connection is considered probable by Davies.[7] The history of the panels is as follows:

1. *Last Supper.* Its Italian origin is not documented, but it was probably acquired in Italy by Sir William Fettes Douglas (1822–91). For the later provenance see below.

2. *Crucifixion* 29 × 36 cm. Bought by the National Gallery, London, from Charles Fairfax Murray, Florence 1883.[8]

3. *Resurrection* 28.5 × 33.7 cm. Bought by the Frick Collection, New York, from Duveen, 1939. According to Duveen it was with Fairfax Murray in 1880 (but this may involve some confusion with the *Crucifixion*, listed as No. 2 above).[9] It is probably the picture of this subject recorded in the Funghini collection in 1891 as by Piero della Francesca.[10] According to Pudelko, it was once in the hands of a Florentine dealer, Constantini, from whom it was acquired by Weisbach.[11]

Two further panels have also been claimed as from the same series.

4. *The Betrayal.* Last recorded as in the collection of Sa. Felice Laschi Vedova Funghini in 1910.[12] In the Funghini collection, 1891, as by Piero della Francesca and as pendant to a *Resurrection*, probably the picture listed as No. 3 above.[13] There is no clear evidence that Funghini owned any of the other panels sometimes considered to be from the series, and statements that he did are perhaps confused.[14]

5. *The Flagellation.* Ex. Berenson collection. Pudelko associated it with the panels, listed as Nos. 1–4 above, and stated that it, like No. 3, was once in the hands of Constantini in Florence.[15]

X-rays and recent technical examinations of the Edinburgh (Fig. 8), London (Fig. 9) and New York (Fig. 10) pictures clearly indicate a common origin. Each of these three panels is made from two wedge-shaped pieces of wood, joined horizontally. The line of the horizontal join, from bottom left to right, runs directly from one panel to the next, after due allowance has been made for the missing sections of equal dimensions, originally placed between the Edinburgh *Last Supper*, on the extreme left, and the London *Crucifixion* followed by the Frick Collection *Resurrection* on the extreme right. On this evidence, there is a *prima facie* case for accepting the tradition that the missing panels from the original predella are *The Betrayal* and *The Flagellation* described above.

The authorship of the panels is uncertain. The panels in London and New York are ascribed to Castagno in the respective museum catalogues. Our panel was acquired as Flemish school and was first attributed to the school of Castagno in the 1919 *Catalogue;* it was attributed to Castagno in the catalogue of the *Exhibition of Italian Art 1200–1900* at the R.A. London 1930 and again by Fry, also in 1930.[16] Salmi, in 1938 and in 1961, then attributed it to Castagno's assistants.[17] Berenson (1932, 1936 and 1963) attributed it to Giovanni di Francesco (Master of the Carrand Triptych) and this was also the view of Richter in 1943[18] and of Levi d'Ancona in 1955.[19] In 1967 Fahy plausibly proposed an attribution to Francesco Botticini,[20] and was supported by Bellosi.[21] In this case it would have to be an early work of *c.* 1465, when Francesco Botticini was still under the influence of Castagno's late style; his much later predella panel of the *Last Supper* from the tabernacle at Empoli, his only documented work, most of which he executed *c.* 1484–91 but which was finally completed by his son, Raffaello, in 1504,[22] does not seem particularly close in style to our panel.

The altarpiece to which this reconstructed predella might have belonged has not been identified conclusively. Langton Douglas suggested, unconvincingly, that it might be the Poggibonsi Altar.[23] Fahy raised the possibility of a connection with the *Pietà*, 196 × 156 cm. attributed to Francesco Botticini in the Jacquemart-André Museum, Paris (Inv. 944).[24] However, this is inconsistent with the probable dimensions of the predella.

Bought at the Lady Fettes Douglas sale, Dowell's, Edinburgh, 17 March 1917 (3).

---

1. See F. Hartt in the *Art Bulletin* XLVIII 1966 pp. 228–30.

2. See M. Davies *National Gallery Catalogue, The Earlier Italian Schools* London 1961 pp. 138–9.

3. See *The Frick Collection An illustrated catalogue. Paintings. French, Italian and Spanish* New York 1968 II pp. 216 ff. illus.

4. R. Van Marle *The Development of the Italian Schools of Painting* The Hague 1928 X p. 350.

5. *Loc. cit.*

6. See *Italian Art 1200–1900* Exhibition Catalogue, R.A. London 1930 (96).

7. *Loc cit.*

8. See Davies *loc. cit.*

9. See *The Frick Collection, An illustrated catalogue, Paintings. French, Italian and Spanish* New York 1968 II p. 219 and note 28.

10. See G. F. Pichi *La Vita e le Opere di Piero della Francesca* Sansepolcro 1892 p. 63.

11. See G. Pudelko in the *Burlington Magazine* LXVIII 1936 p. 239 note 9.

12. See M. Falciai *Arezzo* 1910 p. 158.

13. See Pichi *loc. cit.*

14. Cf. R. Langton Douglas in the *Art Quarterly* VIII 1945 pp. 287–8.

15. *Loc. cit.*

16. R. Fry in the *Burlington Magazine* LVI 1930 p. 84.

17. M. Salmi *Paolo Uccello, Andrea del Castagno, Domenico Veneziano* Rome 1938 pl. 176 b. See also M. Salmi *Andrea del Castagno* Novara 1961 p. 53.

18. G. M. Richter *Castagno* Chicago 1943 p. 14.

19. M. Levi d'Ancona *The Frick Collection, An illustrated catalogue* New York 1955 XII p. 81.

20. E. Fahy in the *Burlington Magazine* CIX 1967 p. 137.

21. L. Bellosi in *Paragone* 211 1967 pp. 10–12. But cf. A. Rizzo in *Antichità Viva* XV 1976 5 p. 15 note 8.

22. See Vasari (ed. Milanesi IV pp. 245 ff.).

23. *Loc. cit.*

24. See *The Frick Collection, An illustrated catalogue, Paintings. French, Italian and Spanish* New York 1968 II p. 219.

Vincenzo CATENA *c. 1480–1531*

Active mainly in Venice.[1] His early style shows him to have been an eclectic follower of the Venetian masters of the late fifteenth century, especially Giovanni Bellini. Although he was later influenced by Giorgione (with whom he had some form of business partnership in 1506), as well as by Titian and Palma Vecchio, his style always retained its essentially conservative *quattrocento* quality.

1675   Portrait of a Venetian Lady

Wood: 35 × 27

Cleaned 1951. Repaints were removed from the face and head, including curly strands of hair running vertically just below her left shoulder. The paint surface is worn, particularly along the edges of the raised craquelure. There are more serious damages in her hair and in the top left background.

Acquired as by Catena. This attribution was first suggested by Bode,[2] and it has been accepted by Van Marle[3] and Robertson.[4] A suggestion by Heinemann that it might be by Bissolo seems much less likely.[5] Comparison with the *Young Woman as Magdalene* in the Dahlem Museum, Berlin (Inv. 7), generally attributed to Catena, also suggests that our picture may be by the same artist.[6] On the other hand, in their present condition, both works are somewhat characterless and neither of them is particularly close to any signed or documented picture by Catena. It is not possible to date our picture with any precision. Robertson's suggestion of a date around 1515 is perhaps most plausible.[7] Bode had earlier suggested *c.* 1520,[8] and Van Marle regarded it as a late work.[9]

A version of our picture in the Borghese Gallery, Rome, attributed to Girolamo da Santacroce, shows the sitter with detached serpentine strands of hair similar to later additions that were removed from our picture when it was cleaned, as described above.[10]

Coll: Said to have been in the collection of Conte Stefano Bardini, Florence. With the dealer Caspari, in Munich, in 1927.[11]

Bought from Knoedler's, London, 1927.

---

1. See G. Robertson *Vincenzo Catena* Edinburgh 1954.

2. Certificate by W. Bode, dated 15 January 1927, in Gallery files.

3. R. Van Marle *The Development of the Italian Schools of Painting* The Hague 1936 XVIII p. 395.

4. *Op. cit.* pp. 51–2 no. 23 pl. 16B.

5. F. Heinemann *Giovanni Bellini e i Belliniani* Venice (1962) p. 94 no. S. 56.

6. See Robertson *op. cit.* p. 49 no. 18 pl. 16A.

7. *Loc. cit.*

8. *Loc cit.*

9. *Loc. cit.*

10. See P. della Pergola *Galleria Borghese. I Dipinti* Rome 1955 I p. 115 no. 205 (Inv. 76) illus.

11. All this information was provided by Knoedler's in June 1927 and is recorded in the Gallery files.

Giovanni Battista CIMA DA CONEGLIANO *c. 1459–c. 1517*

Details of Cima's activity before 1489 are not known, but he was living in Venice by 1492 and remained there until 1516.[1] His earliest surviving works, the polyptych at Olera of *c.* 1489 and the *Madonna and Child with S. James and S. Jerome* at Vicenza, signed and dated 1489, reveal the influence of Giovanni Bellini.

1190   **The Virgin and Child with S. Andrew and S. Peter**

Wood: 55.6 × 47.2; painted surface 47.7 × 39.7

The border, which is part of the original panel, was made up with gilded gesso at a later date to cover the bare wood which once supported an original moulding. The picture was left unfinished, and only the Madonna's head and the Child were completed. However, the entire composition was drawn in detail on the gesso ground prior to painting. There is elaborate hatching and shading, particularly in the modelling of the draperies. The drawing was probably made with a brush in iron-gall ink that has faded from black or bluish-black to brown except where protected by paint. In those areas of the panel which were not protected by paint there has been a considerable loss, by abrasion, of gesso and of the monochrome drawing. The condition of the panel, which has a vertical split in the top centre and which has also suffered from the tunnelling of woodworm, has caused some losses of paint and of the gesso ground. The Madonna's bosom and the draperies over her legs have been seriously affected by damage and flaking paint. The blue paint in the area of the sky is a later addition.[2]

Acquired as an unfinished work by Cima and subsequently accepted as such. The attribution has been endorsed by Borenius,[3] Berenson (1932, 1936 and 1957), Coletti,[4] and Menegazzi.[5] However, Humfrey has suggested it may be by an assistant of Cima and regards it as a later reflection of designs made by Cima in his middle and late career, such as the *S. Mark enthroned* (Venice, Accademia) and *Madonna of the Orange Tree* (Venice, Accademia), both dating from the mid 1490s.[6] More recently, Tempestini has associated our picture, and in particular the draperies of S. Andrew, with the style of Girolamo da Udine, an early sixteenth-century Friulian follower of Cima;[7] and this idea has won some further support from Humfrey.[8]

Coll: Allegedly sold by Prince Abate of Collalto in *c.* 1830 and bought by Ottavio Ellero of Perugia.[9] By descent to his son, Alessandro Ellero, who sold it in 1887 to Miss Margaret Peter Dove.

Presented by Miss Margaret Peter Dove 1915.

1. For biographical details see L. Coletti *Cima da Conegliano* Venice 1959. L. Menegazzi *Cima da Conegliano* Exhibition Catalogue, Treviso 1962; L. Menegazzi *Cima da Conegliano* Treviso 1981; P. Humfrey *Cima da Conegliano* Cambridge 1983.

2. Since the first edition of this Catalogue in 1978, Joyce Plesters, formerly of the National Gallery, London (Scientific Department), has made a detailed examination of the picture and an analysis of paint samples. Her report, dated 26 June 1985, is in the Gallery files.

3. T. Borenius in the *Burlington Magazine* XXIX 1916 p. 164. He suggests that the castle may be identified as the castle of Collalto near Conegliano.

4. *Op. cit.* p. 77 fig. 36.
5. *Op. cit.* p. 89 fig. 18.
6. *Op. cit.* p. 100 fig. 46.
7. A. Tempestini in *Antichità Viva* 1986 no. 1 p. 50.
8. Letter dated 23 August 1988 in the Gallery files.
9. A statement in the Gallery files by Alessandro Ellero, dated Perugia 15 April 1887, reads as follows (translation): 'I, the undersigned, declare the painting on wood by Cima da Conegliano (size 70 × 63 centimetres), unfinished, representing the Madonna and Child with S. Peter and Paul [*sic*], was bought by my father Ottavio, about 1830 at the Castle of San Salvatore near Conegliano (Veneto) when it was sent to the auction of the effects of a younger son of the Princes of Collalto, called Prince Abate. Perugia, 15 April 1887.'

Giovanni Battista CRESPI (Il Cerano) *c. 1575–1632*

Probably born in Lombardy *c.* 1575. He may have studied in Rome *c.* 1595[1] and in Flanders before 1604.[2] Mainly active in Milan, where he influenced G. C. Procaccini. In 1620 he became the first president of the art academy founded in Milan by Cardinal Federico Borromeo.

2129   Head of S. Francis in Ecstasy

Wood: 41 × 35.5
The abrupt termination of the vigorous brush strokes at the edges suggests that our picture might have been cut down from a larger painting. Cleaned 1950. In good condition.

Acquired without attribution and first attributed to Cerano in the 1957 *Catalogue*. It is similar in style and mood to two pictures of *S. Francis*, both attributed to Cerano, in the Museo Civico d'Arte Antica, Turin,[3] and in the Poletti collection, Milan.[4] On this basis it seems reasonable to accept it as the work either of Cerano himself or possibly of one of his close followers or assistants, such as Chignoli or Gherardini, whose artistic activity has never been seriously studied.[5]

Coll: Said to have been acquired early in the nineteenth century by a member of the Stirling family of Kippenross.[6]

Presented by Col. J. A. Stirling of Cauldhame and Kippendavie in 1950.

1. See M. Rosci *Mostra del Cerano* Exhibition Catalogue, Novara 1964 p. 40.
2. See G. Bora *Il Seicento Lombardo. Catalogo dei disegni …* Exhibition Catalogue, Milan 1973 p. 16.
3. See Rosci *op. cit.* p. 101 no. 126 fig. 160.
4. See Rosci *op. cit.* p. 101 no. 127 fig. 161.
5. But see M. Valsecchi in *Arte Antica e Moderna* 13–16 1961 pp. 267–75 for a pioneering study of Chignoli.
6. Letter in Gallery files from Col. J. A. Stirling, dated 2 November 1954.

Bernardo DADDI *active by 1327 died 1348*

Florentine. Strongly influenced by Giotto and the Master of Santa Cecilia. His work included the *Ognissanti* Triptych of 1328, now in the Uffizi, Florence (Inv. 3073); a triptych of 1333, now in the Museo del Bigallo, Florence; a tabernacle of 1334, in the Accademia, Florence (Inv. 8564); and a tabernacle of 1346–7, in Orsanmichele, Florence. He ran a large and busy workshop and many of the works attributed to him were probably completed with the help of assistants.

1904 A Triptych: The Crucifixion

Left wing: Nativity; two prophets, Micah and Zachariah (?); (above) Crucifixion of S. Peter. Right wing: Madonna enthroned with SS. John the Evangelist, Peter, Augustine and Paul; two prophets; (above) S. Nicholas and the golden apples. Above the centre panel: Christ blessing.

Wood: (inside mouldings) centre 53.5 × 28; wings, left 58 × 15.5, right 57.7 × 15.2

An inscription along the base has been repainted or strengthened, evidently before 1854 when Waagen described it; but it appears to be basically authentic. It reads: ANNO DNI MCCCXXXVIII FIORENTIA PER....

Cleaned 1969. There is a small vertical crack in the centre of the main panel. Although the paint surface is in good condition for a work of its age, damages and paint loss affect the group of figures at the bottom right of the central panel, the head of the Madonna in the right-hand panel, the heads of the three young girls in the panel with S. Nicholas immediately above, and the head of S. Joseph in the Nativity scene in the left-hand panel. The gold of the background which is somewhat worn appears to be original. The frame has been extensively restored. The ornaments attached to the central pinnacle are probably nineteenth-century, and the authenticity of the hinges joining the central panel to the wings is also in doubt.

At this date the Madonna enthroned was usually represented in the central panel, as opposed to the wings, of a triptych. According to Offner, there is only one earlier Florentine example of this iconographical arrangement, the *Barnes Tabernacle* by the S. Quirico Master.[1]

By the time the tabernacle was acquired by the Gallery, it had already been attributed to Bernardo Daddi by Sirén (1917),[2] Offner (1919),[3] Berenson (1921,[4] and then again in 1930,[5] 1932 and 1963), MacColl (1924),[6] Van Marle (1924)[7] and Beenken (1932).[8] Offner listed it as by a close follower of Daddi, together with many of the other works usually thought to be by Daddi himself.[9] Earlier, while still in the Fuller Maitland collection, our picture had been attributed to Taddeo Gaddi by Waagen,[10] who was followed by Crowe and Cavalcaselle;[11] and in the catalogue of the *Art Treasures Exhibition* in Manchester in 1857 the central panel was associated with the name of Giottino.[12]

The current association of our picture with the name of Daddi remains entirely acceptable. Many of the details from its design recur in other works generally attributed to him. In particular, both the scene of the *Crucifixion* and the *Nativity* are extremely close to the representation of these two scenes in the wings of a tabernacle in the Dahlem Museum, Berlin (Inv. 1064) where the central panel represents the *Coronation of the Virgin*.[13] However it must also be said that the pictures at present attributed to Daddi are surprisingly uneven in the quality of their execution, perhaps because so many of the products of Daddi's workshop were completed, at least in part, by his assistants; and while the relatively high quality of our picture is in no way suggestive of routine studio work, it still does not match the quality of execution found, for instance, in a tabernacle by Daddi from Count Seilern's collection, now in the Courtauld Institute Galleries, London (fig. 11), which is otherwise close to ours in stylistic character, and which is inscribed with the same date (1338).[14]

Coll: W. Fuller Maitland collection at Stansted Hall by 1854 when described by Waagen.[15] Also listed in the Catalogue of the W. Fuller Maitland collection at Stansted Hall 1872 (p. 5) and again in the Stansted Hall Catalogue 1893 (1) as by Giottino and T. Gaddi. Lent by W. Fuller Maitland to the *Exhibition of Early Italian Art* New Gallery, London 1893–94 (68) as Taddeo Gaddi. Sold to R. Langton Douglas *c.* 1907. Then with Julius Böhler, Munich, by 1917 when noted by Sirén.[16]

Bought from the Spanish Art Gallery, London, 1938.

1. R. Offner *A Critical Corpus of Florentine Painting* Section III vol. IV New York 1934 p. 77.
2. O. Sirén *Giotto and some of his followers* Harvard 1917 I pp. 167 ff. pp. 184 f., and p. 271 and II pl. 146.
3. R. Offner *Art in America* VII 1919 p. 149.
4. B. Berenson in *Bolletino d'Arte* 1921 I p. 298.
5. B. Berenson *Studies in Medieval Painting* New Haven 1930 p. 65. See also in *Dedalo* XI 1931 p. 974.
6. D. S. MacColl in the *Burlington Magazine* XLIV 1924 p. 228.
7. R. Van Marle *The Development of the Italian Schools of Painting* The Hague 1924 III p. 379 and pp. 390–91.
8. H. Beenken in *Zeitschrift für Kunstgeschichte* Berlin 1932 I p. 311.
9. *Op. cit.* Section III IV New York 1934 p. 78.
10. Waagen 1854 III p. 2.
11. J. A. Crowe and G. B. Cavalcaselle *A History of Painting in Italy* (ed. R. Langton Douglas, London 1903 II p. 140). Although Langton Douglas did not question Crowe and Cavalcaselle's attribution at this time, he later concluded that the picture was by Daddi and claimed to have been the first to recognise this. His letter to the Director, Stanley Cursiter, dated 30 May 1938, is in the Gallery files.
12. *Art Treasures Exhibition Catalogue* Manchester 1857 no. 47.
13. See Offner *op. cit.* Section III IV New York 1934 pp. 79–83.
14. Count A. Seilern *Italian Paintings and Drawings at 56 Princes Gate, London.* London 1959 p. 3 no. 69 pls. I-XV.
15. *Loc. cit.*
16. *Loc. cit.*

DOMENICHINO *1581–1641*

Domenico Zampieri, called Domenichino. He was born at Bologna and became a pupil of Ludovico Carracci. He left Bologna for Rome *c.* 1602 and worked in the circle of Annibale Carracci. During this period he made a number of variant copies after Annibale's late works; and in some cases he attempted to adapt their composition to his own severe sense of classical refinement. This is evident, for instance, in Domenichino's *Madonna and Child with S. John* in the Louvre, Paris, after Annibale's original picture in the Royal Collection, London, and in his *Three Maries* (now lost) based on Annibale's picture now in the National Gallery, London.[1] Domenichino's mature works include *The Last Communion of S. Jerome* in the Vatican Gallery, Rome, dated 1614, and his frescoes in S. Andrea della Valle, Rome, documented 1624–8. In 1628 he became President of the Accademia di San Luca, in Rome. From *c.* 1631 onwards he worked mainly in Naples, and in particular in the Cappella del Tesoro in the Duomo.

2313 **The Adoration of the Shepherds**

Canvas: 143 × 115

The blue draperies of the Virgin and the standing shepherd at the right have been affected by chemical change; the yellow draperies of the kneeling child with the dove have also suffered, but to a lesser extent, from a similar process. Otherwise the picture is in good condition.

In the composition, and the dramatic use of nocturnal light, the artist has been influenced by Correggio's *Notte,* now in Dresden, but originally in Reggio Emilia. The sobriety of the Nativity is combined with the more joyful and festive scene of Adoration.[2]

Attributed to Annibale Carracci from 1813–58; then in 1906–7 Tietze identified it as Domenichino's copy of a lost picture by Annibale Carracci, described by Bellori.[3] The whereabouts of the Annibale Carracci version were already unknown to Bellori in 1672 and it seems probable, from his description of it, that he was actually relying on the copy by Domenichino which, he states, had recently been sent to France.[4]

Domenichino's association with the composition of our picture is also documented by a seventeenth-century reproductive engraving by Colbenschlag, inscribed *Dominicus In. St. Colbenschlag fe romae.* However, the print omits the dog and ass and the shepherd's crook in the foreground of the picture, which suggests it might be based on a preparatory drawing.

The quality of the picture is unusually fine for Domenichino and one can readily perceive why it was formerly attributed to Annibale. It has generally been assumed that Domenichino made an almost literal copy of the Carracci composition,[5] and this view was supported by the evidence of a drawing at Windsor (2083 *verso*) clearly by Annibale Carracci, of a kneeling youth with a dove (Fig. 14), which directly relates to the kneeling figure in the right foreground of our picture.[6] There is, however, another drawing at Windsor (5700 *recto* and *verso*) which may probably be attributed on stylistic grounds to Domenichino, consisting of preparatory studies for two of the figures in our picture (Figs. 12, 13); it indicates that Domenichino may have made substantial alterations to the Annibale Carracci composition, since preparatory drawings of this kind would not have been necessary for a literal copy of an earlier painting.[7] Windsor 5700 *verso* is a preparatory study for the figure of S. Joseph in the background of our picture; the position of the hands in the drawing is identical, but the sketch is too exploratory to be judged a later copy made after the lost Carracci picture. Once this connection with our painting is recognised, there is little difficulty in accepting the idea that the figure on the *recto,* a study of a standing male nude, was used for the figure of the bagpiper found in the same picture, even if it may not necessarily have been originally made with this purpose in mind.

The study on the *recto* might be interpreted as an indication that Domenichino either invented the figure of the bagpiper in our picture or at least gave it a much more prominent position than it held in the lost picture by Annibale Carracci. In Giovanni Lanfranco's *Adoration of the Shepherds* (Fig. 15), now at Alnwick Castle, Northumberland, which, as Schleier has already shown, is also based on the lost Carracci, although it is of horizontal format, there is no bagpiper and the left foreground is filled with the seated figure of Joseph.[8] In another horizontal version by Lanfranco, only known from a copy which has also been published by Schleier, there is a bagpiper at the left, but in a much less prominent position than in our picture.[9] In this respect the two Lanfranco versions may be nearer to the Carracci composition than Domenichino's version.[10] On the other hand, Stampfle and Bean have argued that a drawing, now in the Pierpont Morgan Library, New York, which is convincingly attributed to Annibale Carracci and which represents a *Shepherd with pipes ... and the Virgin and Child* might be a preparatory study for his lost picture of *The Adoration of the Shepherds*.[11] But this suggested connection is not convincing; and the drawing, with its horizontal format, is much closer to Annibale's late etching of the *Adoration of the Shepherds* (Bartsch XVIII, 2) of *c.* 1606. It does, however, provide an example of Annibale introducing a prominent bagpiper into an *Adoration* scene, and it is possible that Domenichino was aware of this drawing, and of another closely related sheet (sold at Christie's, London, 1 April 1987, lot 106A), when working on our picture.

If, as Windsor drawing 5700 *recto* strongly suggests, Domenichino did decide to open up the original Annibale Carracci composition and to emphasise its vertical axis by introducing the bagpiper in the left foreground, he might easily have displaced the figure of Joseph. This would explain the necessity for him to make a study for a new figure of Joseph on the back of his study for the bagpiper. This figure of Joseph is placed rather awkwardly in the background of our picture and seems to be quite separate and apart from all the other figures which, with the exception of the bagpiper, are all carefully inter-related. It is therefore easy to believe that this Joseph did not belong to the original composition.

Annibale Carracci's lost painting may have been painted as early as 1598. This view, which has been propounded by Wittkower, Mahon and Posner,[12] and was supported in the first edition of this catalogue, is mainly based on the evidence of his preparatory drawing at Windsor (2083 *verso*), which is made on the back of a drawing connected with one of the *Atlantes* in the Farnese Gallery on which Annibale was working 1597–1600; and on the further evidence of a drawing by Agostino Carracci formerly in the Duke of Sutherland's collection, which seems to be directly derived from Annibale's painting and which almost certainly dates from *c.* 1598–1600, when Agostino was in Rome, and in any event is no later than 1602 when the artist died.

Stampfle and Bean's argument that Annibale's picture should be dated around 1606 or later was based on the fact that the drawing, now in the Pierpont Morgan Library, which they believe to be a preparatory study for this project is on the back of a proof impression of an etching by Annibale (Bartsch XVIII, 3) which in its published state is dated 1606. But it is a theory which fails to account for Agostino's drawing.[13]

Bohlin,[14] followed by Spear[15] has also argued in favour of a late date around 1606 for Annibale's picture, but she regards the Pierpont Morgan drawing as an intermediate stage between 'the recently completed painting' and the etching of the same subject, which she also dates around 1606. She discounts any conflict in the evidence of the Windsor drawing (2083), in the belief that the *recto* is a copy after, rather than a study for, a herm on the Farnese ceiling, and that the study on the *verso*, for the boy holding a dove in the foreground of Annibale's *Adoration*, could easily date from the artist's final years.[16] She further argues that the Agostino drawing from the Duke of Sutherland's collection is not a copy based on Annibale's design but rather a source of inspiration for Annibale when he prepared his painting. Yet Bohlin herself, in advancing this elaborate hypothesis, also concedes that the painting would be the only one to have been executed by Annibale after his serious illness in 1605. If, on the other hand, Bellori was slightly mistaken and Domenichino was working from drawings by Annibale and not a painting, as he did for the figure at S. Mark at Grottaferrata, then Bohlin's proposed date for the Carracci design would be entirely convincing.[17]

Domenichino's picture has been dated *c.* 1610 by Borea and *c.* 1608 by Spear.[18] Lanfranco's version at Alnwick is dated 1607/8 by Schleier.[19] It is arguable that our picture precedes the Alnwick version and that Lanfranco was aware, not only of the lost

Carracci, but also of Domenichino's interpretation. For as Schleier has pointed out, the shepherd boy carrying a bale of hay in the background of Lanfranco's picture is remarkably similar to the figure of St Joseph carrying hay which Domenichino apparently designed himself (Windsor 5700 *verso*) for use in our picture.[20] It seems likely that the obsessive interest in the theme of the *Adoration of the Shepherds* among Annibale's close followers was originally inspired not only by the master's lost picture of c.1598–1600 but also by his own return to the subject in his drawing of 1606 and his late etching, and that both Domenichino and Lanfranco painted their pictures soon afterwards.

Coll: Sent from Rome to an unspecified destination in France by 1672, according to Bellori.[21] A *Nativité de Notre-Seigneur* attributed to Annibale Carracci which might well be the same picture (or else the lost Carracci) was mentioned by Félibien as having been sold in France by Pierre Mignard to M. d'Erval (Barthelemy d'Herwarth); it then passed into the collection of Jean-Baptiste Colbert (1625–83).[22] Then, according to P. J. Mariette (1694-1774), our picture (i.e. the Domenichino *Nativity* engraved by Cobenschlag [sic]) belonged to the Duc d'Orléans,[23] but there appear to be no further readily identifiable references to it in subsequent descriptions of the Orléans collection. The first reference to our picture after its importation into Great Britain dates from 1813 when it is listed in an inventory of the collection of pictures in the house of the late Sir Francis Bourgeois, which had been bequeathed to Dulwich College in 1811.[24] (Although some of the pictures from the Bourgeois bequest had been inherited by him from Noel Desenfans in 1807, and had earlier formed part of the collection Desenfans had been making for Stanislaus, King of Poland, prior to the Polish king's abdication in 1795, there is no evidence that our picture ever passed through the hands of Desenfans). It was sold by the Governors of the Dulwich College Gallery at Sotheby's 24 March 1971 (11).

Bought at Sotheby's, London, 24 March 1971.

---

1. Domenichino's *Three Maries* is now known only from a picture which J. Pope-Hennessy (*The Drawings of Domenichino in the collection of His Majesty the King at Windsor Castle* London 1948 p. 43) has judged to be a copy; it was in the Kinnaird sale Christie's 21 June 1946 (13). It is reproduced by H. Brigstocke in the *Burlington Magazine* CXV 1973 pp. 525–6 fig. 45.

2. See E. Mâle *L'art religieux après le Concile de Trente* Paris 1932 pp. 243 ff.

3. H. Tietze in *Jahrbuch der Kunsthistorischen Sammlungen* des *allerhöchsten Kaiserhauses* XXVI 1906–7 pp. 143 ff. But the first published record of the new attribution to Domenichino is to be found in a *Catalogue of the Pictures ... at Dulwich* London 1892 p. 77 no. 283. According to D. G. Banwell, Clerk to the Governors at Dulwich College, the name of Domenichino was first propounded by S. P. Denning, the Keeper of the Gallery, in 1858. (Letter in Gallery files, dated 8 April 1975). For the attribution to Domenichino see further L. Serra *Domenichino* Rome 1909 p. 20 and H. Voss *Die Malerei des Barock in Rom* Berlin 1924 p. 512

4. Giov. Pietro Bellori *Le Vite de' Pittori* Rome 1672 p.86. He writes: ... *esposto Giesù nella mangiatoa con vivo effetto del lume, che si diffonde sopra la madre, che lo svela, e sopra gli Angeli, che dietro appariscono con le mani in atto di adorarlo, risplendendo all' opposto di un muro in ombra, dove sedono tre Angioletti col titolo della gloria. Stanno i Pastori in adoratione, e prima un giovinetto tiene una palomba, volgendosi al padre appresso, il quale con la berretta in mano piega una gamba in terra & abbraccia un'altro figliuolino che gli pone un piede sù'l ginocchio e giunge le mani rivolto al Bambino. Dietro vi è un huomo raso ginocchione, e s'infrapone la testa di un vecchio in piedi, che con la mano, si fà riparo à gli occhi dallo splendore divino, sollevandosi un altro, che stende il braccio, & addita il nato Giesù, figure ordinate insieme, & espresse all'attione. Dall'altro lato dietro la Vergine vi è un pastore in piedi, che suona la cornamusa: & hò voluto lasciar memoria di questo quadro, benche non si sappia dove sia l'originale, essendone passata in Francia una copia di mano del Domenichino. Annibale osservò in esso i modi di lumeggiare tenuti dal Correggio nella Natività, che era in Reggio, & hora nel palazzo del Serenissimo Duca di Modena;* ...

5. See D. Posner *Annibale Carracci* London 1971 II p. 47 no. 108. He writes that our picture 'would appear to be a fairly exact replica of the original'.

6. R. Wittkower *The Drawings of the Carracci in the collection of Her Majesty the Queen at Windsor Castle* London 1952 p. 144 no. 344 fig. 44. Black chalk on grey-blue paper 353 × 230 mm.

7. Cf. A. Blunt and H. Cooke *Roman drawings of the XVII and XVIII Centuries in the collection of Her Majesty the Queen at Windsor Castle* London 1960 p. 49 no. 216 pl. 4 where it is attributed to Lanfranco. For a discussion of the attribution to Domenichino and the relationship of the drawings to our picture, see Brigstocke *op. cit.* pp. 525–6 figs. 40 and 41. The drawings are made in black and white chalk on green-grey paper 385 × 224 mm.

8. E Schleier in the *Burlington Magazine* CIV 1962 pp. 246 ff. fig. 17. See further E. Schleier *The Age of Caravaggio* Exhibition Catalogue, Metropolitan Museum of Art, New York 1985 pp. 158-60 no. 44.

9. E. Schleier in the *Burlington Magazine* CIV 1962 pp. 246 ff. fig. 18 as a copy after Badalocchio. Erich Schleier now believes it to be after a lost Lanfranco. See E. Schleier *Disegni di Giovanni Lanfranco (1582–1647)*. Gabinetto Disegni e Stampe degli Uffizi, Florence 1983 pp. 26–9 no. II.

10. Two paintings by Badalocchio of the *Adoration of the Shepherds*, which may also be related to the lost Annibale Carracci, offer less reliable evidence of the original composition since they were probably painted later than both the Lanfranco and Domenichino variants. See notes 8 and 9 above.

11. F. Stampfle and J. Bean *The Seventeenth Century in Italy. Drawings from New York Collections II* Exhibition Catalogue, Metropolitan Museum of Art, New York 1967 p. 25 no. 14 illus. The drawing is in pen and brown ink 153 × 217 mm. But cf Posner *op. cit.* II p. 73 no. 175.

12. Wittkower *loc. cit.*; D. Mahon *Mostra dei Carracci Disegni* Bologna 1963 (2nd ed. 1963 p. 62 no. 72 fig. 35); Posner *loc. cit.*

13. Stampfle and Bean *loc. cit.*

14. D. De Grazia Bohlin *Prints and Related Drawings by the Carracci Family. A Catalogue Raisonné* Exhibition Catalogue, National Gallery of Art, Washington 1979 pp. 470–4 no. 22.

15. Spear *op. cit.* p. 151 no. 30 pl. 48.

16. This was earlier suggested by J. R. Martin *The Farnese Gallery* Princeton 1965 p. 267.

17. I am indebted to Aidan Weston-Lewis for this idea.

18. E. Borea *Domenichino* Milan 1965 p. 147. Spear *loc. cit.*

19. See notes 8 and 9 above.

20. See note 9 above.

21. Bellori *loc. cit.*

22. See A. Félibien *Entretiens sur les vies et sur les ouvrages des plus excellens peintres anciens et modernes* Trévoux 1725 III p. 274. See further Posner *loc. cit.* For d'Erval and Colbert see E. Bonnaffé *Dictionnaire des Amateurs Français au XVIIe siècle* Paris 1884 (reprint Amsterdam 1966 pp. 66-9 and 138–9)

23. *Abecedario de P. J. Mariette et autres notes inédites de cet amateur sur les arts et les artistes* ed. P. de Chennevières and A. de Montaiglon, Paris 1859–60 VI p. 149 as follows: *Les pasteurs adorans l'enfant Jésus couché dans la crèche. Gravé à l'eau forte, à Rome, par Et. Cobenschlag. – Mich. de Marolles dicatum. Je ne croy cette pièce gravée que sur un dessein, car il n'est marqué seulement au bas que: Dominiquin in. – M. le duc d'Orléans en a présentement le tableau.* I am indebted to Richard Spear for kindly drawing my attention to this reference.

24. MS. inventory drawn up by J. Britton (Dulwich College archives). The picture is subsequently recorded in the Dulwich College Gallery by A. Jameson *A Handbook to the Public Galleries of Art in and near London* London 1842 p. 503 (no. 349), by J. Sparkes *A descriptive catalogue of the Pictures in the Dulwich College Gallery* London 1876 no. 349, and by J. P. Richter and J. Sparkes *A descriptive catalogue of the Pictures in the Dulwich College Gallery* London 1880 no. 349.

EMILIAN *late fifteenth-century*

1634   Madonna and Child with S. Francis, S. Jerome and Two Angels

Wood: 115.5 × 92.8

The panel is badly damaged at the top centre, seriously affecting the features of the Madonna and Child. The two saints are in a relatively good state.

Acquired as by Leonardo Scaletti, following a suggestion, advanced by Toesca in 1907, that it is by the same hand as an altarpiece of the *Madonna and Saints* in the Pinacoteca

Comunale at Faenza, for which he also tentatively proposed the name of Scaletti.[1] Toesca's view of our picture was followed by Berenson (1932 and 1936) but in 1934 Longhi convincingly demonstrated that there is no real stylistic link between our picture and the Faenza altarpiece, and suggested instead that it might be the work of an artist who was active in Emilia or Romagna around 1490.[2] Longhi's view was followed in the 1957 *Catalogue* and subsequently endorsed by Zeri, who believes it might well be by a Bolognese artist who was working under the predominant influence of Francesco Cossa.[3] No other picture by the same hand has yet been recognised.

Coll: S. Boddington sale Christie's 29 January 1881 (III) as by Mantegna; Howell Wills sale Christie's 17 February 1894 (67) as by Mantegna bought Quilter; Harry Quilter sale Christie's 7 April 1906 (87) as by Mantegna bought for Claude Phillips.[4]

Sir Claude Phillips bequest 1924.

1. P. Toesca in *L'Arte* X 1907 pp. 18 ff. where our picture is reproduced, fig. 3. The Faenza altarpiece is reproduced in the *Catalogo della pittura Ferrarese del Rinascimento* Ferrara 1933 p. 84 no. 97 illus.
2. R. Longhi *Officina Ferrarese* 1934 (*Opere Complete di Roberto Longhi* V Florence 1956 p. 101).
3. Letter from Federico Zeri, dated 19 May 1966, in Gallery files.
4. Toesca *loc. cit.* incorrectly states that Phillips had bought this picture for the Wallace Collection, London.

EMILIAN *seventeenth-century*

19 S. Peter Delivered

Canvas: 108 × 94.5
In good condition

The subject is taken from *Acts of the Apostles* XII, 1–10. Acquired as by Ribera, but this attribution was questioned by Waagen in 1854.[1] Catalogued as school of Caravaggio from 1859 until the 1957 edition when it was described as a later copy of an unidentified design, but not after Caravaggio. There is no good reason to suppose our picture is a copy. It is probably the work of an Italian artist active in Emilia and influenced by Simone Cantarini (1612–48) and possibly by Luca Ferrari (1605–54).

Coll: Bought by Lord Meadowbank on behalf of the R.I., Edinburgh, in 1840.[2]

Royal Institution 1840.

1. Waagen 1854 III p. 270 under Spagnoletto, but described as 'by a later and feebler master'.
2. Recorded in the R.I. Minute Book 2 April 1840 (R.I. MS. deposited in the Scottish Record Office).

FERRARESE *late fifteenth-century*

535 Madonna and Child with Two Angels

Wood: 58.5 × 44
Cleaned 1980. Generally in good condition except for a vertical crack in the panel, running from immediately above the Madonna's head, which has caused some paint loss on her forehead. There are also slight damages on her right shoulder and along the

left side of her neck. The picture surface has suffered from rubbing and minor paint losses along the edges of the rather pronounced craquelure; and the gold leaf has worn away from the haloes of the Madonna and the attendant angels.

The Virgin holds a pomegranate, symbol of the resurrection and eternal life. Pigler has speculated that the fly in the bottom left corner may have been intended as a talisman.[1] Shearman has interpreted the torn material in the foreground of the picture as a paper window covering (impannata), which is a symbol of the Virgin.[2] However this visual conceit did not necessarily have an iconographical significance, and in the 1957 Catalogue it was interpreted as a canvas torn from the stretcher of an illusionistic picture frame; alternatively, it might represent the protective packaging surrounding a picture in transit.

In the nineteenth century when the picture was in the Woodburn collection and then in the Fuller Maitland collection, the painted fly was interpreted as a signature, and the work was ascribed to 'Mosca', in spite of the fact that no painter of that name of the right date was known to have existed. In 1871, however, Crowe and Cavalcaselle had described it as by an artist close to Giorgio Schiavone and Marco Zoppo;[3] and then in 1927 Venturi attributed it to Ercole de'Roberti,[4] a view which was followed in 1933 when it was exhibited at Ferrara,[5] and in all the Gallery catalogues up to 1957. In 1932 and 1936 Berenson described it as by an artist close to Cossa. In 1934 Longhi called it the work of an unknown Ferrarese miniature painter close to G. Giraldi,[6] and in 1950 Fava and Salmi claimed to recognise the artist as one of the hands who painted miniatures in the Missal of Borso d'Este at Modena.[7] Since then, Laclotte[8] pointed out its stylistic affinities with paintings attributed by Longhi to his 'Vicino da Ferrara', also tentatively identified as Baldassare d'Este.[9] Most recently Manca has proposed an attribution to Gherardo d'Andrea Costa who was active in Ferrara 1452–74. Manca dates our picture c.1470.[10]

Coll: Samuel Woodburn sale Christie's 9 June 1860 (54) as Mosca, bought Daniell for W. Fuller Maitland. Recorded in the catalogue of the W. Fuller Maitland Collection at Stansted Hall in 1872 p. 11 as Mosca. Lent by W. Fuller Maitland to the Exhibition of the Works of the Old Masters R.A. London 1873 (165) as by Mosca. Recorded in the Stansted Hall Catalogue 1893 (28) as Mosca.

Bought from W. Fuller Maitland 1921.

1. A. Pigler in Bulletin du Musée Hongrois des Beaux-Arts 24 1964 pp. 47 ff.

2. Verbal communication from John Shearman in April 1977.

3. J. A. Crowe and G. B. Cavalcaselle A History of Painting in North Italy 1871 (ed. T. Borenius, London 1912 II p. 48). See also the drawing made after the picture by G .B. Cavalcaselle, now in the Biblioteca Nazionale Marciana, Venice, reproduced by L. Moretti G. B. Cavalcaselle, Disegni da antichi maestri Exhibition Catalogue, Fondazione Giorgio Cini, Venice 1973 p. 86 no. 56 illus.

4. A. Venturi Studi dal vero attraverso le raccolte artistiche d'Europa Milan 1927 p. 161.

5. Catalogo della esposizione della pittura Ferrarese del Rinascimento Ferrara 1933 p. 109 no. 128.

6. R. Longhi Officina Ferrarese 1934 (Opere Complete di Roberto Longhi V Florence 1956 p. 48).

7. D. Fava and M. Salmi I manoscritti miniati della Biblioteca Estense di Modena Florence 1950 I p. 89.

8. Letter from Michel Laclotte, dated 26 January 1976, in Gallery files.

9. For this artist see Longhi op. cit. (1956 ed. pp. 48–51, pp. 137–8 and pp. 182–4).

10. J. Manca in Gazette des Beaux-Arts November 1990 pp. 157 ff, where he assembles a group of works, including our picture, The Madonna and Child with Angels, National Gallery, Washington inv.

1939. 1.115, and two pictures of *The Meeting of Solomon and the Queen of Sheba*, Houston Museum and Boston Museum of Fine Arts, which he claims are by one hand. Based on his archival researches in Modena, Manca suggests the most likely author is Gherardo d'Andrea Costa, to whom no works have hitherto been convincingly attributed, but who was recorded as a specialist in small panel paintings, executing a wide range of work for the Este 1457–71. See further D. Benati in *Le Muse e il Principe* exhibition catalogue, Poldi Pezzoli Museum, Milan 1991 under no. 77 for the possible association of this group of pictures with a *Madonna and Child* from the Cambo collection; and A. Bacchi in *op. cit.* under no. 88 for stylistic links between our picture and an *Apotheosis of S. Ursula* in the Jacquemart-André Museum, Paris.

FERRARESE? *around 1500*

745

S. Francis Receiving the Stigmata

Wood: 38.5 × 24.
Cleaned 1950. The original panel, excluding fillets which have been added later on all four sides, is 36.8 × 22.2.
An original keyhole on the left has been filled in; there are some traces of an old gold border around its edges. The figure of S. Francis is essentially original but is badly rubbed and damaged, especially an area of drapery at the bottom right. The Crucifix, the rays of the stigmata, and the green foreground area are also authentic, although damaged, but the blue background has been almost totally repainted. The white decorative border, which surrounds the design and which covers the saint's left foot, also appears to be original.

Acquired as by Fiorenzo di Lorenzo, to whom it had been attributed by Venturi in 1913,[1] a view which was endorsed by Berenson in 1968. It had previously been attributed to Perugino by Van Marle,[2] and to Lo Spagna by Fischel.[3] It does not appear to be by any of these Umbrian artists, and recently Zeri has raised the interesting possibility that it might originate from Ferrara.[4] The present condition of the picture probably precludes a more precise identification.

Coll: Said to have been bought by Joseph Spiridon of Paris from Prince Barberini, Rome, in 1896,[5] but not readily identifiable in the Barberini collection inventories of the seventeenth century published by Lavin.[6] Spiridon sale, Paul Cassirer, Berlin 31 May 1929 (20) as Fiorenzo di Lorenzo.

Bought from Thos. Agnew's, London, 1930.

1. A. Venturi *Storia dell'Arte Italiana* Milan 1913 VII Part II p. 585.
2. R. Van Marle *The Development of the Italian Schools of Painting* The Hague 1933 XIV p. 328.
3. O. Fischel in the Spiridon sale catalogue, Paul Cassirer, Berlin 1929 no. 20.
4. Letter from Federico Zeri, dated 3 December 1976, in Gallery files.
5. See the Spiridon sale catalogue, Paul Cassirer, Berlin 1929 no. 20.
6. M. Lavin *Seventeenth-Century Barberini Documents and Inventories of Art* New York 1975.

FLORENTINE *fifteenth-century*

Madonna and Child

Wood: 49.5 × 33.7
In good condition.

One of the better versions of a design frequently used in Florence, which, as Hendy pointed out, very possibly derives from a panel by Pesellino in the Gardner Museum, Boston;[1] another autograph version by Pesellino is in the Keresztény Museum at Esztergom. The version in Edinburgh has been attributed to Piero di Lorenzo by Borenius[2] and to Fra Diamante by Berenson (1932, 1936 and 1963).

Coll: Said to have been in a house in Florence belonging to a family originating from Prato;[3] possibly Conte Stefano Bardini, Florence;[4] Sir Thomas Gibson Carmichael (Lord Carmichael) sale Christie's 13 May 1902 (271) as by Pietro di Lorenzo da Prato, bought in. Lord Carmichael (d. 1926) bequest to the National Gallery, London, received 1956 (Inv. 6266).

National Gallery, London, Loan 1958.

1. P. Hendy in the *Burlington Magazine* LIII 1928 pp. 67 ff. pl. 2b. See further P. Hendy *European and American Paintings in the Isabella Stewart Gardner Museum* Boston 1974 pp. 178–80 illus.; and M. Davies *National Gallery Catalogue, The Earlier Italian Schools* London 1961 pp. 194–5 inv. 6266.
2. T. Borenius in *Apollo* 1925 I pp. 67–8.
3. Borenius *loc. cit.*
4. See Davies *op. cit.* p. 195 note 8.

Mariano FORTUNY *1838–74*

Mariano José Mariá Bernardo Fortuny y Carbo.[1] He was born in Reus, Catalonia, and trained in Barcelona. He travelled in Italy, Morocco and France before settling in Rome *c.* 1862. He produced mainly genre and history paintings, and a relatively small number of bull-fighting scenes.

1189   Le Brindis de l'Espada (The Bull-Fighter's Salute)

Canvas: 100 × 67
Inscribed *Fortuny* with the circular red stamp of the Fortuny atelier sale 1875.
In good condition.

Acquired as by Fortuny under the title *In the Arena* which can be traced back to 1901.[2] Braham has identified our picture as *Le Brindis de l'Espada* which Fortuny is documented as having painted in Seville in 1868.[3]

Coll: Almost certainly Atelier de Fortuny sale, Hôtel Drouot, Paris 26 April 1875 (48) as *Le Brindis de l'Espada à Seville;*[4] Arthur Sanderson who lent it to the *Exhibition of the Works of Spanish Painters,* Guildhall, London 1901 (18).[5]

Bought from Wallis and Son, London, 1915.

1. See J. C. Davillier *Fortuny sa vie, son oeuvre, sa correspondance* Paris 1875, and J. Folch i Torres *Fortuny* Reus 1962.
2. See the catalogue of the *Exhibition of the Works of Spanish Painters* Guildhall, London 1901 (18).
3. See N. Maclaren, revised by A. Braham, *National Gallery Catalogue, The Spanish School* London 1970 p. 8 note 1.
4. In the sale catalogue it is described as follows: *Il demande, suivant l'usage, au président de la Plaza, la permission de tuer le taureau. Toile* — H.1m, ooc, L.om, 67c.

5. The date when Sanderson acquired our picture is not recorded. It is not mentioned in the series of articles on this collection published by C. Monkhouse in the *Art Journal* 1897 pp. 5 ff.

Francesco FURINI *1603–46*

Born in Florence 10 April 1603 and died there 19 August 1646.[1] Son of a portrait painter Filippo Furini, he studied with Domenico Passignano, Giovanni Biliverti and Matteo Rosselli. In 1623–4 he was working in Rome in association with Giovanni da S. Giovanni. In October 1625 he became a member of the *Accademia fiorentina del Disegno* and spent most of his remaining life in Florence, apart from a visit to Venice, and a second visit to Rome in 1645–6. The chronology of Furini's paintings has not yet been established with any precision.

30   **S. Sebastian**

Canvas: 50.5 × 38.5
Cleaned in 1943. In very good condition.

Acquired as by Furini. The traditional attribution is certainly correct; it has been endorsed by Toesca who suggests a date around 1633,[2] by Thiem who dates it in the mid-1630s[3] and by Cantelli who compares it with a *S. John the Evangelist* in a private collection, which he has dated *c.* 1635–6.[4]

Coll: Marchese Gerini, Florence. Gerini sale catalogue 1825 (84).[5] Bought from the Gerini family in Florence by Andrew Wilson on behalf of the R.I., Edinburgh, 1831.[6] Exhibited R.I. 1832 (33).

Royal Institution 1831.

1. For biographical details see F. Baldinucci *Notizie dei professori del disegno* 1681–1728 (ed. Florence 1845–7 IV pp. 629 ff.); E. Toesca *Francesco Furini* Rome 1950; G. Cantelli *Disegni di Francesco Furini e del suo ambiente* Gabinetto Disegni e Stampe degli Uffizi XXXVI Florence 1972 pp. 7 ff.; and G. Corti in *Antichità Viva* X 1971 pp. 14–23.
2. *Op. cit.* p. 12 pl. 17.
3. Letter from Christel Thiem, dated 29 April 1976, in Gallery files.
4. G. Cantelli *Il Seicento Fiorentino. Arte a Firenze da Ferdinando I a Cosimo III Pittura* Exhibition Catalogue, Palazzo Strozzi, Florence 1986/7 p. 274 no. 1.134.
5. *Catalogo e stima dei quadri e bronzi esistenti nella galleria del Sig. Marchese Giovanni Gerini* Florence 1825.
6. See further *Pictures for Scotland* pp. 27 ff.

31   **Poetry**

Paper laid on wood: 41.4 × 34.5
Cleaned in 1943. In very good condition.

Acquired as by Furini. The traditional attribution is certainly correct and has been endorsed by Toesca who suggests a date around 1633.[1] It is similar in style to no. 30 *supra*, but in spite of their common provenance there is no reason to suppose they were originally conceived as companion pieces. A drawing in the Uffizi (Inv. 922 E), executed in red chalk, which is very close to the design of our picture, has sometimes been described as a study for it;[2] but Cantelli has claimed that it is a preparatory sketch for an unpublished picture of an allegorical figure, now in a private collection, for which he suggests a date around 1628–30.[3] After the death of Giovanni da S. Giovanni in 1636, Furini was commissioned to complete the frescoes in the Sala degli Argenti in the Palazzo Pitti, Florence; in his design for the *Accademia Platonica* he included a figure of *Poetry* which is extremely close both to the figure in our picture and to the drawing in the Uffizi.

Coll: Marchese Gerini, Florence. Gerini sale catalogue 1825 (82).[4] Bought from the Gerini family in Florence by Andrew Wilson on behalf of the R.I., Edinburgh, 1831.[5] Exhibited R.I. 1832 (34).

Royal Institution 1831.

1. E. Toesca *Francesco Furini* Rome 1950 p. 12 pl. 16.

2. See Toesca *op. cit.* p. 17 pl. 27.

3. G. Cantelli *Disegni di Francesco Furini e del suo ambiente* Gabinetto Disegni e Stampe degli Uffizi XXXVI Florence 1972 p. 24 no. 6 fig. 17. See further C. Thiem *Florentiner Zeichner des Frühbarock* Munich 1977 p. 378 no. 170.

4. *Catalogo e stima dei quadri e bronzi esistenti nella galleria del Sig. Marchese Giovanni Gerini* Florence 1825

5. See further *Pictures for Scotland* pp. 27 ff.

GAROFALO *c. 1481–1559*

His name was Benvenuto Tisi, and he was called Garofalo after the place of origin of his family, a village in the Polesine. He was born in Ferrara around 1481 and was mainly active there. According to Vasari, he also made two visits to Rome, and his style shows the strong influence of Raphael.

32   Christ Driving the Money-Changers from the Temple

Wood: 45.7 × 37.2

Cleaned 1954. In very good condition apart from some small damages along the centre of the panel, and in particular just under and just above the step in the immediate foreground.

Acquired as by Garofalo and subsequently catalogued as such. The attribution seems to be beyond doubt, in spite of the fact that Berenson omits our picture from his *Lists* in 1932 and 1968. The 1957 *Catalogue* suggests that it may be a relatively late work, and this view has not apparently been questioned.

Coll: Bought from the Duke of Vivaldi Pasqua, Genoa, by Andrew Wilson on behalf of the R.I., Edinburgh, in 1830.[1] Exhibited R.I. 1831 and 1832 (9). Recorded by Waagen in the collection of the R.I. in 1854.[2]

Royal Institution 1830.

1. See further *Pictures for Scotland* pp. 27 ff.

2. Waagen 1854 III p. 269, who writes: 'Although warmly coloured and carefully executed, the picture is not attractive. Subjects of this class … are not within the province of this painter. The figure of Christ is very unsuccessful here'.

GIORGIONE *active from c. 1506 died 1510*

Giorgio da Castelfranco, called Giorgione. He is documented as having worked on a painting (now lost) for the Doge's Palace in Venice in 1507–8, and on a series of frescoes (now virtually destroyed) on the outside of the Fondaco dei Tedeschi, Venice, in 1508. In 1510 he is reported as dead from the plague, apparently at a young age. Apart from the work described above, the only pictures which may be attributed to him with any degree of confidence are a *Portrait of a Lady* and the *Three Philosophers*, both now in Vienna; the *Tempesta* in the Accademia, Venice; and the Castelfranco altarpiece. He appears to have been influenced by Giovanni Bellini, but quickly developed a highly individual style. He already had a considerable reputation as an artist during his lifetime, and after his death quickly became a legend; consequently his style was much imitated.

After, or by an imitator of, GIORGIONE

35   Portrait of a Man Holding a Recorder

Canvas: 45.8 × 34.9
Inscribed lower right in gold: *B.A.*
Cleaned 1937. X-rayed. The paint surface is extensively worn and restored. The man's left cheek is badly damaged; and there are a number of vertical tears in the original canvas, one of them running through the middle of the picture, and another through the man's hand.

Andrew Wilson, who bought the picture in Genoa in 1830 on behalf of the R.I., Edinburgh, considered it to be a self-portrait by Giorgione, in spite of the fact that the Marchesa Pallavicini's house-steward, from whom he acquired it, had been given it by his employer as a 'useless thing'.[1] It remained catalogued under Giorgione's name until 1936 when it was acknowledged to be the work of a later imitator. However, as early as 1871, Crowe and Cavalcaselle had already described it as a fine example of Pietro della Vecchia (1605–78) imitating Giorgione.[2] And although their attribution to Pietro della Vecchia can no longer be sustained, the X-ray of our picture strongly endorses their view that it cannot be an early sixteenth-century work. For the X-ray reveals a quite different composition underneath the present paint surface, representing a bust portrait of a man, framed in an oval-shaped surround, which, to judge from its academic design, might well date from the eighteenth century.

The design of our picture was evidently extremely popular, and is known in many other versions, including those recorded in the following collections:[3] Capodimonte, Naples; Brera Gallery, Milan; New York Historical Society; Earl of Pembroke at Wilton House; Marquess of Lansdowne at Bowood; Lord Bradford at Weston Park; President's Lodgings, St. John's College, Oxford; E. Hockliffe, Somerset; Casa Maldura, Padua; Tadini gallery at Lovere; Camerini collection at Piazzola sul Brenta; and a private collection in Bassano. A half-length version of the design was sold at Parke-Bernet, New York, on 28 March 1946 (78) as ex. Henry Huntington collection, New York. Our 1957 *Catalogue* describes what appears to be another half-length version, showing the figure seated in a chair, in the possession of a Mr Stevenson of New York. A drawing in the

Ambrosiana collection, Milan, attributed by Bora to Lomazzo (1538–1600), may also be derived from the same prototype.[4]

The original version has not yet been identified, and in its absence the identity of the artist responsible for the design also remains a matter of conjecture. Crowe and Cavalcaselle never excluded the possibility that there was once an original painting of the subject by Giorgione.[5] And it is worth noting that the Wilton House version, which seems to have the best provenance of the extant versions, and which can be traced back to 1669 when it was presented to Philip, 5th Earl of Pembroke, by Cosimo III, Grand Duke of Tuscany, was then apparently said to be by Giorgione, although it now has the appearance of a late sixteenth-century or early seventeenth-century copy.[6] More recently Wilde, in 1933, suggested the original design might be by his Master of the Self Portraits.[7] Berenson, on the other hand, has associated some of the extant versions with the name of Sebastiano del Piombo, in particular (1932) those at Capodimonte, Naples, and the New York Historical Society, and (1957) at Bowood in the Marquess of Lansdowne's collection. Of these the Lansdowne version is much the best, but like the Wilton picture it too appears to date from the late sixteenth or early seventeenth century. Garas has further suggested, but perhaps implausibly, that the prototype might be identified as a Sebastiano del Piombo *Self Portrait* recorded in the Farnese collection, Parma, in 1587.[8] She also finds morphological similarities between the man holding a recorder and the third figure in Sebastiano del Piombo's picture of *Cardinal Carondelet*, in the Thyssen collection, Lugano. Hirst has also lent support to the idea that the prototype may have been an early picture by Sebastiano del Piombo.[9]

Notwithstanding these attempts to associate the original design of our picture with Giorgione and with the young Sebastiano del Piombo and to attribute various versions of the design to these artists, there still seems to be no good reason to disagree with Waterhouse's opinion, expressed in the 1957 *Catalogue*, that none of the surviving versions, including the Edinburgh one, appears to be an original by any master of distinction of the early sixteenth century. With less apparent justification, Waterhouse went further and also expressed doubt as to whether the original design goes back as far as Giorgione's time. In any case, the status of our picture as a secondary version now seems to be beyond dispute.

Coll: Said to have been originally in the Grimaldi collection at Venice [*sic*] and to have been inherited by the Marchesa Pallavicini, from whose steward it was bought in Genoa by Andrew Wilson, on behalf of the R.I., Edinburgh, in 1830.[10] Exhibited R.I. 1831 and 1832 (29). Recorded by Waagen in the collection of the R.I. in 1854.[11]

Royal Institution 1830.

---

1. Letter to James Skene, secretary of the R.I., dated Genoa 22 August 1830. The MS. is now in the possession of Major P. I. C. Payne, who kindly made it available for study.

2. J. A. Crowe and G. B. Cavalcaselle *A History of Painting in North Italy* 1871 (ed. T. Borenius, London 1912 III p. 49).

3. See Crowe and Cavalcaselle *loc. cit.*; 1957 *Catalogue* p. 105; P. Zampetti *L'opera completa di Giorgione* Milan 1968 p. 96 no. 41.

4. Cod F 271 Inf. 47. Red chalk 175 × 130 mm. See G. Bora *Disegni di Manieristi Lombardi*, Fontes Ambrosiani XLVI Vicenza 1971 p. 41 no. 49 illus. If this sheet were derived from the same prototype as the pictures listed above, this would perhaps account for a certain timidity in its execution, seen for instance in the indeterminate way the drawing tails off at the bottom.

5. *Loc. cit.*

6. Sidney 16th Earl of Pembroke *A Catalogue of the Paintings and Drawings in the collection at Wilton House* London 1968 p. 4 and p. 83 pl. 88.

7. J. Wilde in *Jahrbuch der Kunsthistorischen Sammlungen in Wien* N.F. VII 1933 p. 124.

8. K. Garas in *Acta Historiae Artium … Hungaricae* XVI 1970 pp. 261−9.

9. Oral communication from Michael Hirst, February 1977. See further M. Hirst *Sebastiano del Piombo* Oxford 1981 p. 4 where he suggests that the Wilton House version 'seems to me to come closest to Sebastiano himself'.

10. See note 1 above. See further *Pictures for Scotland* p. 32. Duchessa Teresa Grimaldi married the Marchese Alessandro Pallavicini: their son was the Marchese Francesco Pallavicini, Duca Grimaldi (b. 1809 d. 1878).

11. Waagen 1854 III p. 270 as by Giorgione.

GIULIO ROMANO *c. 1499–1546*

Giulio Pippi, painter and architect, born in Rome, died in Mantua. He was an assistant of Raphael in Rome until the latter's death in April 1520, when he apparently took over the artistic direction of the workshop, in collaboration with G. F. Penni. In 1524 he became court painter at Mantua.

98   The Holy Family with Infant S. John

Wood: 82.5 × 63.5 (including fillets of oak attached to each side).
Cleaned 1972. X-rayed. The original panel and painted surface 82.5 × 58.4 consists of three planks, measuring from left to right: 16.5; 24.9; 17. There is severe paint loss at the extreme lower left, and some restoration along the line of a split between the left and centre planks, to a depth of 30 cms from the top. There is some abrasion in the shaded areas on the main figures, and on the figures of S. Joseph and the ass in the left background. Otherwise the paint surface is well preserved.

The design of our picture, sometimes known as *La Vierge à la Légende* and *La Vierge de Novar* is based on the now much damaged *Madonna of the Rose* in the Prado, Madrid, which Passavant and many later writers have believed to be by Raphael himself.[1] The main compositional difference between the two versions lies in the treatment of S. Joseph: in Raphael's picture he stands beside the Madonna, but in our picture he is shown in the distance, with an ass, beneath a rusticated stone arch.

The earliest documented record of our picture dates from 1812 when it was in the collection of Lord Gwydir at Grimsthorpe, attributed to Raphael.[2] The attribution to Giulio Romano dates from the Gwydir sale in 1829 (see below) and was followed by Waagen in 1854[3] and by Passavant in 1860.[4] Crowe and Cavalcaselle dissented from this judgement, and argued that the execution 'is feebler than that of Giulio or even Penni and suggests the co-operation of Bagnacavallo'.[5]

After Lord Dudley's sale in 1892, when it was again attributed to Raphael, the picture disappeared from public view. It was rediscovered by Brigstocke in 1972 and published with an attribution to Giulio Romano in 1978.[6] By then the attribution had been endorsed by John Shearman and Philip Pouncey[7] and has subsequently received further support from Russell[8] and Joannides[9].

The unusual exploratory technique of some areas of our picture, which became apparent during restoration in 1972, provides the strongest evidence that we are concerned with the work of a truly creative and experimental artist, such as Giulio Romano is known to have been, rather than with a routine product of Raphael's workshop. For whereas the paint surface in the area of the principal group of figures of the Virgin and Child and Infant S. John has the quality of hardness and high finish which one associates with Raphael's Roman period Madonnas, notwithstanding the very unusual and pronounced craquelure, the subsidiary parts of the picture (the architectural background, the green landscape, the figure of S. Joseph, the transparent veil on the Virgin's shoulders and even the outstretched leg of S. John) none of which occur in Raphael's prototype in the Prado, are all painted more lightly and thinly, and these areas are not affected by the same pronounced craquelure. The distinction in technique between the two parts of the picture is emphasised by the firm outline, visible in the paint surface, isolating the principal figures from the background, except in the area of the Virgin's shoulder where the veil has been superficially imposed, perhaps in order to soften the contour. These observations raise the possibility that the subsidiary features of the design were not painted until some little time after the main figures had been completed and allowed to dry, although the basic outlines of the architecture (but not the rounded columns) were already conceived from the outset and are clearly incised in the gesso.

The most distinctive stylistic features of our picture are the noticeably hard sculptural manner of modelling the figures, the vivid discordant colour scheme, and the mysteriously lit Antique architectural background which together offer a striking contrast to Raphael's prototype, the *Madonna of the Rose*. If each of these qualities independently suggest the hand of Giulio Romano, they also reveal the extent to which he responded to Raphael's own very late paintings, including the recently cleaned Vatican *Transfiguration* and *La Perla* in the Prado (the execution of which may have been completed by Giulio) where remarkably similar effects are deployed.[10] Although it is not impossible that our picture was painted in Raphael's lifetime – Joannides has suggested *c.* 1518[11] – it seems far more likely that it dates from very shortly after Raphael's death in 1520 (and certainly before Giulio left Rome for Mantua in 1524) when Giulio first began to mature as an independent artistic personality. For in our picture the naturalism, humanity, controlled energy and classical understatement of Raphael's late pictures are transformed into a work of polished self-conscious elegance. Raphael's idealised but still intensely animated human figures are removed from their neutral, timeless setting to be transferred, in almost petrified form, deprived of natural vitality, to an inescapably archaeological environment. This view, propounded by Brigstocke in 1978, has recently been supported by Pagden who argues that Giulio Romano's audacious conception of the architectural background in the Edinburgh picture, and in particular the use, unique in his painted oeuvre, of the Tuscan arches for the ancient columns, could only have been realised after the death of Raphael.[12]

Coll: Lord Gwydir Collection, Grimsthorpe by 1812 as Raphael;[13] Gwydir sale Christie's 8 May 1829 (lot 58) as by Giulio Romano; C. J. Nieuwenhuys; his sale Christie's 10 May 1833 (lot 67) as by Giulio Romano; H. A. J. Munro of Novar; Munro of Novar sale Christie's 1 June 1878 (lot 152) as by Raphael; bought Agnew's for Lord Dudley; Lord Dudley sale Christie's 25 June 1892 (lot 82) as by Raphael; bought by James Reid; thence by inheritance.

Bought with the aid of the National Heritage Purchase Grant (Scotland) 1980.

1. Canvas transferred from wood 103 × 84 cms. J. D. Passavant *Raphael d' Urbin et son père Giovanni Santi* Paris 1860 p. 333.

2. Grimsthorpe Castle Inventory 1809–12. Lincolnshire County Archives Anc. 19.

3. Waagen 1854 II p. 132.

4. Passavant *loc. cit.*

5. J. A. Crowe and G. B. Cavalcaselle *Raphael: his Life and Works* London 1882 II pp. 478–9.

6. H. Brigstocke in *Burlington Magazine* CXX October 1978 pp. 665–6 fig. 1.

7. Brigstocke *op. cit.* p. 666 n. 19.

8. F. Russell in *Burlington Magazine* CXXIV May 1982 pp. 297–8.

9. P. Joannides in *Paragone* 45 July 1985 pp. 31–2.

10. See C. Gould in *Burlington Magazine* CXXXIV 198 pp. 479–87. For the X-ray of the Prado picture see *Rafael en España* Exhibition Catalogue Prado, Madrid 1985 p. 100 fig. 23.

11. See note 9 above.

12. S. Ferino Pagden 'Giulio Romano pittore e disegnatore a Roma' in *Giulio Romano*, Exhibition Catalogue, Mantua 1989 pp. 70–2. See further A. Belluzzi and K. W. Forster in *op. cit.* p. 211 and M. Tarfuri in *op. cit.* p. 37 and illus. p. 38 in colour.

13. See note 2 above.

Attributed to GIULIO ROMANO and workshop

538 ### Two Heads from the Massacre of the Innocents

Tempera on paper: 52.3 × 36.1
Laid down on cardboard and trimmed, with a horizontal join *c.* 12.5 cm from the top. There are numerous minor paint losses caused by rubbing and creasing, and the nose of the right-hand figure has been heavily repainted.

A fragment from the original cartoon for a tapestry of the *Massacre of the Innocents*, from the Scuola Nuova series of *Scenes from the Life of Christ*, in the Vatican, Rome. The tapestry is one of three separate panels devoted to this subject, and each of them is woven in the reverse sense to the cartoon.

Acquired as by Raphael and so catalogued until 1936, when described as more probably by a pupil of Raphael. Although the cartoons for the Scuola Nuova tapestries are similar in technique to the seven cartoons illustrating the *Acts of the Apostles*, now in the Victoria and Albert Museum, London, which were reproduced in Raphael's own studio before his death, there is no evidence that Raphael himself was in any way responsible for the designs, and Crowe and Cavalcaselle,[1] Pouncey and Gere,[2] Nicolson,[3] and Byam Shaw[4] have all agreed that the tapestries were probably designed by Giulio Romano and that the cartoons were made under his direction.

Passavant, however, suggested that the three tapestry panels of the *Massacre of the Innocents* were originally conceived by Raphael himself as a single design, and that it was subsequently divided by Raphael's pupils.[5] On the other hand, as Pouncey and Gere have pointed out, in the three tapestries, as well as in three drawings at the Teyler Museum, Haarlem, which are probably variant copies, made by G. F. Penni, after the original designs, the background is not continuous;[6] and since each group of figures was clearly conceived as an entity, it seems more probable that the three panels of tapestry and the related cartoons were originally planned as separate compositions.

Other pieces from the cartoon which relates to the same tapestry panel as our fragment are at Christ Church, Oxford (Inv. 1971), and at the British Museum, London (Inv. 1947–4–14–1). All derive from the elder Richardson's collection.[7] Another related fragment is at Althorp, Northamptonshire, and is said to have been bought in Rome by Lord Spencer in 1785.[8]

Four fragments from the cartoon relating to another of the three tapestries of the Massacre of the Innocents are in the Ashmolean Museum, Oxford, and these too were all previously in the Jonathan Richardson collection.[9] A further piece from this cartoon is in the British Museum (Inv. 1942–7–11–13).

The cartoon for the entire group of figures in the third tapestry panel is in the Foundling Hospital, London, and was previously in the collection of William Hoare (1706–92).[10]

All these cartoon fragments are similar in style and handling. It is not known when the three original cartoons were cut up, but according to della Valle they were already in pieces, in Flanders, by the end of the seventeenth century.[11] Vertue recorded 'The Part of the Cartoon of Raphael the Murder of the Innocents brought from Holland by Mr. Motteux the other part haveing been lost ruind in Holland where they were once all pawn'd …'; and he referred to it again in February 1724 as 'the Carton said to be of Raphael's doing being a third part of the Murder of the Innocents sold in widow Moteuxs sale for 170 guineas …'.[12] This cartoon, which, according to 'Coll. Guise' (i.e. John Guise, the benefactor of Christ Church, Oxford) had once been in the collection of Govaert Flinck (1615–60) and of his son Nicholas Flinck (1646–1723),[13] must be the cartoon now in the Foundling Hospital. There is no evidence that the fragments of the *Massacre of the Innocents* from the Richardson collection also have a Motteux collection provenance.[14]

Fischel dates the commission of the Scuola Nuova series of tapestries 1524.[15] Müntz believed that these tapestries should be identified as those commissioned in a contract with Pieter van Aelst of 27 June 1520, that the work was interrupted by the death of Leo X and the pontificate of Adrian VI, and that a payment of October 1524 signifies a resumption by Clement VII of earlier negotiations.[16]

Coll: Jonathan Richardson sale by Cock, London, 4 March 1747 (52) as Raphael, bought Price. According to Gunn, a fragment ($19^1/_2 \times 15^1/_2$ in.) from the *Massacre of the Innocents* representing 'the heads of two suffering mothers of agonizing expression', probably to be identified as our picture, was sold at the 5th Duke of Argyll's sale at Langfords 1779 (not listed by Lugt) bought John Flaxman. Gunn also records that Mr Flaxman presented it to Mr John Saunders of Bath.[17] Said to have been bought from Mr Saunders by Professor Munro.[18] By descent to his son, Sir David Munro.

Sir David Munro bequest to the Royal Scottish Academy 1878–9; transferred 1910.

---

1. J. A. Crowe and G. B. Cavalcaselle *Raphael, His Life and Works* London 1882 II pp. 539 f.

2. P. Pouncey and J. A. Gere *Italian Drawings … in the British Museum. Raphael and his circle* London 1962 pp. 80–1 nos. 137 and 138.

3. B. Nicolson *The Treasures of the Foundling Hospital* Oxford 1972 pp. 76–7 no. 69.

4. J. Byam Shaw *Drawings by Old Masters at Christ Church, Oxford* Oxford 1976 I pp. 135–6 no. 457 and II pl. 249.

5. J. D. Passavant *Raphael d'Urbin et son père Giovanni Santi* Paris 1860 II pp. 217 ff.

6. *Loc. cit.*

7. See notes 2 and 4 above.

8. According to Kenneth Garlick, there is an inscription on the back of the Althorp picture to this effect; letter in Gallery files dated 23 July 1974.

9. See K. T. Parker *Catalogue of the Collection of Drawings in the Ashmolean Museum* Oxford 1956 II pp. 326–7 nos. 599–602.

10. See Nicolson *loc. cit.*

11. Vasari (ed. G. della Valle, Siena 1791–94 V p. 308).

12. See Vertue *Note Books I in Walpole Society* XVIII Oxford 1930 pp. 36 and 128.

13. See note 12 above.

14. But cf. W. Gunn *Cartonensia* London 1831 pp. 26–7 who may have misunderstood della Valle (see note 11 above).

15. In Thieme–Becker XXIX p. 442.

16. E. Müntz *Les Tapisseries du Raphael au Vatican* Paris 1897 pp. 36 ff.

17. *Op. cit* p. 43 note 19. A copy apparently made from our fragment is in the Soane Museum, London, where it is attributed to John Saunders.

18. This information is recorded in the 1879 *Catalogue* p. 47.

Francisco de GOYA *1746–1828*

Francisco José de Goya y Lucientes. Born at Fuendetodos, near Saragossa. Pupil of José Luzán in Saragossa in 1760 and of Francisco Bayeu in Madrid. In 1771 he visited Italy. By 1775 he had settled in Madrid and began to work on the first of a series of cartoons for the Royal Tapestry Works, an activity which continued to occupy him until 1791. He was appointed *pintor del rey* in 1786, *pintor de cámara* in 1789 and *primer pintor de cámara* in 1799. He died in Bordeaux where he lived from 1824.

1628   **El Médico (The Doctor)**

Canvas: 95.8 × 120.2

Cleaned 1924. There are two vertical seams in the original canvas, one 23 cm from the left, and another 16 cm from the right. The paint surface has suffered from rubbing. The faces and the red draperies now lack modelling and definition, and the red underpaint beneath the black draperies shows through in some places. Some of the highlights, especially the flesh tones of the faces, have also sunk due to the dark red ground. There are a number of more serious damages in the sky, and alongside the bottom edge and in the immediate foreground of the picture, and their effect is accentuated by old discoloured restorations; the most seriously affected area is along a vertical line running down to the tree and foliage on the left.

A tapestry cartoon, painted by Goya and delivered to the Royal Tapestry Factory in Madrid, together with ten further cartoons, on 24 January 1780. These eleven cartoons completed a series representing the costumes and diversions of the time, on which Goya had been working since 1776. The previous delivery of cartoons for this series had been in July 1779, and this suggests that most of the work on our picture was probably carried out in the second half of 1779.

The tapestries from the series were intended as decorations for the Ante–Dormitorio of the Princes of the Asturias in the Palace of El Pardo. Our picture was designed for an overdoor tapestry.[1] Its pendant was *La Cita*, the cartoon for which is now in the Prado, Madrid (no. 792).[2]

The title of our picture originates from Goya's own invoice, which he submitted at the time of delivery, and where he described it as follows: 'A doctor seated, warming himself by a brazier; some books on the ground by his side; behind him, two students…'.[3] Nordström has suggested that the picture might also be interpreted as an allegory of Winter, on the basis both of the man warming his hands and of the leafless branches of the trees.[4]

Coll: Real Fábrica de Tapices, Madrid, 1780; Palacio Real, Madrid; stolen from the Palace during the Revolution in 1869 and reported missing in the *Gaceta de Madrid* 19 January 1870 and in *La Illustracíon de Madrid* 12 February 1870.[5] Bought early in the 20th century by Sr. Linker of Bilbao from an antique dealer in Saragossa when it was said to have been formerly in the collection of a noble family of that province.[6]

Bought from Durlacher's, London, 1923.

1. The most convenient source for the documents relating to our picture is V. de Sambricio *Tapices de Goya* Madrid 1946 pp. 245–46 no. 39 pl. CXXXVIII.
2. See further P. Gassier and J. Wilson, edited by F. Lachenal, *Goya his Life and Work* … London 1971 p. 89 no. 142; J. Gudiol *Goya Biography, Analytical Study and Catalogue of his Paintings* Barcelona 1971 I p. 242 no. 93; Xavier de Salas *Goya* London 1979 p. 174 no. 89; A Braham *El Greco to Goya* Exhibition Catalogue, National Gallery London, 1981 pp. 101–2 no. 63.
3. For this translation of the original Spanish text see P. Troutman *Goya and his times* Exhibition Catalogue, R.A., London 1963–4 p. 22 no. 49. The original text is as follows: *un Medico sentado calentandose a un Brasero, en el sueto a su lado barios Libros, y dos Estudiantes detras.*
4. F. Nordström *Goya, Saturn and Melancholy* Uppsala/Stockholm 1962 pp. 22–6 fig. 4.
5. See Sambricio *loc. cit.* and Troutman *loc. cit.*
6. Information from V. Nieto Linker, dated June 1928.

Benozzo GOZZOLI *1420–97*

Florentine. Pupil and assistant to Fra Angelico in Rome and Orvieto. Much of his work was in fresco.

Style of Benozzo GOZZOLI

953   Christ on the Road to Calvary

Canvas, later mounted on wood: 72 × 116.1
The paint surface is worn and there is some flaking in the trees and bushes. The best preserved areas are the distant landscape and the principal figures. There is a repair along the vertical line of an old stretcher, affecting the standing man to the right of Christ. The statement in the 1970 *Shorter Catalogue* that the present paint surface is very damaged is too pessimistic.

Acquired with a traditional attribution to Benozzo Gozzoli and subsequently catalogued under his name. In 1929 Van Marle advanced the tentative hypothesis that it might be a very early work by Cosimo Rosselli.[1] Then in 1932, 1936 and 1963 Berenson attributed it to his Alunno di Benozzo, an unidentified artist working in a style close to that of Benozzo Gozzoli. More recently Fahy has raised the possibility that it might be by Cosimo Rosselli's brother, Francesco, whose activity as a painter is still ill-defined, which precludes any balanced assessment of this idea.[2] As all these attributions suggest, the design of our picture shows some obvious affinities to Benozzo Gozzoli and Cosimo Rosselli; but the consistently low quality of its execution, especially in the outline of the figures and also in the landscape, raises serious doubts as to whether it was painted by an artist closely associated with the studios of either of these masters.

Coll: Said to have been acquired by the Fine Art Society, London, from the collection of the Marchese Giovanni Rosselli del Turco, Florence.[3] (An old label on the back of the picture is inscribed *Di Proprieta Sig. Giuseppe Pierfrancesco Rosselli del Turco*). Sold anonymously (by the Fine Art Society) Christie's 27 April 1907 (72) bought in. Lent by the Fine Art Society to the *Exhibition of the Works of the Old Masters* R.A. London 1907 (3) as Benozzo Gozzoli.

Bought from the Fine Art Society, London, 1908.

1. R. Van Marle *The Development of the Italian Schools of Painting* The Hague 1929 XI pp. 588–90 fig. 357.
2. Letter in Gallery files, from Everett Fahy, dated 7 April 1977. For biographical information on Francesco Rosselli and a discussion of his activity as a miniaturist and print-maker see M. Levi D'Ancona in *Commentari* XVI 1965 pp. 56 ff.; and K. Oberhuber in *Early Italian Engravings from the National Gallery of Art* Washington 1973 pp. 47–62.
3. Letter in Gallery files, from the Fine Art Society, London, dated 3 February 1908.

EL GRECO *1541–1614*

Domenikos Theotokopoulos, who was known to his contemporaries in Spain as Dominico Greco. He was born in Crete and later travelled in Italy, but the date of his arrival there is not known. He probably went first to Venice where he was almost certainly a pupil of Titian, and then later to Rome. He was in Toledo by 1577 and settled there for the rest of his life. However, the exact chronology of many of his Spanish works has never been firmly established. There are several versions of many of his compositions, and it is often difficult to assess the degree of studio participation in the works attributed to him.

1873   S. Jerome in Penitence

Canvas: 104.2 × 96.5
In quite good condition, apart from surface rubbing and some minor paint losses. The shadows around the head have been strengthened.

The half-length figure of the saint is depicted with his usual attributes: a crucifix, and the stone of self-punishment in his hand; the hour-glass expressing passing time; and the skull, symbol of death, together with books, pen and ink, characterising the saint as a scholar; and his Cardinal's hat hung on a rock to the left. Three other relatively good versions of this composition are known.[1] These are:

1. Madrid, Diputación Provincial (on deposit at the Prado, Madrid).[2] Canvas: 91 × 90. Wethey attributes it to El Greco and workshop and dates it *c.* 1595–1600.
2. Madrid, Marqués de Santa María de Silvela y de Castañar.[3] Canvas: 105 × 90. Wethey considers it to be the work of El Greco *c.* 1600–5.
3. New York, Hispanic Society.[4] Canvas: 80 × 65. Signed. Wethey attributes it to El Greco and workshop *c.* 1600–10, but considers it to be considerably inferior to the other three versions, including our picture.

Our picture was acquired as by El Greco. Wethey,[5] who follows Mayer,[6] Legendre and Hartmann,[7] and Camón Aznar[8] in dating it *c.* 1595–1600, judges it to be the best of the four known versions. He suggests, somewhat surprisingly, that there is little between our picture and no. 2, listed above, which seems to be markedly inferior. On the other hand he probably underestimates no. 3, the only signed version, because of its poor condition. Although our picture is much the best version to have survived in good condition, it appears to have been executed in a relatively lifeless and routine manner when compared to El Greco's *Saviour of the World* (infra), which is usually considered to be of about the same date. This suggests it might be a good studio repetition of a much repeated original, rather than the primary autograph version.

Coll: Condesa de Arcentales (Marquesa Santa María de la Sisla) by 1926.[9]

Bought from Tomás Harris 1936.

1. Another variant of studio quality is published by A. Mayer *El Greco* Munich 1926 p. 45 no. 283.
2. H. Wethey *El Greco and his School* Princeton 1962 II p. 133 no. 247.
3. Wethey *op. cit* II p. 133 no. 246.
4. Wethey op. cit.II p. 133 no. 248.
5. Wethey *op. cit.*II p. 132 no. 245.
6. See note 1 above.
7. M. Legendre and A. Hartmann *El Greco* Paris 1937 p. 440.
8. J. Camón Aznar *Dominico Greco* Madrid 1950 p. 1382 no. 513.
9. See Mayer *op. cit.* p. 45 no. 284a.

2160 The Saviour of the World

Canvas: 73 × 56.5

Signed with the Greek initials: *delta theta*.[1] Cleaned 1963. In excellent condition, apart from some worn areas in the background and around Christ's left hand.

The iconography, with the Saviour raising his right hand in the Latin form of blessing is completely traditional, and similar representations of the Saviour can be traced back as far as the Byzantine era. However, as Davies has pointed out, whereas in Byzantine images of Christ as Pantocrator he is usually shown holding a gospel, in the present picture he holds a globe, a motif that became popular in Netherlandish painting from the fifteenth century.[2] El Greco, on at least three occasions, included closely related versions of this composition in a series of twelve apostles with a Saviour, and our picture might also have originally belonged to such a series. However, the attempt made by Mayer[3] to reconstruct a series which includes it is not convincing and is rightly contested by Wethey.[4] There is also evidence that El Greco sometimes painted the *Saviour* as an independent subject; this is suggested by entries in an inventory of pictures in the artist's possession, at his death, and drawn up by his son Jorge Manuel Theotocópuli in 1614;[5] and also by entries in a 1621 inventory of Jorge Manuel's own possessions.[6] However there is no apparent justification for the claim, which has been made by San Román, that our picture might be identified as *Un Salbador* listed as no. 127 in the 1621 inventory, and the sizes do not correspond.[7]

Our picture is of fine quality and, like a three-quarter length version from the series of Apostles in the El Greco Museum, Toledo,[8] is certainly an autograph work by El Greco, whereas the three-quarter length version from the series in Toledo Cathedral,[9] a half-length version in the Prado, Madrid, from the series which was originally at

Almadrones,[10] and a version in the gallery at Reggio Emilia[11] in Italy which survives on its own, are all of much less quality. A further version from a German private collection, apparently of studio quality, was published by Legendre and Hartmann in 1937.[12]

There is no very sound basis on which to date our picture, but it may well be the earliest version of the subject by El Greco to have been preserved. In handling it is more controlled than the very freely painted version in the El Greco Museum, Toledo, which belongs to a very late series of Apostles on which the artist was still working at the time of his death. Cossío has proposed a date for our picture c. 1594–1604,[13] Mayer dates it 1596–99,[14] and Wethey c. 1600.[15]

Coll: Recorded by Cossío as in the possession of the heirs of Juan de Ibarra, Madrid, and then as having been sold c. 1908 by Luis Maria Castillo.[16] It was bought for the collection of Sra. Da. Trinidad Scholtz-Hermensdorff, viuda de Iturbe, who later became Duquesa de Parcent, and was lent by her to the Exhibition of Spanish Old Masters, Grafton Galleries, London 1913–14 (120) and to the Exhibition of Spanish Painting R.A. London 1920–1 (34). It passed to her daughter, the Marquesa de Belvis de las Navas, who married (1921) Prince Max Hohenlohe-Langenburg, and it was acquired from him in 1951 by Tomás Harris.[17]

Bought from Tomás Harris 1952.

1. H. Wethey El Greco and his School Princeton 1962 II p. 71 no. 113 states that the initials are restored, but this is not correct.

2. D. Davies, El Greco: Mystery and Illumination, Exhibition Catalogue, National Gallery of Scotland, Edinburgh, 1989 p. 71 no. 22.

3. A. Mayer El Greco Munich 1926 p. 22 no. 133.

4. Loc. cit.

5. Transcribed by F. de B. de San Román El Greco en Toledo Toledo 1910 pp. 192–4.

6. Transcribed by F. de B. de San Román in Archivo español de arte y arqueología III 1927 pp. 285–309.

7. See note 6 above. The entry for no. 127 reads Un Salbador, con quadro negro, de bara y terzia y bara y sesma. San Román further suggests that no. 127 in the 1621 inventory might be the same picture as no. 142 in the 1614 inventory, described there as Una cabeza de un Salvador.

8. Wethey op. cit. II p. 105 no. 173.

9. Wethey op. cit. II p. 103 no. 160.

10. Wethey op cit. II p. 107 no. 186.

11. Wethey op. cit. II p. 72 no. 114.

12. M. Legendre and A. Hartmann El Greco Paris 1937 p. 282 illus.

13. M. Cossío El Greco Madrid 1908 pp. 569–70 no. 107.

14. Loc. cit.

15. Op. cit. II p. 71.

16. Op. cit. p. 369 and pp. 569–70.

17. This information is first recorded in the 1957 Catalogue p. 113., and must originate from Tomás Harris.

491   Allegory ('Fábula')

Canvas: 67.3 × 88.6

Inscribed in pen and ink on the lining canvas: Attrib … a Velasquez est du Greco/No 14900 … (?)

In good condition, apart from an extensive tear from lower left to lower centre of the canvas, and smaller tears at upper left and lower right corners. The tacking edges of the original canvas are missing. Some restored damage on the cheek of the right-hand figure.

One of three versions of a still unidentified allegorical subject by El Greco. The earliest version (Fig. 16), perhaps painted in Rome *c.* 1570–5, is on long loan to the Museum of Fine Arts, Boston, from the collection of Stanley Moss, New York.[1] It has been widely accepted as an autograph work, but after it was seen at the exhibition *El Greco: Mystery and Illumination* in Edinburgh in 1989[2] alongside the other two versions Enriqueta Harris classified it as a copy,[3] a view that is still strongly contested by Jordan.[4] The second version (Fig. 17) is in the collection of the Earl of Harewood and is an autograph work by El Greco, probably dating from soon after the artist's arrival in Toledo in 1577.[5] Our picture, which is also unquestionably autograph, is almost identical in design to the Harewood version, apart from the omission of the monkey's chain. It has been dated as early as 1571–6 by Cossío,[6] and to 1576 by Mayer;[7] but a late date in the 1580s now seems far more likely, and this view has been propounded by many writers, including Camón Aznar,[8] Wethey,[9] Braham,[10] Haraszti-Takacs,[11] and Davies.[12] Davies comments on its stylistic kinship with El Greco's celebrated picture *The Burial of the Count of Orgaz* (Santo Tomé, Toledo) which dates from 1586–8.

The central figure of the boy lighting a candle is developed from a picture of this subject at Capodimonte, Naples, that was originally in the Farnese collection, Rome and which may have been painted when El Greco was in the city in 1572.[13] Another version from the Payson collection, Florida, which bears a partially abraded signature, might also date from El Greco's Italian period, and is accepted as an autograph work by most authorities including Wethey[14] and Jordan.[15] However Harris, after seeing the picture in Edinburgh alongside the Naples picture and the three versions of the *Allegory* described above, rejected it as a copy (or else a heavily repainted and seriously distorted original).[16]

El Greco's early stylistic development is still not at all clearly defined and this greatly adds to the difficulty of charting the precise sequence and relationship of the four related paintings which preceded the Edinburgh *Allegory*. In these circumstances it is perhaps premature and certainly unsafe categorically to deny El Greco's responsibility for the two early pictures from the Payson and Moss collections, simply on the grounds that they are more crudely and summarily painted than any of the others. Indeed these are not the normal characteristics of a copy. Harris' unjustified search for consistency in El Greco's early work might equally well have led to doubts about the well documented Naples picture, arguably the earliest of the works under discussion, on the grounds that it is painted in a refined Italianate manner, with a far more muted and less dramatic use of chiaroscuro than any of the other four pictures in the sequence. It seems far better to accept, albeit with caution, all five pictures and to characterise El Greco's development as a progression from a direct and robust, almost genre-like style, reminiscent of Bassano, to the ambiguity, the abstraction, and the technical refinements of the Edinburgh *Allegory*. Harris has commented perceptively on the 'greater coherence of the composition' in the Edinburgh picture and notes its 'more delicate and controlled style'.[17]

The precise meaning of the *Allegory* has still not been fully elucidated, and because of doubts about the status of the Moss collection version there is still disagreement as to whether the idea was originally conceived in Italy or Spain. Bialostocki has argued convincingly that the motif of a boy lighting a candle stemmed from a desire to recreate a lost work from antiquity, as described by Pliny the elder in his *Natural History*.[18] Pliny cites numerous examples of the subject in antique art, including works by the sculptor Lycius and the painters Philisius and Antiphilus. In particular, Antiphilus is praised for his picture of a boy blowing on a fire and for the reflection cast by the fire on the room and on the boy's face.[19] As Jordan has observed: 'Such an evocation of a lost work of antiquity no doubt gave pleasure to the literati in the sophisticated circle of Fulvio Orsini, librarian in the Farnese palace, where El Greco lived after his arrival in Rome and where one version of the painting remained for several decades.'[20] In the context of the more complex design of the *Allegory*, the act of a boy blowing on fire may also imply sexual passion. The monkey is often associated with Vice and the simpleton on the right may epitomise Folly. Davies has made the interesting observation that all these elements are to be found together in the *Ship of Fools*, a moralising treatise by Sebastian Brant, first published in Basle in 1494.[21] Cossío's earlier suggestion that the subject is an illustration of a Spanish proverb 'Man is fire; woman is tow; and the devil blows them into flame' is based on a misconception as to the sex of the central figure.[22]

The early provenance of our picture is not known. A picture of what is probably the same subject is recorded in an inventory made at the death of Juan Ribera in Valencia in 1611.[23] Another picture described as a *Fábula* (the traditional title of the *Allegory*) is listed in an inventory drawn up by El Greco's son Jorge Manuel, in 1621, after the artist's death.[24]

A version listed by Wethey as an early seventeenth-century copy, under no. X149, was later sold Sotheby Parke Bernet, New York 14 January 1988 (lot 129) as a studio work. Other copies are listed by Wethey nos X147–148 and X150–1.[25]

Coll: Féret, Paris; C. Cherfils, Paris by 1908;[26] Dr James Simon, Berlin; his sale Amsterdam 25–26 October 1927 (lot 149); exhibited *Old Masters by Spanish Artists* Tomás Harris Galleries, London 1931 p. 10; exhibited *From El Greco to Goya, The Spanish Art Gallery*, London 1938 no. 3; Mark Oliver collection, lent by him to the Wadsworth Atheneum, Hartford, Connecticut *c*. 1950 and later to the National Gallery of Scotland from 1976.

Acquired by the Gallery from the Estate of Mark Oliver with the aid of the National Heritage Memorial Fund and the N.A.C.F. 1989.

---

1. H. Wethey *El Greco and his School* Princeton 1958 II p. 82 no. 124.
2. D. Davies *El Greco; Mystery and Illumination*, Exhibition Catalogue, National Gallery of Scotland, Edinburgh 1989 no. 14.
3. E. Harris in *Burlington Magazine* CXXXI 1989 p. 729.
4. See W. Jordan in *El Greco of Toledo*, Exhibition Catalogue, Toledo Museum of Art, Prado Museum, Madrid, National Gallery of Art, Washington, Dallas Museum of Fine Arts, 1982–3 no. 5; and letter from W. Jordan in the Gallery files dated 20 October 1989.
5. Wethey *op. cit.* I p. 82 no 125. See further A. Braham *El Greco to Goya*, Exhibition Catalogue, National Gallery, London, 1981 no. 8 and Davies *op. cit.* no. 15.
6. M. Cossío *El Greco*, Madrid 1908 p. 598 no. 296.
7. A. L. Mayer *El Greco*, Munich 1926 p. 49 no. 305. See further A. L Mayer in *Pantheon* April 1930 p. 182, correcting a confusion in the provenance. See also Wethey *op. cit.* p. 83
8. J. Camon Aznar *Dominico Greco* Madrid 1950 (2nd edition Madrid 1970 II, p. 1390 no. 689).
9. Wethey *op. cit.* p. 83 no. 126. See also J. Gudiol *Doménikos Theotokopoulos El Greco 1541–1614* London 1973 p. 348 no. 129.
10. Braham *op. cit.* no. 9.
11. M. Haraszti-Takacs *Spanish Genre Painting in the Seventeenth Century* Budapest 1983 p. 168 no. 25.
12. *Op. cit.* II p. 59 no. 16.
13. Wethey *op. cit.* I p. 78 no. 122; Davies *op. cit.* p. 52 no. 13

14. Wethey *op. cit.* II p. 78 no. 121.

15. Jordan *op. cit.* no. 4. See further Davies *op. cit.* no. 12.

16. *Loc. cit.* (see note 3 above).

17. *Loc. cit.*

18. J. Bialostocki in *Arte in Europa Scritti di Storia dell' Arte in onore di Edoardo Arslan* Milan 1966 pp. 591–5.

19. Pliny *Natural History* IX, Book 35, 138.

20. *Op. cit.* no. 4 (see note 4 above)

21. Davies *op. cit.* pp. 20–21.

22. *Loc. cit.* (see note 6 above).

23. See R. Robres Lluch in *Archivo Español de Arte*, 27 p. 254. See further Wethey *op. cit.* II p. 78.

24. Wethey *op. cit.* p. 78.

25. Wethey *op. cit.* II pp. 196–7.

26. See Cossío *loc. cit.* (note 6 above).

Francesco GUARDI *1712–93*

Born in Venice on 5 October 1712, son of Domenico Guardi, a minor painter. His earliest work was in figure painting, often in collaboration with his elder brother Gian Antonio (1698–1760).[1] He became active as a view painter in around 1750 and was influenced by Canaletto.[2]

1498 Santa Maria della Salute, Venice

Canvas: 50.5 × 40.9
Cleaned 1965. In excellent condition.

1499 San Giorgio Maggiore, Venice

Canvas: 50.5 × 40.7
Cleaned 1965. In excellent condition.

A pair. Acquired with a traditional attribution to Francesco Guardi, which had been endorsed by Berenson in 1907. The attribution is beyond reasonable doubt. The chronology of Guardi's view paintings has not been established with any precision, but most suggestions for the date of our pictures have ranged between c. 1766 and the early 1770s. In 1936 Arslan proposed a date shortly before the cycle of the festivals of the Doge which is datable after 1766.[3] Pallucchini, writing in 1943, preferred a date in the second half of the 1760s,[4] and he was followed by Bauer.[5] In 1965 Zampetti suggested they might be even later in date,[6] and the force of his argument was subsequently accepted by Pallucchini.[7]

A drawing in the Correr Museum, Venice, which appears to be derived from our picture of *Santa Maria della Salute* no. 1498, has been attributed by Pallucchini to Francesco's younger brother, Niccolò Guardi.[8] A close variant of no. 1498 from the Northwick Park collection was sold at Christie's in October 1965.[9]

Coll: Robert Adam Dundas who later changed his name to R. A. Christopher-Nisbet-Hamilton, and who lent them to the B.I., London, June 1856 (138 and 140) and June 1867 (78 and 94), on both occasions as by F. Guardi.[10] Probably the two pictures lent by Miss Nisbet Hamilton to the exhibition *Old Masters and Scottish National Portraits* Edinburgh 1883 (281 and 389) as by Francesco Guardi. By inheritance to Mrs Nisbet Hamilton Ogilvy of Biel.

Mrs Nisbet Hamilton Ogilvy bequest 1921.

1. See P. Zampetti *Catalogo della Mostra dei Guardi* Venice 1965 pp. xxi ff.
2. For the beginning of Francesco's activity as a view painter see D. Mahon in the *Burlington Magazine* CX 1968 pp. 69 ff.
3. W. Arslan in *Bolletino d'Arte* XXIX 1936 p. 447.
4. R. Pallucchini *I disegni del Guardi al Museo Correr di Venezia* Venice 1943 pp. 17 and 60.
5. H. Bauer in *Kunstchronik* 20 1967 pp. 366–7.
6. *Op. cit.* pp. 170 ff. nos. 86 and 87 illus.
7. R. Pallucchini in *Arte Veneta* IX 1965 p. 231. See also A. Morassi *Antonio e Francesco Guardi* Venice 1973 I nos. 438, 470.
8. See note 4 above. See F. Guardi *Metamorfosi dell' imagine* Exhibition Catalogue, Castello di Gorizia 1987, where it is reattributed to Francesco Guardi.
9. Christie's 29 October 1965 (73) illus. See further T. Borenius *Catalogue of the Collection of Pictures at Northwick Park* London 1921 p. 20 no. 37 where the picture was paired with another picture by Guardi, no. 36, a view of the Grand Canal, Venice, looking towards S. Maria degli Scalzi.
10. For Christopher-Nisbet-Hamilton see *Pictures for Scotland* p. 111.

2370   Piazza San Marco, Venice

Canvas: 55.2 × 85.4
Cleaned 1983. In excellent condition.

Morassi has suggested a date of *c.* 1775–80 for our picture.[1] There are many other versions of this well-known view,[2] though ours is of particularly high quality.

Coll: Miss Caldwell, by whom lent to the *Winter Exhibition* Royal Academy 1876 (136); H. B. Caldwell sale Sotheby's 26 April 1939 (144). Duke of Hamilton and Brandon by whom lent to the exhibition *Eighteenth Century Venice* Whitechapel Art Gallery 1951 (34).

Received by the Treasury in lieu of estate duty, and presented 1978.

1. A. Morassi *Guardi I dipinti* Venice 1984 I p. 372 no. 327 fig. 356.
2. See, for example, Morassi *op. cit.* and M. Levey *The Eighteenth Century Italian Schools. National Gallery Catalogues* London 1956 p. 61.

In the style of GUARDI

828   A View in Italy

Canvas: 25.2 × 41.2
In good condition.

829   A View in Italy

Canvas: 25.2 × 41.2
In good condition.

A pair, acquired as by Francesco Guardi. They are later pastiches of Guardi's style and probably date from towards the end of the eighteenth century. The view, expressed by both Muraro and Morassi, that we are concerned with autograph works by Francesco Guardi was presumably based on study of photographs only.[1]

Coll: Our pictures may probably be identified as the two landscapes attributed to Francesco Guardi which were lent by W. Fettes Douglas to the exhibition of *Old Masters and Scottish National Portraits* Edinburgh 1883 (220 and 229).

Bought at the Sir William Fettes Douglas sale, Dowell's, Edinburgh, 10–12 December 1891 (406).

1. See M. Muraro in *Problemi Guardeschi, Atti del Convegno di studi promosso dalla mostra dei Guardi* Venice 1966–7 p. 186 pl. 187 for our no. 828. For the attribution to Francesco Guardi of both no. 828 and no. 829 see A. Morassi *Antonio e Francesco Guardi* Venice 1973 nos, 894, 1004. But cf. G. Fiocco *Francesco Guardi* Florence 1923 p. 77 no. 139 where our picture no. 829 is listed under *Guardi e aiuti.*

GUERCINO *1591–1666*

Giovanni Francesco Barbieri, called Guercino. He was baptised at Cento, near Bologna, on 8 February 1591. At first he was mainly active in Cento, Bologna and Ferrara. Then in 1621 he was invited to Rome by Pope Gregory XV, and remained there until 1623. During this period he painted the *Aurora* on the ceiling of the Casino Ludovisi, and the *S. Petronilla* alterpiece, now in the Capitoline Gallery, Rome. He established a studio in Cento, but, following the death of Guido Reni, moved to Bologna *c.* 1644. His early work shows the influence of artists such as Scarsellino, Bonone, Schedoni and Ludovico Carracci, but he became increasingly preoccupied with academic principles, and his late work is strongly classical in style.

39   S. Peter Penitent

Canvas: 103.7 × 85.8
Cleaned 1962. In very good condition, apart from two damages in the background to the right on a line with the saint's chin.

Acquired as by Guercino and so catalogued until 1957 when it was described as a school copy of a work of Guercino's middle period. After cleaning in 1962 it was again recognised as unquestionably autograph, in particular by Mahon who in 1967 suggested it is very probably the picture of *S. Peter weeping* (*Un. S. Pietro piangente*) described in Malvasia as painted in 1639 for Cardinal Rocci.[1] Another painting of this subject by Guercino is recorded as painted in 1650,[2] but by that date the artist's style had become more delicate and less robust than in our picture. Our picture is, however, consistent in style with a date of 1639; for instance, it is similar in handling to the *S. Joseph and Infant Christ* now in Dublin, which dates from 1637–8.[3]

The picture painted for Cardinal Rocci was paid for on 4 April 1639.[4] Yet by 10 February 1639 Guercino had only just started work on the picture, according to the evidence of a letter of that date from one Fra Gioseffo, who had just visited the artist's studio. Fra Gioseffo was writing to a friend (not named) who apparently hoped to acquire a half-length figure by Guercino, and, after describing Cardinal Rocci's commission for a half-length *S. Peter* which Guercino was about to undertake, Fra Gioseffo ventures to suggest that his friend might like to order a studio copy.[5] In the light of this remark about the possibility of obtaining a studio copy, it is interesting to note that there is a workshop replica of our picture in the Palazzo Venezia, Rome, which was considered to be an autograph Guercino when in the gallery of Cardinal Tommaso Ruffo in 1734.[6]

Coll: Our picture cannot be traced with complete certainty before it entered the Gerini collection, Florence, by 1786, catalogued as by Guercino, and with an engraved reproduction;[7] Gerini sale catalogue 1825 (282).[8] Bought from the Gerini family in Florence by Andrew Wilson, on behalf of the R.I., Edinburgh, 1831.[9] Exhibited R.I. 1832 (35).

Royal Institution 1831.

1. Carlo Cesare Malvasia *Felsina Pittrice Vite de' Pittori Bolognesi* (ed. Bologna 1841 I p. 264). Denis Mahon's view is recorded in a letter, dated 26 August 1967, in the Gallery files. See further L. Salerno *Dipinti del Guercino* Rome 1988 p. 264, no. 179.

2. Malvasia *op. cit.* (ed. Bologna 1841 II p. 269) where it is described as *Un S. Pietro piangente al Sig. Zanchetti da Reggio.* Malvasia *op. cit.* (ed. Bologna 1841 II p. 331) also records a payment for this picture on 11 October as follows: *Dal Signor Aurelio Zanoletti ho ricevuto No. 10 dobbloni d'Italia per la mezza figura del san Pietro piangente, e questi fanno ducatoni No. 59 lir. che sono sc. 74.*

3. See D. Mahon *Il Guercino (Dipinti).* Exhibition Catalogue, Bologna 1968 pp. 166 ff. no. 69.

4. See Malvasia *op. cit.* (ed. Bologna 1841 I p. 318) where it is recorded under an entry for that date as follows: *Dal Cancellier Lombardi si e ricevuto Reali 50 per il San Pietro fatto all' E.mo Sig. Cardinale Rocci Legato di Ferrara – fanno scudi 55.*

5. See Mahon *op. cit.* p. 148. The original manuscript is in the Biblioteca dell' Archiginnasio, Bologna, MS. B. 153, n. 16; it is transcribed by Mahon as follows: *attende parim.te a fare un S. Pietro di mezza fig.ra qual saria approposito p(er) lei, e lo fà all Em. Rocci che tengo sia una delle belle cose si possino cred.re in ordine a pitt.,ra e se V.S. Ill.r volesse ch'io tentassi p(er) haverne una coppia di buona mano, anzi boniss.a vedrò farla servire, pur che si contentino se ne cavi coppia.*

6. Inv. P.V.878. Photograph G. F. N. Rome no. E.35163. For the provenance see Mahon *op. cit.* p. 148. Ruffo had been Papal legate at Bologna and at Ferrara.

7. *Raccolta di ottanta stampe rappresentanti i quadri più scelti de' Signori Marchesi Gerini* Florence 1786. The size of the picture is given as *Palmi 5 once 3 × Palmi 4 once 1.* The engraving is inscribed *Lorenzo Lorenzi del. Carlo Faucci Sc.*

8. *Catalogo e stima dei quadri e bronzi esistenti nella galleria del Sig. Marchese Giovanni Gerini* Florence 1825.

9. See further *Pictures for Scotland* pp. 27 ff.

40   ## The Madonna and Child with the Young S. John

Canvas: 86.5 × 110
Cleaned 1960. In very good condition, apart from some wear in the Virgin's face and the sky.

Acquired as by Guercino and subsequently catalogued under this name. The attribution, which is clearly correct, has never been disputed. Mahon has suggested a date of *c.* 1615–16, and compares it to the *Madonna del Carmine* in Cento which he dates *c.* 1615.[1] A picture of the same composition as ours was engraved by J. H. Mortimer and published by J. Boydell in 1766 with the following inscription: 'From the Original Picture painted by Guercino in the Collection of Mr Reynolds. Size of the picture 2 F. 8$^{1}/_{2}$ by 3 F. 7 in Length'. A copy after our picture, which might be the ex. Reynolds collection version, is at Saltram House.[2]

Coll: Bought from the De Franchi family in Genoa by Andrew Wilson, on behalf of the R.I., Edinburgh, 1830.[3] Exhibited R.I. 1831 and 1832 (13). Recorded by Waagen in the collection of the R.I. in 1854.[4]

Royal Institution 1830.

1. D. Mahon *Il Guercino* (*Dipinti*) Exhibition Catalogue, Bologna 1968 p. 36 no. 14. See further L. Salerno *I Dipinti del Guercino* Rome 1988 no. 22.

2. See *The Saltram Collection* National Trust Catalogue 1967 p. 18 no. 12.

3. See further *Pictures for Scotland* pp. 27 ff.

4. Waagen 1854 III p. 269.

ITALIAN *early sixteenth-century*

645 Madonna and Child with the Young S. John

Wood: circular, maximum diameter 87.5

Cleaned 1971. There are paint losses along a vertical crack to the right of the Virgin's head. There are further extensive paint losses along the Madonna's left arm and the draperies above her waist. The infant Baptist's head and right hand and the torso of Christ are also affected by damage. The paint surface is somewhat worn. An oblong damage along the left edge is due to a technical experiment carried out in 1879, immediately before the picture was accepted by the Gallery.[1]

The design of the figures of the Madonna and Child in our picture is known in various versions:[2]

A weakly executed tondo attributed to Raffaellino del Garbo, in a private collection, advertised for sale in 1968.[3]

A heavily repainted tondo attributed to Raffaellino del Garbo, sold at Parke Bernet, New York in 1962.[4]

A tondo in the National Museum, Stockholm, attributed by Borenius to Piero di Cosimo,[5] and subsequently described by Bacci as a copy.[6]

An octagonal panel in the Johnson collection, Philadelphia, also attributed to Piero di Cosimo, but clearly a feeble derivative work.[7]

A tondo in the Museo de San Carlos, Mexico, attributed to Piero di Cosimo.[8]

A tondo of little artistic quality in the Lindenau Museum at Altenburg, catalogued as Florentine sixteenth-century.[9]

Zeri has noted two further versions of the design, both of fine quality: one was recently with Lorenzelli in Bergamo, and the other was with Giancarlo Baroni in Paris.[10]

The prototype for all these derivative pictures is apparently still lost. The design was probably conceived at the end of the fifteenth century by Piero di Cosimo. One also detects the influence of Filippino Lippi; this is especially evident in the heads of the Madonna and of the Infant Baptist in our particular version.

Our picture was acquired as by Domenico Ghirlandaio, but was first catalogued in 1936 simply as Italian school. Then in the 1957 *Catalogue* it was pointed out that it might be the work of an artist close to Francesco Granacci (who had been a pupil of Domenico Ghirlandaio). The most distinctive feature in the handling of our picture, which distinguishes it from the other versions, is the treatment of the landscape, with its very schematic representation of the rolling hills and the foliage of the trees (Fig. 18). Fahy has pointed out similarities between the treatment of the landscape in our picture and in a panel in the Metropolitan Museum, New York, representing the *Preaching of*

S. John the Baptist (Fig. 19) which is apparently the work of a collaborator of Granacci, active in the first decade of the sixteenth century,[11] and which Zeri has tentatively associated with the hand of the young Raffaello Botticini (born 1477, active until 1520).[12] Zeri compares the landscape of our picture with that in a panel of *S. John the Evangelist* (in the collection of French & Co., New York, in 1967), which Fahy had already listed under the name of Raffaello Botticini.[13]

These comparisons are not conclusive, but both Fahy and Zeri have independently suggested that our picture might have been painted by Raffaello Botticini,[14] and it seems likely that it is either by him or by an artist closely associated with him.

Coll: Probably Captain Thomas Medwyn sale Christie's 2 July 1828 (118) as Ghirlandaio, bought in;[15] David Laing.

David Laing bequest 1879.[16]

---

1. This 'experimental removal of some small part of the re-painting' was carried out with the approval of the Board on the recommendation of the Principal Curator, W. Fettes Douglas (letter dated 8 July 1879 in Gallery files).

2. I am indebted to Everett Fahy and Philip Pouncey for assistance in tracing these versions.

3. In the *Burlington Magazine* CX 1968 June Supplement pl. V.

4. Sale, Parke Bernet, New York 28 November 1962 (3). Photograph by Taylor & Dull Inc., New York, neg. no. 2146–3, in Gallery files.

5. T. Borenius in the *Burlington Magazine* XXXVI 1920 pp. 103–04 pl. II. See also R. Van Marle *The Development of the Italian Schools of Painting* The Hague 1913 XIII pp. 3 50 ff. fig. 241.

6. M. Bacci *Piero di Cosimo* Milan 1966 p. 130.

7. See *Catalogue of Italian Paintings, John G. Johnson Collection* Philadelphia 1966 p. 64 no. 76 illus. p. 191. Also reproduced by Van Marle *op. cit.* p. 352 fig. 240.

8. See *Museo de San Carlos* (Catalogue) 1971 no. 4 illus. There is a photograph in the Gallery files.

9. See R. Oertel *Frühe Italienische Malerei in Altenburg* Berlin 1961 p. 158 no. 165 fig. 64.

10. Letter from Federico Zeri, dated 18 July 1977, in the Gallery files. I have failed to trace photographs of these two versions.

11. Letter from Everett Fahy, dated 17 November 1976, in the Gallery files.

12. See F. Zeri *Italian Paintings. A Catalogue of the Collection of the Metropolitan Museum of Art, Florentine School* New York 1971 pp. 183–6 inv. 1970. 134.2.

13. E. Fahy *Some Followers of Domenico Ghirlandaio. Outstanding Dissertations in the Fine Arts* New York/London 1976 p. 213. A photograph of this picture is reproduced by R. Longhi *Cinquecento Classico e Cinquecento Manieristico* 1951–70 (*Opere Complete di Roberto Longhi* VIII/2 Florence 1976 pl. 3).

14. Letters from Federico Zeri, dated 3 February 1977, and from Everett Fahy, dated 4 March and 7 April 1977, in Gallery files. For Raffaello Botticini see F. Zeri in *Gazette des Beaux-Arts* LXXII 1968 pp. 159 ff. and Fahy *op. cit.* pp. 212–14.

15. Captain Thomas Medwyn was Shelley's cousin and the author of *Conversations with Lord Byron*. He is said to have bought his pictures 'during a residence in the South of Europe.' See D. Lygon and F. Russell in *Burlington Magazine* CXXII February 1980, p. 113, according to whom the reserve of £100 was the highest for a Tuscan quattrocento picture in London sales during the entire period 1801–37.

16. For Laing see *Pictures for Scotland* pp. 67 ff.

ITALIAN *seventeenth-century*

85 Battlefield – Trumpeters Sounding a Recall

Canvas: 105.2 × 232

The paint surface is badly obscured by discoloured varnish. There are heavy paint losses in the sky, and the tree on the right is almost totally repainted. Most of the shadows and middle tones, both in the figures and landscape, have been rubbed and strengthened, but the flesh colours and the areas of relatively heavy paint have survived quite well.

Acquired as Spanish school and catalogued as such until 1936 when it was attributed to Schönfeld, following a suggestion by Voss.[1] This attribution, which was repeated in both the 1946 and 1957 Catalogues, no longer seems convincing. It is more likely that the picture is Italian, and possibly, but not necessarily, Neapolitan. The canvas is of the type often found in Neapolitan painting, with a broad weave, but our picture does not appear to be by the most famous and influential of the Neapolitan battle painters, Aniello Falcone (1606–56), whose work tends to be more schematic and classical. The difficulty of finding a convincing attribution for our picture is greatly aggravated by the present condition of the paint surface.

Presented by James Wardrop (1782–1869) in 1850.[2]

1. Letter from Hermann Voss, dated 7 February 1931, in Gallery files.
2. For Wardrop see *Pictures for Scotland* p. 41.

ITALIAN *late seventeenth-century*

109 Portrait of a Prelate

Canvas 124 × 95.5
Cleaned 1941. The background is badly damaged and heavily repainted. The figure is reasonably well preserved.

There is no apparent basis for the traditional identification of the subject as the Secretary of Pope Leo X. Acquired as by Velázquez. An alternative suggestion that it might be by a follower of Bernardo Strozzi originates from the 1957 *Catalogue*. A further suggestion, in the 1978 *Catalogue*, that it might be by a follower of Pietro da Cortona, or even a copy of a lost picture by him, is discounted by Merz.[1]

Coll: Robert Clouston collection, Edinburgh, by 1843 when he lent it to the R.I., Edinburgh.[2] Also exhibited by the R.I. in 1845.[3] Presented to the R.I. by Robert Clouston in 1850.[4]

Royal Institution 1850.

1. Letter from J. Merz, Gallery files, 16 April 1983.
2. There was no catalogue for the exhibition, but the loan is documented in a list signed by R. Clouston and dated 24 June 1843 (R.I. MS. deposited in the Scottish Record Office).
3. Again, there was no catalogue for this exhibition, but the loan is documented in a letter from R. Clouston to Sir Thomas Dick Lauder, dated 3 May 1845 (R.I. MS. deposited in the Scottish Record Office).
4. Recorded in the R.I. Minute Book 4 August 1850 (R.I. MS. deposited in the Scottish Record Office).

ITALIAN *c. 1630*

812 A Hermit Saint doing Penance

Canvas: 105.4 × 89.4

Cleaned 1941. There are substantial paint losses on all four sides and particularly in the bottom right corner. There are further damages on his right cheek and temple, across his nose and below his left eye, and on his left sleeve. The paint surface generally is badly worn.

The identity of the saint, who flagellates his back with chains, while gazing down at a crucifix and a skull, has not been established.

Acquired as by Ribera and so catalogued up to 1946. In the 1957 *Catalogue* the attribution was questioned by Waterhouse and the picture described as in the manner of Ribera. He further suggested that our picture might be compared stylistically with the works of Cesare Fracanzano, a South Italian artist, born in 1600, who worked as a pupil of Ribera in Naples.[1] The picture also seems close to the style of artists working in Rome *c.* 1630 in the circle of Giovanni Lanfranco, such as Tommaso Luini.[2] It also invites comparison with the *Portrait of a Man*, identified as *Raffaello Menicucci*, in the John Herron Art Museum, Indianapolis, which was formerly attributed to Lanfranco and which is now thought to be by Valentin.[3] The modelling of the head in each of these two pictures is remarkably similar. None of these stylistic comparisons, however, is sufficiently close to provide a reliable basis for attributing our picture, but together they do suggest it was painted in Rome or in the south of Italy around 1630.

Coll: Lent by Messrs Doig and McKechnie [Edinburgh] to the exhibition *Old Masters and Scottish National Portraits* Edinburgh 1883 (406) as Spagnoletto *S. Jerome.*

Presented by Henry Doig 1888.

1. Sir Ellis Waterhouse, in a letter in the Gallery files dated 25 May 1977, again confirmed his opinion that our picture deserves to be considered as a possible work by Cesare Fracanzano. Cesare Fracanzano's work has still not been studied in any detail, and there are difficulties in distinguishing it from that of his brother Francesco Fracanzano. See Thieme-Becker XII pp. 269–70 and E. du Gué Trapier *Ribera* New York 1952 pp. 250–1.

2. The artistic personality of Tommaso Luini is not well defined, and only three pictures can be attributed to him with any certainty. These are *God the Father adored by angels* in S. Carlo al Corso, Rome, for which payment was made between 1627–32; and two pictures on the lateral walls of the chapel of S. Filippo Benizzi in S. Maria in Via, Rome. See A. Sutherland Harris and E. Schaar *Die Handzeichnungen von Andrea Sacchi und Carlo Maratta* Düsseldorf 1967 I pp. 30–1.

3. See J. P. Cuzin in *Revue de l'Art* 28 1975 p. 53 fig. 1.

ITALIAN *eighteenth-century*

638   Portrait of a Man

Canvas: 81.5 × 61
The sitter's cuff and hand are badly damaged. The background has been extensively repainted. The paint surface generally is worn.

Acquired as by Alessandro Longhi, to whom it had been attributed since 1918, and hitherto catalogued under his name, although in the 1957 *Catalogue* it was rightly pointed out that it is not good enough in quality to be by Alessandro Longhi himself. Pignatti has subsequently cast doubt on whether it is even Venetian, and firmly rejects the possibility that it might be a work from Longhi's studio.[1] The picture's condition and its mediocre quality both impede precise identification, but it appears to be a genuine eighteenth-century work and it is probably of Italian origin.

Coll: Sir Kenneth Matheson sale Christie's 26th July 1918 (155d) as by A. Longhi.

Sir Claude Phillips bequest 1924.

1. Letter from Terisio Pignatti in Gallery files, dated 11 March 1975.

ITALIAN *eighteenth- or nineteenth-century*

910   A City Square

Canvas: 68 × 93.5
The paint surface is somewhat worn, especially in the sky, and with some minor paint losses.

Hitherto described as a Venetian scene, but the location has never been positively identified and it is by no means necessarily Venetian. Acquired as eighteenth-century Spanish school and catalogued as such in 1936 and 1946. Catalogued as eighteenth-century Venetian school in 1957. Although it is painted in an eighteenth-century style, incorporating elements derived from Venetian and Spanish painting of this period, it may well be a nineteenth-century pastiche. In any case the quality of the execution is poor and it is not possible to attribute the picture with any precision.

Patrick Shaw bequest 1903.

LEONARDO DA VINCI *1452–1519*

Painter, sculptor, architect, engineer. He was born at Vinci near Florence on 15 April 1452. According to Vasari he was a pupil of Verrocchio in whose house he was living by 1476. He also worked in Milan and visited Rome. He died in France at Cloux, near Amboise, on 2 May 1519.

After LEONARDO DA VINCI

2270   Madonna of the Yarnwinder

Wood: 62 × 48.8
Cleaned 1965. In reasonably good condition apart from some quite heavy paint losses on the body of Christ, especially around his right hip and his left thigh, as well as in the foliage beneath the tree on the left, and along the right-hand and bottom edges of the picture.

Our picture is a sixteenth-century copy after the *Madonna of the Yarnwinder* which Leonardo da Vinci is recorded in 1501 as working on for Florimond Robertet, a favourite of the King of France.[1] The original has been presumed lost, though the two paintings now in the collection of the Duke of Buccleuch and a New York private collection (formerly in the Reford collection) have both had strong claims advanced for their authenticity.[2] An opportunity to compare these two pictures, our own and other related versions and drawings was provided by an exhibition held in 1992 at the National Gallery of Scotland and organised by Martin Kemp.[3] According to Kemp's most recent hypothesis,[4] the Buccleuch picture (incontestably the finer of the two prime versions) is the painting commissioned by Robertet, begun in 1501 by Leonardo and perhaps finished in 1506–7 with studio participation. The ex-Reford version, following Kemp, is later c.1516, and was completed in Leonardo's studio under the master's supervision.[5] Penny, however, has drawn attention to the evidence which has recently emerged from infra-red reflectography of the two pictures.[6] This reveals extensive underdrawing in both works including, to the left of each, details of the Holy Family grouping which are also found in our picture. Although the quality of our painting is not high, it and its related variants[7] may, therefore, provide intriguing evidence as to the appearance of the original of the *Madonna of the Yarnwinder*, whether that was in painted or drawn (ie a cartoon) format.

Coll: Bequeathed by Sir J. Stevenson Barnes to the grandfather of Captain Douglas Hope.[8]

Presented by Captain Douglas Hope 1964.

1. The account is given by the Carmelite friar Fra Pietro da Novellara in a letter to Isabella d'Este dated 14 April 1501 (letter published by various authors, for example by E. Möller in the *Burlington Magazine* XLIX 1926 p. 62 note 2).

2. See, for example, C. Gould *Leonardo. The Artist and the Non Artist* London 1975 p. 107 fig. 52 and M. Kemp *Leonardo da Vinci. The Marvellous Works of Nature and Man* London 1981 pp. 219–27 pl 60.

3. *Leonardo da Vinci. The Mystery of the Madonna of the Yarnwinder* Exhibition Catalogue, National Gallery of Scotland, Edinburgh 1992, with essays by M. Kemp and T. Crowe

4. *Op. cit.*, see Kemp's essay and his catalogue entries for the Buccleuch (no. 1) and ex-Reford (no. 2) pictures.

5. C. Gould, on the other hand, in the light of recent evidence provided by infra-red reflectography, has suggested the reverse sequence. See *Apollo* CXXVI 1992 pp. 12–16.

6. N. Penny *Burlington Magazine* CXXXIV 1992 pp. 542–46.

7. Our picture is particularly close to a version from the E. W. Edwards collection in Cincinatti, Ohio (reproduced by M. Goldblatt in *The Connoisseur* CXXV March 1950 p. 3 fig. 1 where it is erroneously claimed to be Leonard's original). Goldblatt (*op. cit.* p. 5 pl VI), also reproduces a similar version in the Dijon Museum and another, recorded in the Harrach collection, Vienna, which omits the subsidiary group of figures on the left (*ibid.* p. 5 pl. V). In his entry (no. 5) for our picture in the Edinburgh exhibition catalogue Kemp suggests a comparison with the work of Fernando Yañez, for example the *Madonna and Child with S. John* in the National Gallery of Art Washington, though he affirms our picture is of considerably lesser quality.

8. Information from Captain Douglas Hope; letter in Gallery files dated 14 May 1963.

Filippino LIPPI *1457?–1504*

Son of Fra Filippo. Probably born in 1457 and brought up in Prato. He was in Spoleto with his father from 1467–1469/70. In *c.* 1472 he was apparently living with Botticelli in Florence. He was in Rome for a few years from *c.* 1488–93 when he painted the fresco cycle in the Caraffa chapel of S. Maria sopra Minerva. His style shows the influence both of his father and of Botticelli.

1758 **The Nativity, with Two Angels**

Wood: 25 × 37

X-rayed. The condition of the paint surface is very good and the report on the picture's condition in the 1970 *Shorter Catalogue* is too pessimistic.[1] There is no good reason to doubt the authenticity of the hair and of the highlights and edges of the draperies. The background is slightly worn, and there are superficial restorations affecting the Child and the Virgin's pale blue under-robe. There is also a damage on Joseph's yellow drapery and his hand has been strengthened.

Presumably from the predella of an altarpiece, but no companion panels are known, and the altarpiece to which it belonged has not been identified. It was acquired as by Filippino Lippi and the attribution has been accepted by Borenius,[2] Berenson (1932, 1936 and 1963), Scharf,[3] and Neilson.[4] In view of the delicate quality of the handling it is almost certainly by Filippino Lippi himself rather than any studio assistant or follower. Fahy[5] has pointed out that it is particularly close in style to the small tondo on copper of the *Virgin Adoring the Child with Six Angels* in the Hermitage Museum, Leningrad,[6] and to the tondo of the *Holy Family with the Infant S. John and S. Margaret* in the Cleveland Museum,[7] both of which are generally attributed to Filippino Lippi. The Cleveland picture, in particular, has the same colour range and the same figure types as our panel. There is no sound basis on which to date our picture and published opinions have varied considerably. Berenson (1963) described it as an early work; Van Marle suggested a date *c*. 1484–5;[8] Scharf proposed *c*. 1496;[9] and Neilson considered it no later than 1497.[10] A date in the early 1490s is perhaps most likely, on the basis of stylistic comparison with Filippino's work in the Caraffa chapel of S. Maria sopra Minerva, Rome.

Coll: Said to have been in Hungary in the collection of Marie and Christine Sergievna Barishnikov, a family of Russian origin; Silbermann Galleries, Vienna;[11] private collection Paris when seen by Van Marle;[12] Knoedler's, London, by 1928.

Bought from Knoedler's, London, 1931.

---

1. *Shorter Catalogue* 1970 p. 51.
2. T. Borenius in *Pantheon* VII 1931 pp. 222 ff.
3. A Scharf *Filippino Lippi* Vienna 1935 p. 57 and p. 107 no. 21 fig. 96. See also A. Scharf *Filippino Lippi* Vienna 1950 p. 56 no. 100.
4. K. B. Neilson *Filippino Lippi* Cambridge (Mass.) 1938 pp. 136–7 fig. 64.
5. Letter from Everett Fahy, dated 3 June 1969, in Gallery files.
6. Reproduced by A. Scharf *Filippino Lippi* Vienna 1950 p. 56 no. 100.
7. See *The Cleveland Museum of Art Catalogue of Paintings: Part One, European Paintings before 1500* Cleveland 1974 pp. 76–9 no. 29 fig. 29. Everett Fahy's letter, dated 17 November 1976, is in the Gallery files.
8. R. Van Marle in *Apollo* XX 1934 pp. 70–1 fig. 1.
9. See note 3 above.
10. *Loc cit.*
11. Information from Knoedler's at the time of its acquisition by the Gallery. See further Borenius *loc. cit.*
12. See R. Van Marle *The Development of the Italian Schools of Painting* The Hague 1931 XII pp. 314 ff.

LOMBARD *late sixteenth- or early seventeenth-century*

60   **Christ on the Mount of Olives**

Canvas: 91.4 × 179

In good condition, apart from minor damages and paint losses which do not affect the principal features of the picture.

Acquired as by Giovanni Antonio Pordenone. This attribution was rejected by Waagen as early as 1854,[1] yet our picture remained catalogued under Pordenone's name until 1957 when it was listed as a work of the Lombard school. The Lombard character of our picture had already been noted by Crowe and Cavalcaselle as early as 1871.[2] It is probably by an artist from the circle of Moncalvo (c. 1568−1625) who worked mainly in the area around Milan, Pavia and Turin.[3] A stylistic clue to the artist's identity may lie in the rather unusual articulation of hands and feet, a stylistic feature which is not characteristic of Moncalvo himself.[4]

Coll: Bought from the Doria family, Genoa, by Andrew Wilson, on behalf of the R.I., Edinburgh, in 1830;[5] exhibited R.I. 1831 and 1832 (18).

Royal Institution 1830.

1. Waagen 1854 III p. 269.
2. J. A. Crowe and G. B. Cavalcaselle *A History of Painting in North Italy* 1871 (ed. T. Borenius, London 1912 III p. 183).
3. A generic attribution to Moncalvo was suggested (verbally) by Philip Pouncey in 1970.
4. For Moncalvo see A. Venturi *Storia dell'Arte Italiana* IX Part VII Milan 1934 pp. 552 ff; V. Moccagatta in *Arte Lombarda* VIII (2) 1963 pp. 185 ff.; A Griseri in *Paragone* 173 1964 pp. 17 ff.
5. See further *Pictures for Scotland* pp. 27 ff.

LORENZO DI CREDI *born 1456/9 died 1536*

Lorenzo d'Andrea d'Oderigo. Born between 1456 and 1459. A pupil of Andrea del Verrocchio, but he later ran his own busy workshop in Florence, where his somewhat unoriginal designs were further imitated and repeated by assistants.

Follower of LORENZO DI CREDI

646 Holy Family

Wood: circular, diameter 30
In reasonably good condition, but there are small paint losses in all areas. The paint surface in the area of the landscape in the right background is worn. An oblong area of paint loss above the Infant Baptist's head is due to a technical experiment, carried out in 1879 immediately before the picture was acquired by the Gallery.[1]

Acquired as by Lorenzo di Credi and catalogued as such until 1957 when it was attributed to his school. In 1931 Van Marle had already classified it as a school work.[2] Although our picture shows some similarities in style with the group of pictures which Berenson isolated under the name of Tommaso, an artistic personality close to Lorenzo di Credi, the routine workshop quality of its execution is hardly sufficient to justify such a specific attribution. Berenson himself omits our picture from his *Lists* (1932 and 1963) of both Lorenzo di Credi and Tommaso.

Coll: David Laing collection by 1862, when it is shown in the background of a portrait of Laing by W. Fettes Douglas, now in the S.N.P.G.[3]

David Laing bequest 1879.

1. This 'experimental removal of some small part of the re-painting' was carried out with the approval of the Board of Trustees on the advice of the Principal Curator, W. Fettes Douglas (his letter, dated 8 July 1879, is in the Gallery files).

2. R. Van Marle *The Development of the Italian Schools of Painting* The Hague 1931 XIII p. 317. See further G. Dalli Regoli *Lorenzo di Credi* Cremona 1966 p. 187 fig. 249 where it is listed as workshop of Lorenzo di Credi.

3. For Laing see *Pictures for Scotland* pp. 67 ff.; his portrait by Fettes Douglas is reproduced pl. 55.

LORENZO MONACO *born before 1372–1422/24*

Piero di Giovanni of Siena.[1] In 1390 he entered the Camaldolese monastery of S. Maria degli Angeli, Florence, and took the name of Lorenzo. Active from 1399 or earlier, but only two documented paintings by him are preserved: the Monte Oliveto altarpiece (1410) and the *Coronation of the Virgin*, from S. Maria degli Angeli (1414), both of which are now in the Uffizi, Florence. He also worked as a miniature painter.

2271 **LORENZO MONACO and workshop**

Madonna and Child

Wood: 101.6 × 61.7

The painted area goes up to the edges except round the arched top. Cleaned 1965. X-rayed. The heads of the Madonna and Child are affected by old restoration in the areas of shadow, but their feet and hands are in good condition. The Madonna's dark blue draperies have suffered from extensive paint losses, but her light blue draperies and the Child's draperies are not affected. There are substantial areas of repaired damage in the gold around the Child's head and in the centre of the floor. The lions' heads on the throne have been strengthened.

The lion-headed throne is the throne of Solomon or *Sedes Sapientiae* (I *Kings* X, 18–20). It is also found in the central panel from a triptych in the Collegiata di S. Andrea at Empoli, usually attributed to the studio of Lorenzo Monaco,[2] and in a triptych in the Fitzwilliam Museum, Cambridge, by Francesco di Antonio (Inv. M.33), dated 141(5).[3]

Our picture was very probably the central part of an altarpiece. A fragment of crimson drapery at the left-hand edge of the panel might have belonged to a subsidiary figure; but the lateral sections of the original altarpiece have not been convincingly identified.[4]

Our picture was acquired as by Lorenzo Monaco to whom it had also been attributed when in the Drury-Lowe collection.[5] Although almost certainly designed by Lorenzo Monaco, it may have been executed with some workshop assistance, to judge from the superior quality of works firmly attributed to the master such as the *Coronation of the Virgin* in the Uffizi.

The Madonna and Child in our picture appear to have been developed from the equivalent figures in Lorenzo Monaco's Monte Oliveto altarpiece, of 1410. In view of the relatively fluid modelling of the figures and draperies, our picture is very probably a somewhat later work, although it is less advanced in style than Lorenzo Monaco's

Adoration of the Magi, also in the Uffizi, which apparently dates from *c.*1420.[6] Eisenberg's suggestion that our picture might date from *c.* 1418–20 therefore seems quite plausible:[7] especially on comparison with the *Annunciation* in the Accademia, Florence.

Coll: William Drury-Lowe of Locko Park who probably bought it in Italy between 1840–65.[8] It may well be the picture by Lorenzo Monaco which Drury-Lowe is documented as having bought in 1863.[9] Lent by William Drury-Lowe to the *Exhibition of Works by the Old Masters* R.A. London 1884 (224). Lent by Lieut-Col. J. Packe-Drury-Lowe to *Works of Art from Midland Houses* Birmingham Museum and Art Gallery 1953 (164) as by Lorenzo Monaco. By descent to Captain P. J. B. Drury-Lowe.

Bought at the Locko Park sale Sotheby's 24 March 1965 (56).

---

1. See M. Levi d'Ancona in *Art Bulletin* XL 1958 pp. 175 ff.

2. In spite of some superficial stylistic similarities, the picture does not appear to be by the same hand as ours.

3. See J. W. Goodison and G. H. Robertson *Fitzwilliam Museum Cambridge, Catalogue of Paintings Volume 2. Italian Schools* Cambridge 1967 pp. 55–8, with discussion of possible dates between 1415 and 1418.

4. Frederico Zeri (letters in Gallery files dated 22 February 1966, 19 May 1968 and 31 December 1970) has suggested that a panel in the National Museum, Kraków (Inv. XII–187), representing *S. Catherine of Bologna and S. John the Baptist* might originally have been the left wing of a triptych to which our picture belonged; his idea is also reported by M. Boskovits *Pittura Fiorentina alla vigilia del Rinascimento* Florence 1975 pp. 340–41. Yet there is no evidence in favour of this hypothetical reconstruction, and it is also strongly contested by Marvin Eisenberg (letter dated 29 July 1977 in Gallery files), and again in his subsequent monograph *Lorenzo Monaco* Princeton 1989 p. 93.

5. See *Exhibition of Works by the Old Masters* R. A. London 1884 (224) as Lorenzo Monaco, and J. P. Richter *Catalogue of Pictures at Locko Park* 1901 no. 25 as Lorenzo Monaco. See also O. Sirén *Lorenzo Monaco* Strasbourg 1905 p. 190.

6. The Uffizi picture is usually identified with an altarpiece Lorenzo Monaco painted for Sant' Egidio and for which he was paid between 1420 and 1422. See Levi d'Ancona *op. cit.* p. 176.

7. Letter in Gallery files from Marvin Eisenberg, dated 4 May 1969, and confirmed in his recent monograph, see no. 4 above.

8. Richter *loc. cit.*

9. See J. Cornforth in *Country Life* 19 June 1969 pp. 1602–03.

Lorenzo LOTTO *c. 1480–1556/7*

Almost certainly born in Venice.[1] His early signed works in Asolo, dated 1506, and in S. Cristina al Tivarone (Treviso) show the influence of Alvise Vivarini and, above all, of Giovanni Bellini. A polyptych executed for the church of San Domenico in Recanati and now in the Pinacoteca there, inscribed with the date 1508, marks the end of this *quattrocento* style. In the next few years Lotto was influenced by Raphael's work, some of which he could have seen in Rome, where he had stayed by 1509; this influence is already evident in his *Entombment* at Jesi, dated 1512. Thereafter he evolved a highly individual style, and its progress can be followed through his numerous signed and dated works in Bergamo, Venice, and several of the cities in the Marches, such as Ancona, Jesi and Loreto.

418   **Virgin and Child with SS. Jerome, Peter, Clare (?) and Francis**

Canvas transferred from wood: 82.5 × 105; painted surface 80.5 × 102.5.

Signed on the scroll: L. LOTUS. F.

Cleaned 1991. X-rayed. The picture still had a wooden support in 1727 when described by Dubois de Saint Gelais.[2] It seems probable that the transfer took place when the picture was still in the Orléans collection; other pictures from the same collection such as Raphael's *Bridgewater Madonna* (q.v.) and his *Holy Family with a Palm Tree* (q.v.) were definitely transferred before they reached Britain.[3] Comparison with a photograph published by Cust in 1903 suggests that the picture was restored at some time between that date and 1946 when it was placed on loan in the Gallery.[4] The 1991 cleaning has revealed the high quality of the picture, although the paint surface has suffered, as is to be expected, from damages resulting from both flaking paint and the consequences of the transfer to canvas. Although these damages are fairly extensive, they are clearly visible and the overall design is quite unaffected. The effect of the damages was magnified by old restorations.[5]

The woodcutters in the landscape background, here symbolising Christ's Passion according to Béguin[6], may have been inspired by similar figures in a picture, from the studio of Giovanni Bellini, representing the *Death of S. Peter Martyr*, now in the National Gallery, London.[7] Lotto again introduced woodcutters in his *Assassination of S. Peter Martyr* at the Collegiata of Alzano Lombardo.[8]

Our picture has been generally accepted as an early work by Lotto, still showing the strong influence of Giovanni Bellini. Berenson has dated it *c.* 1505–10,[9] and Banti has suggested *c.* 1505.[10] It is particularly close in style to the signed *Madonna and Saints* in S. Cristina al Tivarone (Treviso). Documents, published by Liberali in 1963,[11] show that the S. Cristina picture was completed by May 1506, and it seems likely that our picture dates from about the same moment.

Coll: In the collection of Louis Duc d'Orléans by 1727, when catalogued by Dubois de Saint Gelais,[12] but not recorded three years earlier in the 1724 Orléans inventory.[13] Sale Lyceum, London, 1798 (234) reserved for the 3rd Duke of Bridgewater; thence by inheritance[14] to the 6th Duke of Sutherland, by whom lent to the Gallery 1946–84.

Purchased by Private Treaty from the Ellesmere Trustees with a grant from the National Heritage Memorial Fund 1984.

---

1. For full biographical details see B. Berenson *Lorenzo Lotto* London 1956.

2. L. F. Dubois de Saint Gelais *Description des tableaux du Palais Royal* Paris 1727 pp. 294–95.

3. B. Berenson's description of the picture as still on panel (*Lorenzo Lotto* London 1895 p. 6) as well as Cust's similar statement in 1903 (Cust and Bourke 1903 no. 16) may well be based on the picture's style, which is certainly that of a panel painting, rather than on a close physical examination of the support. In the photograph reproduced by Cust, the picture has a flattened appearance and shows no signs of flaking, which indicates that the transfer had already been carried out.

4. Cust and Bourke 1903 no. 16.

5. The areas most seriously affected by damage are the beard, cheek, and both hands of S. Peter; the face of S. Jerome; the face and legs of the infant Christ; the cheek, chin and forehead of the Virgin (but not her eyes, mouth and nose); the cheek of S. Clare, and the forehead, cheek, and ear of S. Francis.

6. S. Béguin in *Lorenzo Lotto. Atti del Convegno Nazionale di Studi per il V Centenario della Nascita,* ed. P. Zampetti and V. Sgarbi, Treviso 1981 p. 100.

7. For the attribution and status of the London picture see M. Davies *National Gallery Catalogue. The Earlier Italian Schools* London 1961 pp. 65–7 Inv. no. 812; and G. Robertson *Giovanni Bellini* Oxford 1968 pp. 125–7 pl. CX. See further J. Fletcher and D. Skipsey *Apollo* CXXXIII 1991 pp. 4–9.

8. See B. Berenson *Lorenzo Lotto* London 1956 pp. 32 and 461 pl. 81. He suggests a date of *c.* 1514 for this picture.

9. B. Berenson *Lorenzo Lotto* London 1956 pp. 8 and 463 pl. II.

10. A. Banti *Lorenzo Lotto* Florence 1953 p. 57. See further G. M. Canova *L'opera completa del Lotto* Milan 1975 p. 89 no. 13 as *c.* 1506.

11. See G. Liberali *Lotto, Pordenone e Tiziano a Treviso. Cronologie, Interpretazioni ed Ambientamenti inediti* in *Memorie dell'Istituto Veneto di Scienze, Lettere ed Arti* 1963 pp. 7 ff.

12. *Loc. cit.*

13. See C. Stryienski *Galerie du Regent Philippe Duc d'Orléans* Paris 1913 p. 151 no. 43.

14. Recorded by Otley and Tomkins 1818 II no. 7; Passavant 1836 I p. 130; Waagen 1838 II pp. 51–2; Jameson 1844 p. 109 no. 59; *Catalogue of the Bridgewater Collection* 1851 no. 90; Waagen 1854 II p. 33: Cust and Bourke *loc. cit.; Catalogue of Bridgewater House* 1926 no. 90.

Francesco MARMITTA *active c. 1500*

A painter, illuminator, and gem cutter from Parma.[1] Although Franciscus Maria Grapaldus, writing in the 1506 edition of *De partibus aedium* refers to Marmitta as a painter of altarpieces,[2] his only firmly authenticated work is the illumination of a manuscript of Petrarch in the library at Cassel.[3] Other miniatures have been convincingly attributed to him on the basis of stylistic comparison with the Cassel illuminations; they include a Missal at Turin, executed for Cardinal Domenico della Rovere (died 1501), and a Book of Hours in the Palazzo Bianco at Genoa.[4] Drawings attributed to Marmitta include a *Crucifixion* in the Louvre, Paris,[5] and an *Entombment* in the British Museum, London.[6] His style appears to derive from Ercole de'Roberti but also shows some affinities with that of Lorenzo Costa. Marmitta is said to have died in 1505,[7] but this testimony should perhaps be treated with some caution.

Attributed to Francesco MARMITTA

573 ### The Scourging of Christ

Wood: 35.8 × 25

Cleaned 1955. In basically good condition. This impression is not seriously affected by numerous small paint losses, due to flaking, which are readily discernible and which mainly affect the figures of Christ and of the flagellator on the left.

Attributed to Francesco Bianchi Ferrari at the time of its acquisition. An equally tentative attribution to Bramantino was proposed in 1930 when our picture was exhibited at the R.A. London.[8] This suggestion was then followed by Berenson, but with some reservations, in 1932 and 1936; and our picture continued to be catalogued under Bramantino's name up to 1946. In 1934 Longhi had suggested it was by Marmitta,[9] and this view was accepted by Toesca in 1948.[10] Our picture was listed under Marmitta's name in the 1957 *Catalogue*, and the attribution was further endorsed by Levi d'Ancona in 1967[11] and Brown in 1988.[12] On the basis of stylistic comparison with the illuminated Missal at Turin (Fig. 20),[13] the attribution to Marmitta is certainly quite convincing, even if it must still be regarded as tentative. However a complication seems to arise inasmuch as our picture does not have any obvious stylistic connection with the only other painting to have been attributed to Marmitta, an altarpiece in the Louvre, Paris, representing the *Virgin and Child with S. Benedict and S. Quentin* (Fig. 21).[14] Of these two paintings, ours seems much the closer in style to Marmitta's more securely identified miniature paintings. The large scale of the Louvre picture inevitably precludes serious stylistic comparison with illuminated manuscripts, but the fact remains that Marmitta was described by a contemporary writer as a painter of altarpieces. Although in these circumstances the attribution of the Louvre picture to Marmitta cannot be excluded, equally it does not provide a secure basis from which to question the attribution of our small picture to Marmitta.

The development of Marmitta's style and the chronology of his work cannot be traced with any precision, but Toesca has argued that our picture might be a relatively early work, when Marmitta was still influenced by Ercole de'Roberti.[15]

Coll: Said to have belonged to Emile Gavet,[16] but it cannot be traced in the catalogue of his picture sale in Paris on 5 June 1897. Later, apparently in the collection of Sir George Donaldson.[17]

Bought from Durlacher's, London, 1927.

1. See Vasari (ed. Milanesi V p. 383).
2. F. M. Grapaldus *De partibus aedium* Parma 1506 Lib II ch. VIII f. 125.
3. P. Toesca *Monumenti e Studi per la Storia della Miniatura Italiana. La collezione di Ulrico Hoepli* Milan 1930 pp. 95 ff.
4. Toesca *loc. cit.* See also P. Toesca in *L'Arte* XVII 1948 pp. 33–9, and M. Levi D'Ancona in *Bollettino dei Musei Civici Veneziani* XII 4 1967 pp. 9–28.
5. See R. Longhi *Officina Ferrarese* 1934 (*Opere Complete di Roberto Longhi* V Florence 1956 p. 57 fig. 183).
6. See P. Pouncey in *Proporzioni* III 1950 pp. 111–13; and A. E. Popham and P. Pouncey *Italian Drawings … in the British Museum. The Fourteenth and Fifteenth Centuries* London 1950 pp. 106–7 no. 171 pl. CLVIII.
7. See P. Toesca in *L'Arte* XVII 1948 p. 33 note I.
8. *Italian Art 1200–1900* Exhibition Catalogue, R.A., London 1930 (264).
9. *Op. cit.* p. 57 fig. 184
10. In *L'Arte* XVII 1948 p. 34.
11. *Op. cit.* p. 10
12. D. A. Brown in *Prospettiva* 53–6, 1988–9 p. 305 fig. 10.
13. See note 4 above.
14. Inv. 1167. For the attribution to Marmitta see P. Toesca in *L'Arte* XVII 1948 p. 39 figs. 8 and 9. The attribution has also been put forward by P. Pouncey in *Proporzioni* III 1950 p. III and by Popham and Pouncey *op. cit.* pp. 107–8 no. 174 pl. CLIX.
15. In *L'Arte* XVII 1948 pp. 34 ff.
16. Information from Durlacher's in 1927; receipt in Gallery files.
17. See note 15 above.

MASTER OF THE ADIMARI CASSONE *active mid-fifteenth century*

An artistic personality first defined by Longhi,[1] followed by Pudelko,[2] on the basis of the Adimari *cassone* in the Accademia, Florence.[3] He may have been trained around 1435 under the influence of Vecchietta and Paolo Schiavo. Longhi has further speculated that he might be identified as Lazzaro Vasari of Arezzo. Bellosi suggested that the Master of the Adimari Cassone might be Giovanni di Ser Giovanni, called Lo Scheggia (1406–after 1480), the brother of Masaccio.[4] Among the other works attributed to the Master of the Adimari Cassone, who is also sometimes known as the Master of Fucecchio, are the *Madonna and Child Appearing to S. Sebastian and S. Lazarus, Mary Magdalen and Martha on the Voyage to Marseilles* in the museum at Fucecchio,[5] and a *desco da parto* representing the *Triumph of Fame* and dated 1449, in the collection of the New York Historical Society,[6] as well as numerous cassone panels.[7] Many of the works now associated with the Master of the Adimari Cassone were listed by Berenson (1963) under the name of Francesco di Antonio di Bartolomeo (born 1394) who was active a generation earlier.

75   Triumph of a Roman General

Canvas transferred from wood: 40.5 × 70.5

Transferred from the original panel in 1967 because of extensive flaking of the paint surface. A particularly severe paint loss affects the rump of the horse in the centre foreground. Otherwise, both the horses and the human figures are in fair condition. The grey paint of the men's armour is badly rubbed. The trees and foliage in the middleground and background are also rubbed and discoloured.

Catalogued in 1946 as Sienese school, and in 1957 under Florentine as by a close follower of Pesellino. Since then Zeri has pointed out, quite convincingly, that it is very close in style to works attributed to the Master of the Adimari Cassone.[8] Both the distinctive and skilful rendering of the horses, and the character of the tooling, are recognisable features of this hand.

Coll: Bought in Florence in 1865 from William Blundell Spence, by the 9th Earl of Southesk, as a work of Uccello, according to a MS. inventory of the Southesk collection.[9]

Bought from the 11th Earl of Southesk in 1942.

1. See R. Longhi '*Me Pinxit*' *e Quesiti Caravaggeschi* 1928–34 (*Opere Complete di Roberto Longhi* IV Florence 1968 p. 25) and *Fatti di Masolino e di Masaccio e altri studi sul Quattrocento* 1910–67 (*Opere Complete di Roberto Longhi* VIII Florence 1975 p. 43 and pp. 56 ff. note 24).
2. See G. Pudelko *Studi sopra Domenico Veneziano* in *Mitteilungen des Kunsthistorischen Instituts in Florenz* IV 1934 p. 163.
3. Reproduced by B. Berenson 1963 II pls. 733a and b.
4. See *Arte nell' Aretino* Exhibition Catalogue, San Francesco, Arezzo 1974/75 pp. 88 ff. for a discussion of Luciano Bellosi's hypothesis.
5. Reproduced by Berenson 1963 II pl. 723.
6. Reproduced by Berenson 1963 II pl. 732.
7. Listed by Pudelko *loc. cit.* and Longhi *op. cit.* 1975 p. 58.
8. Letter from Federico Zeri, dated 19 April 1966, in the Gallery files.
9. Copy of the MS. in Gallery files. For W. Spence see J. Fleming in the *Burlington Magazine* CXV 1973 pp. 4 ff.

MASTER OF THE S. LUCCHESE ALTARPIECE

A Florentine artist, active in the mid-fourteenth century and probably a close follower of Maso di Banco. His individual style has been defined by Offner on the basis of a triptych, formerly in the church of S. Lucchese, Poggibonsi, and now destroyed;[1] but his precise identity remains unknown. Other works which Offner attributed to him[2] include a *Coronation of the Virgin* at the Lindenau Museum at Altenburg (Inv. 18);[3] a tabernacle at the Musée Bonnat, Bayonne (Inv. 966);[4] a *Madonna and Child* in the Cleveland Museum of Art (Inv. 68.206);[5] a *Coronation of the Virgin* formerly in the

Pasquinelli collection, Milan;[6] a series of *Scenes from the life of S. Christopher* formerly in the Monte Carlo museum; a tabernacle formerly in the collection of Felix Gouléd, New York;[7] a tabernacle in the Mark Brandenburg collection, Radensleben; a *Coronation of the Virgin* in the Palazzo Barberini (Galleria Nazionale), Rome (Inv. F.N. 700);[8] a tabernacle in the S. Louis City Art Museum (Inv. 51.26);[9] and the Baronci triptych in the Archiepiscopal Museum, Utrecht (Inv. N.K. 1726).[10] Some of these works have recently been attributed to Orcagna by Boskovits,[11] but his definition of Orcagna's style is not always convincing and he does not offer sufficient evidence seriously to undermine the basis of Offner's attributions to the Master of the S. Lucchese Altarpiece.

1539A A Baptism

Wood: 18.6 × 31.8
The edges of the panel are trimmed. Cleaned 1951. A horizontal break running just above the level of the heads of the two kneeling figures has been filled. Otherwise in fair condition, but with some paint loss along the edges of the cupped craquelure.

1539B A Martyrdom

Wood: 18.6 × 29.6
The edges of the panel are trimmed. Cleaned 1951. There are damages in the top left corner, in the area of the male saint's halo, and around the outstretched hand of the further of the two Roman judges. There is also some paint loss along the edges of the cupped craquelure.

The legend depicted in these two panels has not been convincingly identified. The female figure, dressed in green, who is shown being beaten to death in no. 1539B, has no halo, and therefore is not necessarily a saint.[12]

Two panels from a predella which had been joined together some time after the Woodburn sale in 1860 (see under *Coll.* below) and were re-separated in 1951. Another fragment from the same predella, representing the *Man of Sorrows*, is at the City of York Art Gallery.[13] A fourth panel, which shows the male saint, dressed in white and visited by an angel, was published by Zeri in 1965, but its present location is not recorded.[14] A fifth panel, which has yet to be identified, was last recorded, together with the four other sections of the dismembered predella, at the Woodburn sale in 1860; it was lot 40 and was described in the catalogue as: 'The martyrdom of a Saint who is beheaded by an executioner, two Roman officers seated on a tribune, a group of soldiers in attendance and two singular diminutive figures in the foreground – gold ground.'[15] The original sequence of the five panels must remain a matter of conjecture so long as the subjects are unidentified, but it seems quite likely that the panel published by Zeri in 1965 came first, followed by our no. 1539A, then the York panel in the centre, followed by our no. 1539B and the missing panel depicting the death of a male saint. Alternatively, the panel published by Zeri might have been the fourth in the sequence, dividing our no. 1539B from the missing panel.

Our panels were acquired together as by Giotto and were catalogued under this name in 1924. Then, from 1929 to 1946, they were catalogued under the name of Daddi, and in 1957 they were described as mid-fourteenth-century Florentine. Berenson had begun by attributing them to Maso (1932 and 1936) but later revised this view, and in 1963 described them as the work of an unidentified Florentine active *c.* 1350–1420. The attribution to the Master of the S. Lucchese Altarpiece was advanced by Offner in 1958[16] and was followed in the 1970 *Shorter Catalogue*. It is entirely convincing inasmuch as our two panels are extremely close in style to many of the other pictures which Offner groups together under the same name.

Coll: Samuel Woodburn sale Christie's 9 June 1860 (37 and 41) bought Daniell for W. Fuller Maitland. Recorded in the catalogue of the W. Fuller Maitland collection at Stansted Hall 1872 (p. 6) as by Giotto, and again in the Stansted Hall Catalogue 1893 (12) also as by Giotto.

Bought from W. Fuller Maitland 1921.

---

1. Reproduced in *The Cleveland Museum of Art Catalogue of Paintings: Part One, European Paintings before 1500*. Cleveland 1974 p. 94 fig. 34b.

2. I am indebted to Klara Steinweg who provided me with an unpublished list of pictures attributed by Richard Offner to this hand, and who kindly invited me to make use of it in the biographical section of this catalogue. I am also grateful to the Curators of the Richard Offner Collection (Photographic Archive), Institute of Fine Arts, New York University, for assistance in obtaining photographs (now in the Gallery files) of most of these pictures. See further R. Offner ed. H. Maginnis *Corpus of Florentine Painting. A Legacy of Attributions. The Fourteenth Century. Supplement.* 1981 pp. 21–3.

3. See also R. Offner *A Critical Corpus of Florentine Painting* Section III V New York 1947 p. 249. Offner's attribution is followed by M. Boskovits *Pittura Fiorentina alla viglia del Rinascimento* Florence 1975 p. 200.

4. Reproduced by Berenson 1963 pl. 222 as by Jacopo di Cione. Offner's attribution is followed by Boskovits *loc. cit.*

5. See *The Cleveland Museum of Art Catalogue of Paintings: Part One, European Paintings before 1500* Cleveland 1974 pp. 93 ff. no. 34 fig. 34. See further Boskovits *loc. cit.*

6. But cf. M. Boskovits in the *Burlington Magazine* CXIII 1971 p. 248 note 32 fig. 20 where it is attributed to Orcagna.

7. See also Offner *op. cit.* Section III V New York 1947 p. 212 note 1. Offner's attribution has been questioned by M. Boskovits *Pittura Fiorentina alla vigilia del Rinascimento* Florence 1975 p. 200.

8. See also Offner *op. cit* Section IV II New York 1960 p. 95 note 9. But cf. M. Boskovits in the *Burlington Magazine* CXIII 1971 p. 247 fig. 10 where it is attributed to Orcagna.

9. But cf. M. Boskovits in the *Burlington Magazine* CXIII 1971 pp. 244–5 note 22 fig. 11 where it is attributed to Orcagna.

10. See also Offner (with K. Steinweg) *op. cit.* Section IV IV New York 1967 p. 68 note 10. But cf. M. Boskovits in the *Burlington Magazine* CXIII 1971 p. 243 note 15 where it is attributed to Orcagna.

11. See notes 6, 8, 9 and 10 above. For the views of M. Boskovits on the Master of the S. Lucchese Altarpiece see *Pittura Fiorentina alla vigilia del Rinascimento* Florence 1975 p. 200.

12. G. Kaftal *Iconography of the Saints in Tuscan Painting* Florence 1952 nos. 328 and 329 figs. 1179 and 1180 as unidentified. In the 1957 *Catalogue* it was tentatively suggested that the two figures might be SS. Felix and Regula, a brother and sister who, at the time of the martyrdom in Switzerland of S. Maurice and the Theban Legion, escaped only to be captured and put to death near Zurich.

13. Wood 18.4 × 47.6 cm. See *City of York Art Gallery Catalogue of Paintings* York 1961 I p. 29 and *City of York Art Gallery Catalogue Supplement* York 1975 p. 7. The connection between the York and Edinburgh panels was first proposed by Offner (unpublished lists, for which see note 2 above), and was later endorsed in the 1957 *Catalogue*. In 1965 the three panels were all exhibited together in London (see St. John Gore *The Art of Painting in Florence and Siena from 1250 to 1500* Exhibition Catalogue, Wildenstein, London 1965 pp. 9 ff. nos. 14–16) and this provided an excellent opportunity to confirm, beyond reasonable doubt, the close stylistic connection between them.

14. Wood 18.4 × 33 cm. See F. Zeri in the *Burlington Magazine* CVII 1965 p. 254 fig. 54.

15. By the time of the Woodburn sale, the predella had already been taken apart and the five sections were not even sold consecutively. Our two panels were lots 37 and 41; the York panel was lot 39, and the panel published by Zeri was lot 47. For a detailed discussion of the connection between these five panels and their common origin in the Woodburn sale, see H. Brigstocke *City of York Art Gallery Preview* 82 1968 pp. 755–59.

16. *Op. cit.* Section III VIII New York 1958 p. 166 note 2; in his unpublished lists (see note 2 above); and *op. cit.* 1981 p. 21. The attribution has been supported by Zeri *loc. cit.* and by M. Boskovits *Pittura Fiorentina alla vigilia del Rinascimento* Florence 1975 p. 200.

MASTER OF 1419

Named by Pudelko after a *Madonna and Child,* in the Cleveland Museum (Inv. 54.834), which is dated 1419.[1] The same artist is sometimes known as the Master of S. Julian, after the *S. Julian* polyptych in the Museo Civico at San Gimignano.[2] Other pictures which have been convincingly associated with the same hand include the two lateral sections of the altarpiece of which the *Madonna and Child* in Cleveland forms the centrepiece;[3] a *Madonna of Humility* sold at the Hôtel Drouot, Paris, 8 June 1937 (38);[4] a *Madonna and Child* formerly on the Munich art market;[5] and a *Madonna and Child with Saints* sold at Sotheby's 30 June 1965 (33).[6] The Master of 1419[7] was influenced by the style of Lorenzo Monaco, and he sometimes appears to anticipate the relatively early works of Masolino, such as the *Madonna of Humility* in the Kunsthalle, Bremen, dated 1423.

1540A   **The Stigmatization of S. Francis**

Wood: 21.6 × 30.5
Cleaned 1950. The paint surface is in reasonably good condition for a predella panel of its age. There are a number of small damages, including a heavy vertical scratch through the figure of the Franciscan friar on the right. The gold is severely rubbed.

1540B   **S. Anthony Abbot Exorcising a Woman Possessed by the Devil**

Wood: 21.6 × 30.5
Cleaned 1950. The paint surface is in reasonably good condition for a predella panel of its age. There are a number of small damages, and the panel has a crack, running horizontally, along the centre left.

Two panels from a predella. They had been joined together and were re-separated in 1950. The other panels from the predella have not been identified.

Acquired as by Giotto and catalogued under his name in 1924.[8] Berenson (1932, 1936 and 1963) tentatively attributed them to Andrea di Giusto, and this view was then followed in the 1936 and the 1946 *Catalogues*. In 1940 Longhi suggested they might be the work of a miniature painter, active *c.* 1420.[9] In 1951 Offner attributed them to the Master of 1419,[10] and this view was then followed by Kaftal.[11] The stylistic connection between our panels and the *S. Julian* polyptych in the Museum at San Gimignano (Fig. 22), which is generally attributed to the Master of 1419, was also noted in the 1957 *Catalogue*. Although the attribution of our panels to the Master of 1419 cannot be firmly established, the stylistic evidence deserves very serious consideration; the main difficulty lies in the lack of further predella panels associated with the same hand, for detailed comparison. In any case, this tentative attribution is indicative of the belief that our panels are probably by an artist active in Florence around 1420, and whose style is close to artists such as Andrea di Giusto and Giovanni Toscani.

Coll: Recorded in the catalogue of the W. Fuller Maitland collection at Stansted Hall in 1872 (p. 6) as 'Gaddi?', and again in the Stansted Hall Catalogue 1893 (7) also as 'Gaddi?'

Bought from W. Fuller Maitland 1921.

1. G. Pudelko *Art in America* XXVI 1938 p. 63. For the Cleveland picture see also W. Cohn in *Rivista d'Arte* XXXI 1956 pp. 49–52 and *The Cleveland Museum of Art Catalogue of Paintings: Part One, European Paintings before 1500* Cleveland 1974 pp. 89 ff. no. 33.
2. Pudelko *loc. cit.* See also R. Longhi in *Critica d'Arte* V 1940 II p. 185 note 21.
3. See Pudelko *loc. cit.*; Berenson 1963 II p. 550; P. Pouncey in the *Burlington Magazine* XCVI 1954 pp. 291–2 fig. 30; Cohn *loc. cit.*
4. See Longhi *loc. cit.*; also noted by Richard Offner in an unpublished list, dated 1951, kindly made available by Klara Steinweg (copy in Gallery files). A photograph of the picture was kindly provided by the Curators of the Richard Offner collection (Photographic Archive), Institute of Fine Arts, New York University.
5. Listed by Offner in 1951 (see note 4 above).
6. See Longhi *loc. cit.*, also listed by Offner in 1951 (see note 4 above).
7. Pudelko *loc. cit.*; and Offner list (1951), also attributed a number of other pictures to the same hand.
8. Also listed by R. Van Marle *The Development of the Italian Schools of Painting* The Hague 1924 III p. 272 as Giotto school.
9. Longhi *op. cit.* p. 182 note 15.
10. Offner's 1951 list (see note 4 above).
11. G. Kaftal *Iconography of the Saints in Tuscan Painting* Florence 1952 no. 24 fig. 71 as Master of S. Julian at S. Gimignano.

MATTEO DI GIOVANNI *active 1452 died 1495*

Matteo di Giovanni di Bartolo. His family came from Sansepolcro, but he was active as an artist in Siena from *c.* 1452. His style was influenced by Vecchietta, Sano di Pietro, and Girolamo da Cremona, as well as the Florentine artists Antonio and Piero Pollaiuolo. His principal pupil was Guidoccio Cozzarelli.

1023 ### Madonna and Child with S. Sebastian, S. Francis and Angels

Wood: 51.3 × 39.7

Cleaned 1956. There is no evidence to support a statement in the 1957 *Catalogue* that the picture has been cut down on all four sides. A further statement that the punched border at the top and left side is a later addition is equally questionable. The appearance of the gold is uniform throughout and does not appear to have been subjected to later interference in the area of the punched border. The overall paint surface is in a reasonable state for its age. The Madonna's face and hands are in good condition, but there are serious paint losses, due to flaking, on her dark outer robe, and the glazes on her mauve robe have been lost. There is some rubbing in the area occupied by the children at the bottom of the picture.

Acquired as by Matteo di Giovanni. The attribution has been endorsed by Van Marle[1] and Berenson (1932, 1936 and 1968), but the possibility of studio assistance cannot be excluded.

Coll: Arthur Severn who lent it to the *Exhibition of Pictures of the School of Siena* B.F.A.C., London 1904 (42), where it was said to have been formerly in the collection of John Ruskin.

Bought from R. Langton Douglas 1910.

1. R. Van Marle *The Development of the Italian Schools of Painting* The Hague 1937 XVI p. 358 fig. 204.

Pier Francesco MOLA *1612–66*

Born in Coldrerio, near Lugano, in February 1612.[1] His family then moved to Rome by 1616. He made two journeys out of Rome, the first *c.* 1633–40 and the second *c.* 1641–7. He had probably visited Venice by 1640–1, and was almost certainly there again in 1644. From *c.* 1645–7 he studied under Albani in Bologna. He was also strongly influenced by Guercino. He worked in Rome from *c.* 1647 and in 1662 was elected President of the Accademia di San Luca.

Attributed to a follower of Pier Francesco MOLA

29 S. Jerome

Canvas: 61 × 79
Cleaned 1962. In good condition.

Czobor suggests that our picture does not represent S. Jerome, because of the apparent absence of some of the Saint's traditional attributes, such as the lion, crucifix, angel and trumpet.[2] But a lion can in fact be seen in the landscape to the right, and this confirms the traditional identification of the Saint. He is also shown with the stone of self-punishment, together with books, pen and ink, characterising him as a scholar.

Acquired as by Franceschini and so catalogued until 1957 when it was attributed to either Guercino or a good early imitator. An attribution to Guercino was already ruled out by Mahon by 1962,[3] and at the Guercino exhibition in Bologna in 1968 it became perfectly evident that our picture could not possibly be by him, and probably not by any other artist working principally in Emilia. A suggestion (by Mahon in 1962) that it might be by Mola was adopted by Czobor who published it as a late work.[4] The attribution was rejected by Cocke.[5] In favour of Cocke's negative view it may be said that although our picture is stylistically close to Mola its decorative quality is not altogether characteristic of his work, which is usually more vigorous in modelling and more robust in handling. Since the predominant influence is that of Mola, our picture may well be by one of his many pupils, most of whom have yet to be seriously studied.[6]

Coll: Bought as by Franceschini, form the De Franchi family, Genoa, by Andrew Wilson, on behalf of the R.I., Edinburgh, 1830.[7] Exhibited R.I. Edinburgh 1831 and 1832 (16).

Royal Institution 1830.

1. Mola's biography, and the relevant literature, are fully summarised by A. Sutherland Harris in the *Burlington Magazine* CVI 1964 pp. 363 ff.; and by R. Cocke *Pier Francesco Mola* Oxford 1972 pp. 1–10.
2. A. Czobor in the *Burlington Magazine* CX 1968 p. 569 fig. 46.
3. Verbal communication from Sir Denis Mahon recorded in the Gallery files, and reported in the *Shorter Catalogue* 1970.
4. *Loc. cit.*
5. *Op. cit.* p. 66 no. R. 18,
6. For Mola's pupils and followers see E. Schleier 'Pier Francesco Mola e la pittura a Roma' in *Pier Francesco Mola*, Exhibition Catalogue, Lugano, 1989 pp. 89 ff.
7. See further *Pictures for Scotland* pp. 27 ff.

Francesco MONTI *1685–1767*

Born in Bologna where he was a pupil of Giovanni Gioseffo dal Sole. Also influenced there by Giuseppe Maria Crespi, Donato Creti and Antonio Gionima. In 1725 he became president of the Accademia Clementina in Bologna. From the 1730s onwards he was also active in Brescia (where, among other commissions, he decorated the church of S. Maria della Pace), Cremona, and Bergamo. During the period of his activity in Lombardy, he appears to have studied and been influenced by the work of Venetian artists such as Giovanni Battista Tiepolo and Giovanni Battista Pittoni.[1]

120

Rebecca at the Well

Canvas: 78.7 × 84.5
Cleaned 1978. The paint surface is in fair condition but with some considerable loss by abrasion. The dark ground is visible in some areas.

For the subject see *Genesis* XXIV, 22 ff. Acquired as Venetian eighteenth-century and catalogued as such until the first edition of this catalogue (1978), by which date it had been recognised by the present writer as by the same hand as a group of pictures which Roli, in 1962, convincingly identified as the work of Francesco Monti.[2] The attribution was subsequently supported by Philip Pouncey and Renato Roli.[3] It is consistent in style with a number of pictures which came to light after Roli's 1962 article and which have also been attributed to Francesco Monti: a *Moses and the Daughters of Jethro* in the City of Manchester Art Gallery (Inv. 1928–39);[4] and a *Shepherd and Shepherdesses resting in a Landscape* and *The Expulsion of Hagar* which were both sold at Sotheby's, London, in 1967.[5] The chronology of Monti's work cannot be defined with any precision, but to judge from the strong Venetian influence apparent in our picture it is probably a relatively late work, perhaps dating from the period when Monti was working in and around Brescia.

Miss Ida Hayward bequest 1950.

1. See G. P. Zanotti *Storia del' Accademia Clementina* Bologna 1739 II pp. 217 ff.; L. Crespi *Vite de' Pittori Bolognesi* Rome 1769 pp. 313 ff. See further R. Roli in *Arte Antica e Moderna* 17 1962 pp 86–98 and D. Miller in *Painting in Italy in the Eighteenth Century: Rococo to Romanticism* Exhibition Catalogue, Chicago 1970 p. 140.
2. *Loc. cit.*
3. Letters supporting this idea from Philip Pouncey, dated 12 November 1975 and Renato Roli dated 7 September 1976 are in the Gallery files. Roli subsequently published our picture. See *Pittura Bolognese 1650–1800 Dal Cignani ai Gandolfi* Bologna 1977 p. 281 pl. 235b.
4. See D. Miller in *Arte Antica e Moderna* 25 1964 p. 99 fig. 342. According to records at the Manchester City Art Gallery, the attribution to Monti was first proposed independently by Ulrich Middeldorf and Hermann Voss in 1961.
5. Sale Sotheby's 22 February 1967 (23 and 24).

Giovanni Battista MORONI *active by 1547 died 1578*

His home town was probably Albino, to the north east of Bergamo, but his early training was in Brescia where he was a pupil of Moretto. After Moretto's death in 1554,

Moroni appears to have been active mainly in Bergamo. He was particularly successful as a portrait painter, establishing a naturalistic style that was later to influence Lombard painters such as Carlo Ceresa, Giuseppe Ghislandi and Giacomo Ceruti.

2347   Portrait of Giovanni Bressani

Canvas: 116.2 × 88.8; original painted surface 114.2 × 81. Inscribed on the base of the inkwell: IO; BAP. MORON. PINXIT QVEM NON VIDIT (Giovanni Battista Moroni painted him whom he did not see), and inscribed and dated on the manuscript in the centre: CORPORIS EFFIGIEM ISTA QVIDEM BENE PICTA TABELLA/EXPRIMIT, AST ANIMA TOT MEA SCRIPTA MEI./ M.D.LXII. (This painted picture well depicts the image of my body but that of my spirit is given by my many writings 1562.) The manuscript in his left hand begins with the word SEMPRE.

Cleaned 1977/8.[1] X-rayed (details of the head, both hands, the still life and the left-hand edge). The canvas has been made up c. 7 cm on the left and c. 2 cm at the top. These additions probably date from after 1855 when Eastlake saw the picture in the Manfrini collection, Venice, and recorded its size (probably in the frame) as 44 x 32 in. (i.e. 111.7 x 82.5 cm.).[2] The clearly accentuated swagging threads in the original canvas which are pulled towards the left-hand edge, suggest this is an original edge. Tack marks, visible on the painted surface, are common to all four sides and suggest that the picture was originally nailed to the front of the stretcher. This may have been a relatively standard practice in Moroni's studio, since similar marks are to be found on several of his pictures now in the National Gallery, London (including Inv. 697, 1022, 1023, 1024, 2094, 3123 and 3124); of these much the clearest example is the portrait of *Canon Ludovico di Terzi*, Inv. 1024, which has remained virtually unaltered and only strip-lined.[3] The paint surface of our picture is in good condition, with no major damages. The green tablecloth is badly worn. The lack of definition on the sitter's black clothes is due to darkening and sinking of the pigment. His ear is also affected by the sinking of the pigment on the dark red ground. There are *pentimenti* below the window and along the top edge of the paper in the sitter's hand. There is serious doubt as to the autograph status of the inscription at the foot of the paper on the table in the foreground. There are traces of an earlier inscription beneath it. The execution of the lettering of the present inscription is surprisingly heavy handed, with the preliminary drafting still evident underneath, and the pigment is not the same as that used for the hieroglyphics on the same sheet of paper which are definitely original. These doubts extend to the inscription on the inkwell which is also drawn in a clumsy manner that is uncharacteristic of Moroni. Nevertheless, the inscriptions may well date from the sixteenth century and probably record authentic information.

During the nineteenth century our picture was known as a portrait of Michelangelo. It was described as such in the Manfrini collection, Venice, and the title was still current in 1870 when the picture was exhibited at the R.A. London.[4] In the earliest known reference to what is probably our picture, which dates from 1793 when Tassi described it in the collection of Conte Canonico Giambattista Zanchi in Bergamo, the sitter is identified as Gio. Crisostomo Zanchi.[5] Giovanni Crisostomo Zanchi was at one time Abate Lateranense in the convent of S. Spirito and subsequently became General of the order in 1559. Yet he did not die until 1566, and was still living in Bergamo in 1562 when Moroni is supposed to have painted our picture, without physical access to the sitter. Since 1960, when the picture was exhibited in London, various writers have suggested that Tassi might have confused Giovanni Crisostomo for his brother Basilio.[6] However, more recently, Mina Gregori has convincingly argued that our picture represents Giovanni Bressani, a poet from Bergamo who died in 1560. The identification is based on a portrait of Bressani in the Biblioteca Civica, Bergamo, which itself derives from a medal of Bressani, struck in 1561 and signed by Arsensio (Fig. 23).[8] This identification is supported by the evidence of Maironi da Ponte who in 1803 notes that Moroni painted Bressani and describes the picture in the collection of the Milanese engraver, Giuseppe Longhi, with the same inscription as that found on ours.[9] However since this provenance conflicts with Piccinelli's statement that our picture was in the Manfrini collection by 1785 (see below), Maironi da Ponte may have known another version, possibly an old copy. Alternatively Piccinelli's date may be incorrect. Mina Gregori notes a copy of our picture, now in the Casa dell' Orfano di Ponte Selva.[10]

No serious doubt surrounds the attribution of the picture to Moroni. It is particularly close in handling to Moroni's *Portrait of a Monk* in the Städelsches Kunstinstitut, Frankfurt, where one finds the same distinctive use of light impasto highlights in the rendering of the flesh.[11] Our picture may also be compared stylistically with some of Moroni's most celebrated portraits of seated old men, such as the portrait known as *Titian's Schoolmaster* in the National Gallery of Art, Washington,[12] the *Portrait of Giovanni Antonio Pantera* in the Uffizi, Florence,[13] and the *Portrait of an Unidentified Old Man* in the Accademia Carrara in Bergamo.[14] The most unusual and distinctive feature of our picture is its design. In most of Moroni's portraits of seated men, such as the three pictures described above, and the *Portrait of Bartolomeo Bonghi* in the Metropolitan Museum, New York,[15] the figure is shown, three-quarter length, in the same wooden chair, close to the picture frame and facing sideways, but with the head turned towards the spectator: an intimate and relaxed pose, derived perhaps from earlier prototypes found in the work of Titian and in pictures such as Lorenzo Lotto's *Man in a Fur Coat* in New York.[16] In our picture, on the other hand, the figure seems physically remote and emotionally detached from the spectator, largely on account of his position behind a large table which fills the foreground. This disturbing compositional device may well have been adopted to underline the fact that the sitter was already dead and that Moroni had never seen him (as explained in the inscription on the base of the inkwell). Moroni's lack of direct acquaintance with the sitter might also account for the disproportionate emphasis given to the elaborate still life of objects on the table. The books are probably intended as an allusion to the sitter's publications. These deviations from Moroni's standard pose for three-quarter length portraits of seated men, which give our picture its haunting and original quality, seem also to have given rise to unforeseen problems: the table is uncomfortably low in relation to the level of the chair, and the lower part of the sitter's legs, instead of being cut off below the knee by the picture frame, stick out awkwardly in a crossed position. Notwithstanding these uncharacteristic weaknesses in the design, the status of our picture as an autograph work by Moroni seems assured.[17]

Coll: Probably Conte Giambattista Zanchi collection, Bergamo, by 1793 when what appears to be our picture is described by Tassi;[18] according to Piccinelli (writing *c.* 1863–65) this picture was acquired by Girolamo Manfrini in 1785.[19] In 1852 our picture was described in the Manfrini collection, Venice, by Selvatico and Lazari as a portrait of Michelangelo by Moroni;[20] also recorded in the Manfrini collection by Eastlake in 1855[21] and by Zanotto in 1856,[22] but not included in the 1856 Manfrini sale catalogue;[23] bought from the Manfrini collection, probably in 1856, by Alexander Barker, apparently with a view to subsequent sale to Baron Meyer Amschel de Rothschild of Mentmore;[24] Rothschild collection, Mentmore, by 1860;[25] lent by Baron Meyer de Rothschild to the *Exhibition of the Works of the Old Masters* R.A. London 1870 (20); by inheritance to his daughter Hannah who in 1878 married the 5th Earl of Rosebery; recorded in the 1883 Mentmore Catalogue (8); lent by the 6th Earl of Rosebery to the exhibition *Italian Art and Britain* R.A. London 1960 (72). Mentmore sale catalogue IV, Sotheby's 25 May 1977 (2049), withdrawn for sale to the Gallery by private treaty.

Bought by private treaty from the estate of the 6th Earl of Rosebery 1977.

1. For a full discussion of the picture since it was cleaned, see H. Brigstocke in the *Burlington Magazine* CXX 1978 pp. 457 ff. figs. 15–19.

2. Charles Eastlake *Notebooks* (National Gallery, London MSS) 1855 II. On f. 6r. he notes: '25. Good portrait by Morone (posthumous) books and papers – seated in a chair holding pen' and then on folio 8 v. he records the size and the two principal inscriptions, and observes that the 'accessories, books etc [are] better than [the] head'. I am indebted to the National Gallery for permission to publish Eastlake's notes.

3. I am indebted to Allan Braham for kindly investigating the edges of the Moroni pictures in the National Gallery, London, in response to my enquiry; his letter of 6 April 1978 is in the Gallery files. See also D. Bomford in *National Gallery Technical Bulletin* 3, 1979 p. 34 fig. 1.

4. See P. Selvatico and V. Lazari *Guida di Venezia e delle isole circonvicine* Venice-Milan-Verona 1852 p. 297; F. Zanotto *Nuovissima Guida di Venezia* Venice 1856 p. 343; and *Exhibition of the Works of the Old Masters* R.A. London 1870 (20).

5. F. M. Tassi *Vite de' Pittori Scultori e Architetti Bergamaschi* Bergamo 1793 I p. 169 (also Milan 1970 ed. p. 202). He described the picture as follows: *il ritratto del famoso nostro letterato Gio: Grisostomo (sic) Zanchi Abate Lateranense nel convento di Santo Spirito: un vecchio con lunga barba seduto con molti libri intorno, in uno de' quali sta scritto. "Jo: Bap. Mor. pinxit quem non vidit 1562". spicca al più alto segno al confronto de' più celebri, ed accreditati maestri, de' quali è abbondevolmente adorna la scelta galleria del Co: Canonico Giambattista Zanchi.* In view of the discrepancies in Tassi's transcription of the inscription, one cannot entirely exclude the possibility that he is in fact describing a variant version or a copy of our picture, but this seems most unlikely, given A. Piccinelli's nineteenth-century statement, first printed in *L'Arte* XXIV 1959 p. 127 and also in the 1970 edition of Tassi's *Vite*, that the Zanchi collection picture was sold in 1785 to the Manfrini collection, from which our picture was acquired by Barker for Rothschild in 1856 (see under *Coll.*).

6. For biographical information on the Zanchi family see B. Belotti *Storia di Bergamo e dei Bergamaschi* Bergamo 1959 III pp. 427 ff. and pp. 476 f. For Basilio Zanchi see further *Enciclopedia Italiana* 1937–45 XXXV p. 881 and R. de Maio in *Collectanea Vaticana* Città del Vaticano 1962 I pp. 285–86 and 312–13. In the exhibition catalogue *Italian Art and Britain* R.A. London 1960 (72) our picture was tentatively identified as Basilio Zanchi. This was followed in the first edition of this catalogue in 1978. See further A. Braham *Moroni 400th Anniversary Exhibition* National Gallery, London 1978 ed. p. 35 no. 7 fig. 47. Cf also H. Brigstocke's review of the above exhibition in *Arte Lombarda* 51 1979 pp. 93–7 where the ambiguity of Tassi's text and the difficulty of identifying the sitter is discussed.

7. M. Gregori in *Giovanni Battista Moroni* Exhibition Catalogue Bergamo 1979 pp. 154–7 illus.; also *I Pittori Bergamaschi: Giovan Battista Moroni Tutte le opere* Bergamo 1979 pp. 256–8 no. 100 illus. p. 349.

8. For the medal see B. Belotti *Storia di Bergamo e dei Bergamaschi* 1959 Volume 6 III p. 469. Both the medal and picture are reproduced by F. Rossi in *Giovanni Battista Moroni* Exhibition Catalogue, Bergamo 1979 p. 327 nos. 24 and 25.

9. G. Maironi da Ponte *Aggiunta alle Osservazioni sul Dipartimento del Serio presentate dall' ottimo vice presidente della Repubblica Italiana F. Melzi d'Eril* Bergamo 1803, p. LXXXXIX. See also G. Maironi da Ponte *Dizionario Odeporico o sia storico-politico-naturale della provincia bergamasca* Bergamo 1819/20 III p. 89.

10. See Footnote 7 above.

11. Inv. 904. Canvas 55.2 × 50.5 cm.

12. Reproduced *National Gallery of Art, European Paintings and Sculpture. Illustrations* Washington 1968 p. 84 inv. 641.

13. Reproduced A. Venturi *Storia dell' Arte Italiana* IX Part IV Milan 1929 p. 255 fig. 217.

14. Reproduced by Venturi *op. cit.* IX Part IV p. 256 fig. 218.

15. Reproduced by D. Cugini *Moroni Pittore* Bergamo 1939 pp. 151 ff. pl. 28.

16. Reproduced by B. Berenson *Lorenzo Lotto* London 1956 pl. 273.

17. It is not discussed in the monographs on Moroni by Cugini (see note 15 above) and by G. Lendorff (*Giovanni Battista Moroni II Ritrattista Bergamasco* Bergamo 1939) but it is listed by Berenson 1968 as *Portrait of a Rabbi* by Moroni.

18. Tassi *loc. cit.*

19. See note 5 above.

20. Selvatico and Lazari *loc. cit.*

21. See note 2 above.

22. Zanotto *loc. cit.*

23. *Catalogo dei Quadri esistenti nella Galleria Manfrini in Venezia* 1856 (photocopy in the library of the National Gallery, London). Waagen 1857 p. 77 records: 'Mr Barker has recently become the possessor of a number of pictures from the well-known Manfrini collection in Venice, including some of the chefs d'oeuvre of the gallery. They were not arrived before I left England.'

24. Alexander Barker, the son of a fashionable boot-maker and an important collector (see Waagen 1854 II pp. 125 ff. and 1857 pp. 71 ff.) appears to have been in charge of the interior decorations and furnishings at Mentmore. Letters from Barker to Baron Meyer de Rothschild are still preserved by the Rosebery family; I am indebted to John Fleming for this information.

25. See Mentmore [Catalogue] Edinburgh 1883 no. 8 as *Portrait of a Man, Unknown*, by Moroni, acquired 'from the Manfrini Gallery at Venice before 1860'.

NEAPOLITAN *second quarter of the seventeenth century*

21   Cain Killing Abel

Canvas: 190 × 143

Cleaned 1970. The paint surface is generally in fair condition, but there are abrasions to the flesh colour of the figure of Abel, and serious losses of blue pigment in the sky, which is now discernible only in small areas.

The subject of *Cain Killing Abel* (see *Genesis*, IV, 8) became very popular among Italian artists during the seventeenth century.[1] Several of the pictures on this theme show a direct or indirect relationship, with particular emphasis given to the physical struggle between the two figures. They may have been inspired originally by late sixteenth century sculptures of fighting men by Giambologna and his circle. One of the earliest examples of this type is in the museum at Valletta, in Malta;[2] it has been attributed to Orazio Riminaldi, and different compositions of the same subject, also attributed to this artist, are in Florence[3] (a second version in Potsdam)[4] and in Pommersfelden.[5]

Our picture was acquired in 1834 with an attribution to Ludovico Carracci, and hitherto it has been catalogued under this name. It is clearly not by Ludovico Carracci and is probably by a South Italian artist, perhaps active in Naples in the second quarter of the seventeenth century. Schleier has compared it, stylistically, with pictures by Francesco di Maria,[6] and in particular with his *Calvary* in the church of San Giuseppe a Pontecorvo, Naples, which dates from the 1660s.[7] Although in some respects this comparison is striking, particularly with regard to the facial types and the baroque style of the draperies, the connection is not conclusive. The figures in our picture are more robustly modelled and the design is less decorative, which suggests it may also be a little earlier in date than an attribution to Francesco di Maria would suggest.

A picture of *Cain Fleeing from the Body of Abel*, now in the Corsini collection, Florence, and formerly in the Barberini collection, Rome, is extremely close in style to our picture and might well be by the same hand. The figure of Abel in each of these two works is almost identical, both in design and in the distinctive silvery tone of the flesh (see Figs. 24, 25). Unfortunately the Corsini picture is listed in the old Barberini inventories without an attribution.[8]

Coll: Sir Alexander Crichton,[9] who presented it to the R.I., Edinburgh, in 1834. Recorded by Waagen in the collection of the R.I. in 1854.[10]

Royal Institution 1834.

1. See A. Pigler *Barockthemen* Budapest 1974 I pp. 19 ff.
2. See M. Gregori in *Paragone* 269 1972 p. 37 pl. 43.
3. See Gregori *op. cit.* p. 40 pl. 50.
4. Inv. 5051.
5. See Gregori *op. cit.* p. 42 pl. 47.
6. Letter from Erich Schleier, dated 22 May 1972, in the Gallery files. Schleier's opinion was based on a photograph.
7. For biographical details of Francesco di Maria see O. Ferrari in *Storia di Napoli* VI 2 pp. 1223 ff.
8. Marilyn Lavin (letters in Gallery files, dated 24 February and 4 May 1972) has suggested that this is almost certainly the picture listed in the inventory of Prince Maffeo Barberini in 1655 without attribution as follows: *Un Quadro con dentro una figura di 'Abelle con Caino', e Dio Padre Cornice d'Albuccio tinta di nero con filetto, e fiori d'oro alto palmi dieci, e mezzo largo otto.* (For the transcription see M. Lavin *Seventeenth-century Barberini Documents and Inventories of Art* New York 1975 p. 265 VII Inv. 55 no. 24).
9. For Sir Alexander Crichton, who was Physician to the Emperor Alexander I of Russia, see *The Dictionary of National Biography*.
10. Waagen 1854 III p. 270 where it is described, unjustly, as 'a feeble production'.

NEAPOLITAN *second half of the seventeenth century*

84 The Martyrdom of S. Sebastian

Canvas: 202 × 146.5

The picture is discoloured by old varnish; it is therefore difficult to evaluate the paint surface. There are numerous damages which affect both the Saint's body and the background, but the face, hands and feet are in good condition.

Acquired as by Ribera and hitherto catalogued under his name. In the 1957 *Catalogue* it was pointed out that the rather mannered elegance of the figure is not characteristic of Ribera's style, and his responsibility for the design was questioned. It is probably an original work by a rather minor artist working in Naples in the second half of the seventeenth century.

Coll: Presented by Charles O'Neil (a picture dealer) to the R.I., Edinburgh, in 1834. Recorded by Waagen in the collection of the R.I. in 1854.[1]

Royal Institution 1834.

1. Waagen 1854 III p. 270 where it is described as: 'Spagnoletto – The Martyrdom of St. Sebastian, by a later and feebler master'.

Pietro NOVELLI 1603–47

Born in Monreale, Sicily, in 1603.[1] His early style as a painter in Palermo was influenced by Van Dyck, whose *Madonna del Rosario* was in S. Domenico, Palermo, by *c.* 1628. Novelli's early documented works include a fresco of *Daniel in the Den of Lions* in the refectory of the Convent of S. Martino delle Scale (1629), and a painting of the *Appearance of the Madonna to S. Andrea Corsini* in the church of the Carmine, Palermo (1630). It has been generally assumed that he visited the mainland of Italy in the early 1630s because of a marked change in his style, apparently due to the influence of artists, active in Naples, such as Massimo Stanzione and Ribera. By 1633 he was back in Palermo. The *S. Benedict and Sancho III of Castille* in S. Martino delle Scale, Palermo, is dated 1635; and the documented *Filiation of S. Benedict*, in the Convent at Monreale, also dates from this year. His later work includes the *Marriage of the Virgin* in S. Matteo, Palermo, dated 1647.

83 'A Mathematician'

Canvas: 116.9 × 91.5
Cleaned in 1960, when eighteenth-century additions to all four sides of the original canvas were removed. In good condition.

A quite similar composition of *Democritus*, shown holding a sheet of diagrams and a pair of dividers, was painted by Ribera; it is now in the Prado Museum, Madrid.[2] An almost identical version of the present picture, in a private collection, Solesino, inscribed 'Tales Milesio' (one of the Seven Sages of ancient Greece), has recently been published by Spinosa with an attribution to Ribera.[3]

Our picture was catalogued under the name of Ribera up to and including the 1957 *Catalogue*. Although it may well be based on a design by Ribera, it is closer in handling to pictures attributed to Pietro Novelli. An attribution to Novelli was first tentatively suggested by Mahon in 1962;[4] and later in the same year our picture was exhibited under Novelli's name at the Bowes Museum, Barnard Castle.[5] It was also given to Novelli in the 1970 *Shorter Catalogue*. On the other hand, it is not included in Moir's list of pictures by this artist which was published in 1967.[6]

Our picture is particularly close in style both to an undocumented picture of *S. Paul* at Capodimonte, Naples, first attributed to Novelli by Delogu, in 1928,[7] and also to an undocumented picture of *S. James Major* in the Corsini Gallery, Rome, first attributed to Novelli by Hermanin in 1910,[8] followed by de Rinaldis in 1929.[9] It may also be compared with a picture of a *Man Holding a Set Square*, recorded in a private collection in Rome and attributed to Novelli by Colasanti.[10]

Several other versions of our picture have been recorded as follows:

1. London, with Alex Wengraf; formerly Carvalho collection, Rome.

2. Spain, formerly Casa Torres collection,[11] now known only from unpublished photographs.

3. Stockholm, from the collection of O. Falkmann,[12] as school of Ribera.

4. Sintra, Portugal, in the Lower Palace (photograph in Gallery files).
5. London, Christie's, 17 November 1972 lot 46.
6. Collection Earl of Wemyss, Gosford, entitled *Galileo*.

Acquired by the Royal Scottish Academy by 1859;[13] transferred 1910.

1. For biographical details see G. Di Stefano *Pietro Novelli* Palermo 1940 and A. Moir *The Italian Followers of Caravaggio* Cambridge (Mass.) 1967 I pp. 192 ff.
2. See *Ribera* Exhibition Catalogue, Naples, Castel Sant'Elmo 1992 no. 32.
3. *Ibid.* p. 32 illus.
4. Sir Denis Mahon's attribution is recorded in the Gallery files.
5. *Neapolitan Baroque and Rococo Painting* Exhibition Catalogue, Bowes Museum, Barnard Castle 1962 no. 14.
6. See note 1 above.
7. G. Delogu in *L'Arte* XXXI 1928 pp. 153–54 fig. 10.
8. F. Hermanin in *Bolletino d'Arte* IV 1910 pp. 226 ff.
9. A. de Rinaldis *Neapolitan Painting of the Seicento* Florence 1929 pl. 80.
10. A. Colasanti in *Bolletino d'Arte* XXVIII 1935 pp. 542–4.
11. See E. Frankfort in *Archivo Español de Arte* XXXVI 1963 pp. 131 ff. Photographs of these pictures are in the Gallery files.
12. *Stora Spanska Mästare* Exhibition Catalogue, Nationalmuseum, Stockholm 1959–60 no. 90.
13. See the 1859 *Catalogue* p. 40.

Giovanni Battista PAGGI *1554–1627*

Born in Genoa, but banished after a quarrel and lived in Florence at the Medici court. In 1599 he was allowed to return to his native city. His style is strongly influenced by Luca Cambiaso whom he apparently knew from an early age. His own studio pupils included Sinibaldo Scorza.

55   Rest on the Flight into Egypt

Canvas: 86.5 × 68
Signed bottom left: G.BTA PAGGI F. Apart from minor paint losses overall and more substantial damages along the edges, the condition of the paint surface is still reasonably good for a picture of its age.

The mark of the Doria family, a D surmounted by a Ducal coronet, was recorded on the back of the canvas in 1831;[1] but since then the picture has been relined.

Coll: Bought by Andrew Wilson from one of the Doria family villas near Genoa, on behalf of the R.I., Edinburgh, in 1830.[2] Exhibited R.I. 1831 and 1832 (24).

Royal Institution 1830.

1. See the *Catalogue of the Fifth Exhibition of Ancient Pictures* Edinburgh 1831 (24).
2. See further *Pictures for Scotland* pp. 27 ff.

Gonzalo PÉREZ *active early fifteenth century*

He was a follower of the Valencian painter, Pedro Nicolau, and was formerly known under the pseudonym Maestro de los Martí de Torres, after the name of the patron of his S. Martin altarpiece, now in the Provincial Museum at Valencia and formerly in the monastery at Portaceli.[1] His identity was first established by Saralegui, who published the results of his documentary studies in 1954.[2] Those of Gonzalo Pérez's works which have been identified, including the panel of *S. Martha and S. Clement*, dating from 1412, in the Cathedral Museum at Valencia,[3] indicate that he was already active in the first quarter of the fifteenth century. Young[4] has questioned Saralegui's assumption[5] that the artist with whom we are concerned may be identified as the same Gonzalo Pérez who was still active as late as 1451.

Attributed to Gonzalo PÉREZ

021   S. Michael Killing the Dragon

Wood: including frame, which is original except at the bottom 191.8 × 104.5; painted surface 183.4 × 92.
The saint's face, the figure of the devil, the landscape and the gold background, are all in very good condition. On the other hand the saint's armour is badly rubbed and repainted; there are a number of local damages to the gold patterned drapery where the paint has broken away; and much of the pattern on the red drapery has been lost.

Probably the centre panel of a composite altarpiece. It has been suggested by Saralegui[6] that a panel depicting *Three Scenes from the Legend of S. Michael*, once in the possession of Prince Leon Ourousoff,[7] might have formed part of the same altarpiece, but there is no evidence for this. A suggestion by Mayer, in 1947, that a panel representing *S. Bartholomew* in the Worcester Art Museum (Mass.) might be from the same altar as our picture[8] has been questioned by Wethey, not without reason, since the embossed pattern in the gold background of the Worcester panel does not correspond to the plain gold in the background of our picture, and the original frames also differ in detail.[9] Mayer's attempt to establish a physical connection between our picture and the *S. Bartholomew* in Worcester was a development of an idea, first propounded by Post in 1930,[10] that they were both painted by the same hand.

Our panel was acquired as Spanish fifteenth century and has hitherto been catalogued as such. However, in 1942, Saralegui had already argued that it might be the work of his Maestro de los Martí de Torres[11] whom he subsequently identified as Gonzalo Pérez. And Saralegui's suggestion also received qualified support from Post in 1947,[12] before it was strongly endorsed by Young in 1964.[13] It now seems reasonable to accept this attribution on the basis of stylistic comparison with other pictures generally associated with Gonzalo Pérez, including the S. Martin retable in Valencia and a retable with S. Barbara in the Museo de Arte de Cataluña at Barcelona.[14]

Bought from The Spanish Art Gallery, London, 1910.

1. See L. de Saralegui in *Boletín de la Sociedad Española de Excursiones* XLVI 1942 pp. 98–152. The *S.*

Martin altarpiece is reproduced by C. R. Post *A History of Spanish Painting* Cambridge (Mass.) 1930 III pp. 96 ff. and fig. 285. See further Post *op. cit.* 1947 IX Part II pp. 759–60, and *El Siglo XV Valenciano* Exhibition Catalogue, Palacio de Exposiciones del Retiro, Madrid 1973 p. 54 no. 29 illus.

2. L. de Saralegui *El museo provincial de Bellas Artes de San Carlos – Tablas de las Salas 1a y 2a de Primitivos Valencianos* Valencia 1954 pp. 77–105. See further L. de Saralegui in *Archivo de Arte Valenciano* XXVIII 1957 pp. 5–24.

3. See *El Siglo XV Valenciano* Exhibition Catalogue, Palacio de Exposiciones del Retiro, Madrid 1973 p. 53 no. 27 illus.

4. Letter in Gallery files from Eric Young, dated 1 April 1971.

5. L. de Saralegui *El museo provincial de Bellas Artes de San Carlos …* Valencia 1954 p. 87.

6. In *Boletín de la Sociedad Española de Excursiones* XLVI 1942 p. 129.

7. Published by W. Suida in *Oesterreichische Kunstschätze* I 9 pls. 62 and 63.

8. A. L. Mayer *Historia de la pintura española* Madrid 1947 p. 71 fig. 59.

9. H. Wethey in *European Paintings in the Collection of the Worcester Art Museum (Spanish School)* Worcester (Mass.) 1974 pp. 507–09 Inv. no. 1919.315 and illus. p. 650.

10. *Op. cit.* III pp. 96 ff. For the attribution see further Saralegui in *Boletín de la Sociedad Española de Excursiones* XLVI 1942 p. 129 and Wethey *loc. cit.*

11. See note 6 above.

12. *Op. cit.* IX Part II pp. 759–60.

13. E. Young in *Apollo* LXXIX 1964 p. 13 fig. 4.

14. See *El Siglo XV Valenciano* Exhibition Catalogue, Palacio de Exposiciones del Retiro, Matrid 1973 pp. 53–4 no. 28 illus.

Pietro PERUGINO *c. 1445/6–1523*

Pietro Vannucci, known as Perugino. Born at Città della Pieve, according to Vasari around 1445–6. By 1472 he was in Florence, where he probably worked in Verrocchio's workshop. At an earlier date he may also have been influenced by Piero della Francesca. By 1479 he was in Rome where, in 1481–2, he painted some of the frescoes on the lateral walls of the Sistine Chapel. Thereafter he was mainly active in Florence and Perugia where he ran busy workshops. Raphael is said to have been one of his pupils.

1805   Four Male Figures

Canvas: 73.3 × 55.5

Cleaned 1983. The paint surface is badly worn and deteriorates progressively from left to right, with the figure at the extreme right particularly seriously affected. Some of the outlines of each of the figures, as well as of the lyre and of the patterned highlights of the column, had been strengthened. The draperies, which are original, are in good condition. The figure third from the right has suffered from a serious damage which runs vertically from the top to the very bottom of the picture. The painted frame, which probably dates from the sixteenth century, has been cut down to fit the picture.

A fragment from the lower left corner of what appears to have originally been a much larger composition. The left-hand edge of the present fragment appears to be the original edge, to judge from the clearly accentuated swagging threads in the canvas, pulled towards the nails. On the twin assumptions that the bottom edge of our picture is also close to the line of the original edge, and that we are dealing with a fragment of a picture originally constructed on symmetrical principles which used a one-point perspective system, with a vanishing point in the centre, Bury has calculated that the width of the original picture was between 344 and 367 cm.[1] The upper end of this scale would give a vanishing point about 13 cm. above the head of the figure holding a lyre; this corresponds with the high viewpoint suggested by the comparative height of the remaining figures. The stretcher of our picture probably dates from the seventeenth or eighteenth century, suggesting that the picture's present format precedes its most recent relining which dates from the nineteenth century; this view is reinforced by signs of an earlier relining on the stretcher.

There is no basis for the picture's former title, *The Court of Apollo*, which was invented in 1930.[2] Our picture was acquired under an attribution to Perugino which is entirely convincing, on stylistic grounds, and which has been widely accepted by most writers, including Gnoli,[3] Berenson (1909 *Central Italian Painters*, 1936 and 1963), Borenius,[4] Fischel,[5] Van Marle,[6] and Camesasca.[7] The only writers to have questioned the attribution are Venturi[8] and Canuti.[9]

Fischel suggested that it might be a fragment from a large picture of *Mars and Venus in the Net of Vulcan* offered by Perugino's widow, Chiara Fancelli, to Isabella d'Este, Duchess of Mantua, on 6 October 1524.[10] This view received further support in the 1957 *Catalogue* on the grounds that Perugino's non-devotional paintings are so rare. There is, however, absolutely no positive evidence to justify this supposition; and since the style of our picture is characteristic of Perugino's work c. 1505 when he completed the *Combat between Love and Chastity*, now in the Louvre, Paris,[11] it seems unlikely that it would still have been in the artist's studio at the time of his death.

Coll: Acquired from Conte Stefano Bardini, Florence, by Sir Thomas Gibson Carmichael Bt.; Sir Thomas Gibson Carmichael (Lord Carmichael) sale Christie's 13 May 1902 (269) as Perugino bought Thos. Agnew's. Frederick Anthony White collection, London, 1902, and lent by him to the B.F.A.C. 1902 (53),[12] to the B.F.A.C. 1909 (44),[13] to the Winter Exhibition B.F.A.C. 1928–9 (64) and to the *Exhibition of Italian Art 1200–1900* R.A., London 1930 (246) all as by Perugino. F.A. White sale Christie's 20 April 1934 (127) bought by the N.A.C.F. who presented it to the Gallery in the same year.

Presented by the N.A.C.F. 1934.

---

1. Letter from Michael Bury, University of Edinburgh, dated 21 June 1977, in Gallery files. I am greatly indebted to Michael Bury for his very helpful interest in this problem. This conclusion, first published in the 1978 edition of this catalogue, was misinterpreted by P. Scarpellini *Perugino* Milan 1984 p. 111 no. 133.

2. See *Exhibition of Italian Art 1200–1900* R.A., London 1930 pp. 152–3 no. 246.

3. U. Gnoli in *Rassegna d'Arte Umbra* 1910 p. 51 and *P. Perugino* Spoleto 1923 p. 56.

4. See J. A. Crowe and G. B. Cavalcaselle *A History of Painting in Italy* (ed. T. Borenius, London 1914 V p. 371).

5. O. Fischel *Die Zeichnungen der Umbrer* Berlin 1917 p. 70.

6. R. Van Marle *The Development of the Italian Schools of Painting* The Hague 1933 XIV pp. 379 ff. fig. 251.

7. E. Camesasca *Tutta la pittura del Perugino* Milan 1959 p. 106 tav. 178, and *L'opera completa del Perugino* Milan 1969 p. 110 no. 105 illus.

8. A. Venturi *Storia dell'Arte Italiana* Milan 1913 VII Part II p. 566 as by Andrea da Assisi.

9. F. Canuti *Il Perugino* Siena 1931 p. 363 under studio works and works of questionable attribution.

10. See Fischel *loc. cit.* For Chiara Fancelli's letter to the Duchess of Mantua, see W. Braghirolli *Notizie e Documenti Inediti intorno a Pietro Vannucci detto il Perugino* in *Giornale di Erudizione Artistica* II September 1873 pp. 281–2 no. LV.

11. For the picture in the Louvre, which was painted for Isabella d'Este, see E. Camesasca *L'opera completa del Perugino* Milan 1969 p. 107 no. 94 illus.

12. *Catalogue of a Collection of Pictures, Drawings, Bronzes and Decorative Furniture* B.F.A.C. London 1902 no. 53.

13. *Catalogue of a Collection of Pictures of the Umbrian School* B.F.A.C. London 1909 no. 44.

PESELLINO *c. 1422–57*

Francesco di Stefano, known as Pesellino. Active in Florence. His only documented work is part of an altarpiece of *The Trinity* in the National Gallery, London, which was completed in the studio of Fra Filippo Lippi.[1]

Nineteenth-century imitator of PESELLINO

1250 Madonna and Child with the Young S. John

Wood: 70.6 × 41.7

The damages to the panel are superficial and appear to have been artificially induced to give a false impression of age. Although the paint has not been subjected to scientific analysis, the picture is clearly a nineteenth-century fake.

The design of our picture is based on a *Madonna and Child* attributed to Pesellino, formerly in the Aynard collection, Lyons.[2] Our picture was acquired in 1919 as by Pier Francesco Fiorentino, and was catalogued under this name up to 1946. It was listed by Berenson in 1932, 1936 and 1963 under the Pseudo Pier Francesco Fiorentino.[3]

Coll: Said by Knoedler's to have been in the collection of Lady Henry Somerset, of Eastnor Castle, Ledbury, and of her son H. C. Somers Somerset, of The Priory, Reigate.[4]

Bought from Knoedler's, London, 1919.

---

1. See M. Davies *National Gallery Catalogue, The Earlier Italian Schools* London 1961 pp. 413–19.

2. For Pier Francesco Fiorentino and the Pseudo Pier Francesco Fiorentino see F. M. Perkins in *La Balzana* II 1928 pp. 188 ff.; B. Berenson in *Dedalo* XII 1932 pp. 692 ff.; and F. Zeri *Italian Paintings in the Walters Art Gallery* Baltimore 1976 I pp. 80–1.

3. The Aynard picture is reproduced by Berenson 1963 II pl. 834.

4. This information is recorded on the receipt from Knoedler's, dated 15 July 1919, now in the Gallery files. According to this source, our picture may be identified as the picture at Eastnor Castle, described by Berenson 1909 p. 168 as: 'Pier Francesco Fiorentino *Madonna against Rosehedge* (version of M. Aynard's Compagno di Pesellino at Lyons).'

PIERO DI COSIMO *c. 1462 after 1515*

He was born in Florence, the son of Lorenzo di Piero *c.* 1462. A pupil of Cosimo Rosselli, with whom he may have worked in the Sistine Chapel in Rome in *c.* 1481–2.

Style of PIERO DI COSIMO

1633 Two Censing Angels Holding a Crown

Wood: arched top 93.3 × 183.5

Cleaned 1977. A break along a join in the panel runs through the left shoulder and arm of the angel on the left. A further break, on the right, deviates from the vertical line of an old join and runs through the right wing and hand of the other angel. Another break, also along a join in the panel, runs down to the angel's censer on the extreme right. The paint surface is so extensively damaged and repainted that it is not possible to isolate, with confidence, any areas of genuine sixteenth-century paint. The damage is particularly serious around the left arm and shoulder of the right-hand angel.

Acquired as by Melozzo da Forlì, to whom it had been attributed by Phillips in 1914.[1] In 1932 Berenson attributed it to Piero di Cosimo, an opinion he repeated in 1936 and 1963. In the meantime the attribution had received further support from Gamba,[2] Langton Douglas,[3] and Morselli;[4] and more recently it has been accepted by Bacci.[5]

A very similar pair of angels is shown above an enthroned Madonna in an altarpiece by Piero di Cosimo, now in Borgo San Lorenzo, and our picture may be based on a prototype of this kind.[6] A suggestion by Gamba that it might have been part of a lost altarpiece by Piero di Cosimo from San Pier Gattolini,[7] which was described by Vasari,[8] cannot be sustained, both for lack of any positive evidence, and on account of the questionable standing of our picture, so far as it can be judged in its present condition.

Coll: Sir Claude Phillips collection by 1914.[9]

Sir Claude Phillips bequest 1924.

1. C. Phillips in the *Burlington Magazine* XXV 1914 pp. 273–80 illus.
2. C. Gamba in *Illustrazione toscana e dell'Etruria* May 1940 p. 10.
3. R. Langton Douglas *Piero di Cosimo* Chicago 1946 p. 106.
4. P. Morselli in *L'Arte* XXIII 1958 p. 77.
5. M. Bacci *Piero di Cosimo* Milan 1966 p. 97 no. 43. See further *L'opera completa di Piero di Cosimo* Milan 1976 p. 97 no. 56.
6. Reproduced by Bacci *op. cit.* pl. 44.
7. See Gamba *loc. cit.*
8. Vasari (ed. Milanesi IV p. 141) where it is described as *una Nostra Donna a sedere, con quattro figure intorno, e due Angeli in aria che la incoronano…*
9. See note 1 above.

PIETRO DA CORTONA *1596–1669*

Pietro Berrettini, generally known as Pietro da Cortona, after his birthplace. He practised as a painter, decorator and architect. His early training was with Andrea Commodi, first in Cortona and then, after 1612, in Rome. By 1620 he was working for Marcello Sacchetti for whom he painted the *Triumph of Bacchus* in the Capitoline Gallery, Rome. By then he was developing a baroque style which culminates in his decoration of the vaults of the Palazzo Barberini executed 1632–9. He also worked in the Palazzo Pitti, Florence from around 1637 to 1647.

Attributed to PIETRO DA CORTONA

2378   Landscape with Mary Magdalen

Canvas: 49 × 64.5
Cleaned shortly before its acquisition by the Gallery in 1979. The paint surface is in good condition. There are some paint losses along the inner edge of the stretcher, especially top and bottom left.

Acquired with an attribution (due to Clovis Whitfield) to Pietro da Cortona. It was subsequently discussed in an article by Brigstocke, who suggested a date c. 1629 towards the end of the period when the artist was working for Marcello Sacchetti at Castel Fusano, near Ostia.[1] The Magdalen in our picture has exactly the same pose, but reversed, as the Magdalen in a closely related fresco at Castel Fusano.[2] Her pose also recurs in a female figure in the extreme bottom left of a *Landscape with Two Temples*, now in the Vatican Museum, which was recorded in the Sacchetti Collection, as by Pietro da Cortona, from 1688 until 1747.[3] Yet the attribution of our picture has nevertheless been doubted in several quarters: by Briganti,[4] by Merz[5] and by Rice,[6] and although Sutherland Harris catalogued it as by Pietro da Cortona c. 1630 for a New York exhibition in 1985 she too expressed some reservations, pointing out that it is executed 'in a blotchier manner, and with a more heavily loaded brush than in Cortona's accepted landscapes, which have a rather dry brush stroke that gives leaves and foliage pointed tips and sharp edges rather than the more rounded ones seen in this canvas'.[7] Even if our picture does appear to be more fluidly and loosely painted than comparable small oil paintings which have long been associated with Pietro da Cortona, including two oval landscapes in the Capitoline Museum, Rome,[8] *The Calling of S. Peter and S. Andrew* in the Fitzwilliam Museum, Cambridge[9] and the closely related version at Chatsworth,[10] there is still a *prima facie* case for associating it with Pietro da Cortona's immediate circle at the time he was working for Marcello Sacchetti. Since no alternative artistic personality within this circle has yet been identified, either by name or even through a group of stylistically homogeneous paintings, it seems best to catalogue our picture, albeit with some caution, under Pietro da Cortona's name. It is also pertinent to raise the question of whether the artist's manner of executing small, informal landscapes might not have been susceptible to more stylistic variation than is generally allowed for by some modern critics.

Coll: Bought from Colnaghi's, London, 1979.

1. H. Brigstocke in *Burlington Magazine* CXXII May 1980 pp. 342–5 fig. 76.
2. See G. Briganti *Pietro da Cortona* Florence 1982 ed. pp. 393–4.
3. See L. Rice in *Burlington Magazine* CXXIX February 1987 pp. 73–6 fig. 10.
4. *Op. cit.* pp. 393–4.
5. Letters in Gallery files 16 April 1983 and 17 March 1989.
6. See note 3 above.
7. A. Sutherland Harris *Landscape Painting in Rome 1595–1675* Exhibition Catalogue, Richard L. Feigen and Co., New York 1985 pp. 157–8 no. 23 illus. 7.
8. Briganti *op. cit.* p. 171 nos. 15 and 16 pl. 95 and 96.
9. J. W. Goodison and G. H. Robertson, *Fitzwilliam Museum Cambridge, Catalogue of Paintings, Volume II Italian Schools*, Cambridge 1967 pp. 40–1 pl. 49.
10. Briganti *op. cit.* p. 181 no. 25 pl. 98

Giovanni Battista PITTONI *1687–1767*

Probably born in Venice. Worked as a pupil of his uncle Francesco Pittoni. He was also influenced, at different stages of his artistic development, by numerous other artists, including Luca Giordano, Francesco Solimena, Antonio Balestra, Federico Bencovich, Giovanni Battista Piazzetta, Sebastiano Ricci and Giovanni Battista Tiepolo.[1] The chronology of his work has not been satisfactorily established and is complicated by his very eclectic style. His early manner, in particular, has still not been clearly defined, but securely attributed early works by him include *The Death of Agrippina* and *The Death of Seneca*, formerly in Dresden, which were completed before 1722,[2] and the *Martyrdom of San Tommaso* in the Church of S. Stae, Venice, which can be dated 1722–3 on documentary evidence.[3] On the other hand, Boccazzi's claim to have recognised Pittoni's earliest style in three pictures of *Prophets*, from the series in the Church of the Ospedaletto, Venice, which date from c. 1716, has not yet found general acceptance.[4]

238 The Apotheosis of S. Jerome with S. Peter of Alcántara and an Unidentified Franciscan

Canvas: 275 × 143

The canvas originally had an arched top. The upper-left and right-hand corners are later additions. The paint surface is in excellent condition.

S. Jerome (347–420) is shown with his traditional attributes, including the cardinal's hat and the lion. S. Peter of Alcántara (1499–1562) was canonised in 1669 but was rarely included in Italian pictures.[5] He was a Franciscan and was a central figure in the Spanish Counter-Reformation movement. He is associated with a wooden cross which he carried around, while fixing his eyes downwards as an expression of modesty. He was a celebrated visionary, and as Howard has pointed out, his presence in the picture serves not only to exemplify Franciscan self-denial and physical suffering but also to assist the viewer in experiencing the vision of S. Jerome's apotheosis.[6] Howard further suggests that while S. Jerome's apotheosis is revealed to us, the saint himself is experiencing a vision of his own: his outstretched hand and transfixed gaze are not directed towards the heavenly glow above him but are focussed on the miraculous image of the Virgin on the high altar of the church of S. Maria dei Miracoli, for which our picture was originally commissioned (Fig. 26).

Our picture was acquired as by Pittoni, and was then convincingly identified by Haskell as the Pittoni altarpiece in the church of S. Maria dei Miracoli, Venice,[7] where it had been noted by Zanetti as early as 1733.[8] Later guide-books describe it as placed at the last altar on the left of the church; this explains the curve in the step at the bottom of the picture which would have directed the viewer towards the altar.[9] An engraving of the interior of the church, first published in 1840, and reproduced by Howard, shows a tall, arched picture space, set in a grand stone or marble frame flanked by columns and topped by a heavy segmental pediment. The picture was set high, over an altar raised on two steps, bringing its base to shoulder height. The low vanishing point within the present picture indicates Pittoni's response to the intended placing of the picture; and the perspective suggests a viewpoint from the left.[10]

Our picture was probably completed not long before 1733. It is more fluid and vigorous in handling, more delicate in colour, and more assured in design than some other early works by Pittoni such as the *Martyrdom of San Tommaso* in S. Stae of 1722–3;[11] the *S. Peter, S. Paul and Pius V adoring the Virgin* in S. Corona, Vicenza, which dates from 1723–5;[12] the *Virgin and Child with Saints* in S. Germano dei Berici, Vicenza, which is usually thought to date from soon after the S. Corona altarpiece;[13] a *Rest on the Flight into Egypt* at Sidney Sussex College, Cambridge, where the Virgin is reminiscent of the Virgin in the S. Corona altarpiece, and which might well also date from the mid 1720s;[14] and the *Miracle of the Loaves and the Fishes*, originally in the church of SS. Cosma and Damiano, Venice, and now in the Accademia, which Zanetti had seen before 1733.[15] Together these comparisons indicate that our picture is a relatively mature work from Pittoni's early period, and Zava Boccazzi's suggested date of c. 1725, which she does not support with any detailed argument, is perhaps, too early.[16]

A drawing in the Brera Gallery, Milan, published in 1937, and described by Haskell in 1960 as a preparatory study for our picture,[17] is not characteristic of Pittoni's well defined graphic style, and is probably a copy made after the painting. It shows the original arched top of our picture but omits the step in the foreground of the composition. Two interesting sheets of preparatory studies are in the Fondazione Cini, Venice.[18]

Coll: Originally in the church of S. Maria dei Miracoli, Venice.[19] It was still in the church in 1815 when it was described there by Moschini,[20] and was apparently removed between 1837 and 1855. It next turned up in Paris, at the Hochhom sale 11/12 June 1903 and was acquired by the Cooper Union, New York around 1903.[21] Anonymous sale Sotheby's 23 March 1960 (69) as by Pittoni, bought Colnaghi's.

Bought from Colnaghi's, London, 1960.

---

1. For Pittoni's biography see F. Zava Boccazzi *Pittoni. L'Opera Completa* Venice 1979. See further R. Pallucchini *I Disegni di Giambattista Pittoni* Padua 1945 and P. Zampetti *Dal Ricci al Tiepolo* Exhibition Catalogue, Palazzo Ducale, Venice 1969 pp. 205–7 and with a full bibliography pp. 428–9.

2. See M. Goering in *Mitteilungen des Kunsthistorischen Instituts in Florenz* IV 1934 p. 207.

3. See L. Moretti in *Arte Veneta* XXVII 1973 pp. 318–20.

4. See F. Zava Boccazzi in *Arte Veneta* XXVIII 1974 pp. 179 ff.

5. See *Les Petits Bollandistes: Vie des Saints* XII Paris 1878 p. 457; this reference is cited by F. Haskell in the *Burlington Magazine* CII 1960 p. 366 note 2.

6. D. Howard in *Burlington Magazine* CXXI 1989, pp. 684–92.

7. Haskell *op. cit.* p. 366 fig. I.

8. A. M. Zanetti *Descrizione di tutte le pubbliche pitture della Città di Venezia ... di Marco Boschini, colla aggiunta di tutte le opere, che uscirono dal 1674 fino al presente 1733* Venice 1733 p. 380.

9. See Howard *loc. cit.*

10. See A. M. Zanetti *Della Pittura Veneziana* Venice 1771 p. 461 who says *alla sinistra*; and G. A. Moschini *Guida di Venezia* Venice 1815 I part 2 p. 651 who says *nell' ultimo altare*. See further Haskell *loc. cit.*

11. See Moretti *loc. cit.*

12. See D. Bortonal *S. Corona, Chiesa e convento dei domenicani in Vicenza* Vicenza 1889 p. 229; L. Pittoni in *Dedalo* VIII 1928 p. 678; and F. Zava Boccazzi in *Atti del Congresso internazionale di studi su Sebastiano Ricci e il suo tempo* Venice 1976 p. 51 note 4. The picture is reproduced by Goering *op. cit.* p. 206 fig. 6.

13. See F. Valcanover in *Arte Veneta* XI 1957 p. 221 and Zampetti *op. cit.* p. 208 no. 93 illus.

14. Unpublished; but see M. Levey *National Gallery Catalogue, The Seventeenth and Eighteenth-Century Schools* London 1971 pp. 182–83 note 12.

15. A. M. Zanetti *Descrizione di tutte le pubbliche pitture della Città di Venezia ... di Marco Boschini, colla aggiunta di tutte le opere, che uscirono dal 1674 fino al presente 1733* Venice 1733 p. 374.

16. See F. Zava Boccazzi in *Arte Veneta* XXVIII 1974 pp. 203 n. 49. See further Zava Boccazzi 1979 (see note 1 above) pp. 128–90 no. 59 fig. 131.

17. *L'Arte* VIII 1937 p. 141. Haskell, *op. cit.* p. 366. This view was also followed in the *Shorter Catalogue* 1970 p. 67.

18. A. Binnion, *I disegni di Giambattista Pittoni* Florence 1983 pp. 42–3, 62–3, figs. 150–1.

19. See note 7 above.

20. *Loc. cit.*

21. By this time it was attributed to Sebastiano Ricci, but c. 1952 A. Morassi re-attributed it to Pittoni.

This information was kindly provided by Calvin S. Hathway, Director of the Cooper Union for the Advancement of Science and Art (letter dated 4 August 1960 in Gallery files). He suggests that the picture was probably bought by the Misses Hewitt who were founders of the Cooper Union Museum, and were grand-daughters of Mr Peter Cooper, the founder of the Cooper Union.

POLIDORO DA LANCIANO *c. 1515–65*

Polidoro di Paolo di Renzi, born in Lanciano in the Abruzzi. Active as an artist in Venice. His style was derived from Titian, and he appears to have specialised in the production of small scale Titianesque religious pictures. He also painted on a large scale, including a *Descent of the Holy Spirit* now in the Accademia, Venice, dated 1545. He died in Venice in 1565.

105   Holy Family

Wood: 42.6 × 52
Cleaned 1969. X-rayed. The figure of Joseph is repainted. Otherwise, apart from minor local damages, the picture is in good condition. The X-ray (Fig. 27) reveals a bust portrait of a female figure beneath the present paint surface; this design was of vertical format, and the left-hand edge was originally the bottom edge.

Acquired by the R.I., Edinburgh under an attribution to Titian, but the design, although possibly inspired by Titian's early work,[1] is more immediately connected with the design of a picture at Budapest which was attributed to Polidoro da Lanciano in a 1659 inventory (no. 227) of the collection of Archduke Leopold Wilhelm of Brussels.[2] The principal difference between our picture and the design of the Budapest picture is that S. Joseph replaces a figure of S. Louis of Toulouse, and a parapet separates him from the Child. Our picture is also painted in a style that seems entirely characteristic of Polidoro da Lanciano, to whom it has been attributed since the 1909 *Catalogue*, following earlier suggestions by Crowe and Cavalcaselle[3] and Berenson (1907).[4]

Coll: An inscription on the back states that the picture belonged to the family of Conte Cornian degli Algarotti at Venice. Bought in Venice from the dealer Felice Schiavone by Lord Wood, on behalf of the R I., Edinburgh, 1852.

Royal Institution 1852.

1. The arrangement of the Madonna and Child is found in a picture in Munich traditionally attributed to Titian, but attributed to Francesco Vecellio by J. A. Crowe and G. B. Cavalcaselle *The Life and Times of Titian* London 1877 II p. 452. For this picture and a further variant in the Museo Civico, Verona, also now attributed to Francesco Vecellio, see H. Wethey *Titian. The Religious Paintings* London 1969 pp. 175–6 pls. 205–6.
2. The inventory is printed by K. Garas in *Jahrbuch der Kunsthistorischen Sammlungen in Wien* LXIV 1968 pp. 201 ff. The Budapest picture is reproduced by K. Garas in *Jahrbuch der Kunsthistorischen Sammlungen in Wien* LXIII 1967 p. 47 pl. 46. The picture is also engraved in reverse by L. Vorsterman in the *Theatrum Pictorium* 1660 as by Titian.
3. *Op. cit.* II p. 468.
4. Also listed by Berenson in 1932 and 1936, but excluded in 1957.

1931 **Madonna and Sleeping Child**

Canvas: 53 × 67.3; painted surface 50.5 × 65
Cleaned 1943. The paint surface is very worn. The green pigment both of the trees and of the foliage in the foreground is discoloured.

Acquired as by Titian and catalogued as such until 1957. The design, with the addition of a figure of S. Joseph, is engraved in reverse by P. Lisebetius as after a picture by Polidoro da Lanciano in the *Theatrum Pictorium* 1660.[1] The original picture on which the engraving was based is also listed in a 1659 inventory (no. 11) of the collection of Archduke Leopold Wilhelm of Brussels, as by Polidoro da Lanciano.[2] Our variant is also consistent in style with the work of Polidoro, a view expressed by Berenson in 1907, 1932, 1936 and 1957.

Coll: Listed as no. 586 in a nineteenth-century inventory of Lord Lothian's collection as by Titian, and said there to have been bought in Rome in 1861 (i.e. by the 8th Marquess).[3] Lent by Lord Lothian to the exhibition *Old Masters and Scottish National Portraits* Edinburgh 1883 (393), as by Titian.

11th Marquess of Lothian bequest 1941.

  1. See also a copy, painted on panel, by David Teniers the younger, which is now on loan to the Iveagh Bequest, Kenwood, from the executors of the late Princess Royal.
  2. The inventory is printed by K. Garas in *Jahrbuch der Kunsthistorischen Sammlungen in Wien* LXIV 1968 pp. 201 ff.
  3. There is a copy of this inventory in the files of the S.N.P.G., Edinburgh. For the Lothian collection see further *Pictures for Scotland* pp. 111 ff.

POPPI (Francesco Morandini) *1544–97*

Francesco Morandini, generally called Poppi after his birthplace, a small mountain village between Florence and Arezzo.[1] He was mainly active in Florence where he was a pupil of Giorgio Vasari, with whom he collaborated on some of the decorations in the Palazzo Vecchio. His own independent work in the same palace includes the frescoed vault of the *Studiolo* of Francesco I de' Medici.

2268 **The Golden Age**

Wood: 43 × 32.6
Cleaned shortly before entering the collection. X-rayed. The figures are generally in good condition, except for numerous minute paint losses in the areas of shadow. The landscape is also in quite good condition, except that the dark green of the trees and of the foliage has discoloured to dark brown and is affected by cracking and some paint loss.

The first of the four ages of the world in classical mythology. The figures at the top represent the four seasons, winter and spring on the left, summer and autumn on the right. The ram in the centre signifies Aries, first sign of the zodiac, an attribute of spring and the birth of a new year (the sun enters the sign of Aries at the spring equinox on 21

March). The theme of the Golden Age was conceived as alluding to the prosperity of Florence under Medici rule.[2]

The design of our picture is based closely on a drawing in the Louvre, Paris (Inv. 2170) (Fig. 28), which has been attributed to Giorgio Vasari by Barocchi and Goguel,[3] and Pouncey.[4] As Barocchi has pointed out, the design in its turn follows almost exactly a programme written by Vincenzo Borghini, the manuscript of which is now in the Biblioteca Nazionale in Florence.[5] Borghini's text appears to date from c. 1565–7, and an annotation to the manuscript states that the drawing based on it was made on 25 September 1567.[6] As Armstrong has already pointed out, Vasari and Borghini had by then already collaborated in planning a pageant of the *Genealogy of the Gods* which took place in Florence on 21 February 1566 in celebration of the marriage of Francesco de' Medici to Joanna of Austria, and Vasari's responsibility had included the design of a float symbolising the reign of Saturn in whose suite featured the Golden Age. In preparing the programme of our picture, Borghini may also have recalled the festivities at the time of the wedding of Cosimo I de' Medici in 1539, since the motto displayed by an angel in the Louvre drawing and by a cupid in our picture, 'Oh beautiful years of gold' (*O begli anni dell'oro*), is a quotation from a *canzonetta* sung at the 1539 ceremonies.[7] According to a letter from Vasari to Borghini, dated 20 September 1567, the painting based on their programme was to be executed by Poppi. This was at the specific request of Francesco de' Medici.[8]

It seems very probable that our picture is the painting by Poppi described above, although Baldinucci later stated that the Medici's picture had been painted on stone or slate (*pietra lavagna*) rather than wood.[9] Francesco de' Medici's picture was probably still in the family collection in 1730 but later disappeared. The early history of our picture is not known.[10] The attribution to Poppi is not in doubt and has been accepted by Barocchi.[11] It is very close in style to Poppi's work for the *Studiolo* of Francesco de' Medici.[12]

A panel, of the same subject, with similar iconography, by Jacopo Zucchi is in the Uffizi, Florence.[13]

Bought from Colnaghi's, London, 1964.

1. For a general study of Poppi see P. Barocchi in *Mitteilungen des Kunsthistorischen Instituts in Florenz* XI 1964 pp. 117.

2. See T. Puttfarken in *Journal of the Warburg and Courtauld Institutes* XLIII, 1980, pp. 130–49, pl. 16a. See also J. Kliemann in *Giorgio Vasari Principi, letterati e artisti nelle carte di Giorgio Vasari* Exhibition Catalogue, Arezzo 1981 pp. 156–7.

3. P. Barocchi *Vasari Pittore* Milan 1964 pp. 64 and 141–2 and illus. pl. 92. C. Monbeig-Goguel *Giorgio Vasari Dessinateur et Collectionneur* Exposition du Cabinet des Dessins, Musée du Louvre, Paris 1965 p. 26 no. 36: pen and ink 420 × 282 mm.

4. Letter in Gallery files from Philip Pouncey, dated 28 October 1970.

5. The relevant text was printed by Barocchi *op. cit.* pp. 141–2. It reads as follows: *Vorrei si dipignessi l'età dell'oro in questo modo, che innanzi fussi un bel prato, per il quale passassi un rio cor un principio di boschetto da una parte e nel lontano qualche colle o poggetto con boschi e fonti, e situato il paese che si andassi dolcemente allontanando. Le figure davanti fussero giovani e giovane che s'andassino diportando per il prato in diverse attitudini, come – v.g. – una bella giovane che avessi in sulle braccia un figliolino e lo porgessi al padre che gli desse o pome o fiori, e vi fussi a piè un altro fanciulletto, che stendendo le braccia in alto mostrasse di chiedere anch'egli quel pome. Da un'altra parte un giovane con una giovane posto a sedere in sul rio tenessin le gambe in sull'acqua et una mano in sulla spalla*

dell'altro: vi si potrebbe fare un fanciullino adormentato in grembo a quella giovane. Potrebbonsi fare per il prato, allontanandosi un poco, diverse attitudini, come sarebbe un ballo, come sarebbe uno sopra un frutto che cogliessi pomi e gli gettassi a' piè chi gli sta d'intorno: cosí chi dormisse, chi sonasse ecc.: et in aria vorrei un angioletto cor un breve: 'o begli anni dell'oro'; pel prato vorrei diversi animali fieri e domestichi, ma tutti mansueti [un piuttosto che cavalcassi un leone che giacessi]. I vestimenti pochi, e que' pochi la maggior parte di pelle selvaggie con quella antica rozeza, con qualche ghirlanda di fiori non solo in testa, ma ovunche accomodasse per la persona; qualche poco di velo non disdirebbe. Nel mezzo del cielo sia il segno d'Ariete, perché 'tunc formosissimus annus', e nell'aria in alto le quattro stagioni, cominciandosi dal verno, e poi la primavera che viene accanto all'Ariete, e seguendo l'estate che lo mette in mezzo, e fin sie l'autunno. Tutti con l'ali e col corno della dovizia in mano, assedere sopra certi nuvoli, i quali si faranno appropriati alle stagioni, cosí bianco azzurrino, fiorito e vario, giallo cangiante, rosso ... Or vorrei pieni di frutti convenienti alla stagione. Mostrando che ogni ha dalla natura quel che può satisfare a' bisogni umani, e l'alie perché il tempo vola.

6. A photograph of the MS., showing the annotation, is in the Gallery files.

7. E. Armstrong *Ronsard and the Age of Gold* Cambridge 1968 pp.115–6.

8. *Der Literarische Nachlass Giorgio Vasaris* ed. H. W. Frey 1930 II p. 351. See also *Il Riposo di Raffaello Borghini* Florence 1584 IV p. 642: *Ha di sua mano il Gran Duca Francesco un quadro in cui son figurati gli anni dell'oro, un'altro di lastra Genovese fintovi l'arte del fondere ...*

9. F. Baldinucci *Notizie dei professori del disegno* (ed. F. Ranalli, Florence 1846 III p. 531).

10. L. Berti *Il Principe dello Studiolo Francesco I dei Medici e la fine del Rinascimento fiorentino* Florence 1967 p. 231 n. 51. It was listed as a lost work by Barocchi in 1964 (see note l) p. 146.

11. Letter in Gallery files dated 3 January 1965. See further Berti *op. cit.* p. 82.

12. See Berti *op. cit.* p. 288 and pls. 59, 60 and 63.

13. Reproduced by A. Venturi *Storia dell' Arte Italiana* Milan 1933 IX Part VI p. 386 fig. 225, and E. Pillsbury in *Master Drawings* XII 1974 pp. 12–13 fig. 5 and p. 27. See also Kliemann *loc. cit.*

Giulio Cesare PROCACCINI 1574–1625

Born 30 May 1574.[1] First active *c.* 1591 as a sculptor in Milan. His earliest recorded work as a painter is in the church of S. Maria presso S. Celso, Milan, where he began to paint the frescoes in the vault of the chapel of the Pietà in 1602. Then in 1604 he delivered an altarpiece of the *Pietà* for the same chapel. Other important paintings which can be firmly dated include: *The Martyrdom of S. Nazaro and S. Celso* (1606), also in S. Maria presso S. Celso; *The Deposition from the Cross*, signed and dated 1606, in the Capuchin Church at Appenzell, Switzerland; the six large *Miracles of S. Carlo* (1610), in the Duomo, Milan; the *Holy Family*, the *Annunciation*, and the *Visitation* (1612), in S. Antonio Abate, Milan; the *Circumcision* now in the Estense Gallery, Modena, commissioned in 1613 and delivered early in 1616; *The Death of the Virgin* in the Cremona Museum, commissioned on 12 June 1616; and the *Constantine Receiving the Instruments of the Passion*, commissioned in 1605 but dated 1620, now in the Castello Sforzesco, Milan. G. C. Procaccini's work up to *c.* 1616 is strongly influenced by Parmesan artists, such as Correggio and Parmigianino, and to a lesser extent by Cremonese artists, such as Camillo Boccaccino and the Campi. Around the middle of the second decade, his paintings show greater balance in composition and more breadth and vigour in handling, but by the end of the decade, in the *Constantine,* he had begun to revert to retardataire mannerist principles of composition. Died 14 November 1625.

63 Cupid

Canvas: 70 × 95.5

Cleaned 1941. The figure of the Cupid, together with the red draperies to his right and the red draperies at the bottom left up to the level of his elbow, has been cut from a larger picture and set into another canvas. The quiver and the red drapery towards the upper left of the present picture both belong to this new canvas. The Cupid was probably cut from the bottom right of the picture to which it belonged, to judge from the clearly accentuated swagging threads in the canvas, pulled towards the nails along the original edges. The paint surface is in good condition, apart from some losses along the seam where the two canvases were joined.

Our picture was acquired as by G. C. Procaccini and the principal section, including the Cupid, is certainly characteristic of his style. To judge from the picture's provenance, this section might well date from around 1618, when, according to Soprani, G. C. Procaccini visited Genoa.[2] The section of the picture on the second canvas, including the quiver, probably dates from the eighteenth century, and is not by the same hand as the Cupid.

Coll: Bought from the De Franchi family in Genoa by Andrew Wilson on behalf of the R.I., Edinburgh, in 1830.[3] Exhibited R.I. 1831 and 1832 (14).

Royal Institution 1830.

1. The fundamental pioneering study of G. C. Procaccini is by N. Pevsner in *Rivista d'Arte* XI 1929 pp. 321 ff. For a bibliography of later studies up to 1973 see M. Valsecchi *Il Seicento Lombardo, Catalogo dei dipinti e delle sculture* Exhibition Catalogue, Milan 1973. For a detailed summary of studies since Pevsner, and further new material, see H. Brigstocke in *Jahrbuch der Berliner Museen* 18 1976 pp. 84–133 and in *Revue de l'Art* 85 1989 pp. 45–60.
2. R. Soprani *Vite de' Pittori, Scultori e Architetti Genovesi* 1674 (ed. C. Ratti, Genoa 1768 I pp. 441 ff.).
3. See further *Pictures for Scotland* pp. 27 ff.

2276   The Raising of the Cross

Canvas: 218 × 148.6

Cleaned 1965/66. There is an old and illegible inscription on the back of the original canvas, possibly in Spanish (photograph in Gallery files). Apparently slightly reduced in size before 1965, probably because of damaged edges. There is a vertical seam which runs *c*. 47 cm. from the right-hand edge of the picture. The right-hand section of the picture also has a horizontal seam on a line just below Mary's outstretched left arm. There are a number of tears in the canvas. One of these runs from Christ's right hand down to the top of the head of the bald-headed man on the left; another affects the biceps of the man kneeling in the foreground; and there is a patch across the calf of Christ's right leg. Otherwise the paint surface is in very good condition.

The representation of the erection of the Cross, with Christ's body already nailed to it, does not strictly belong to the sequence of the Passion of Christ. Scattered examples of this subject are found in German paintings and woodcuts around 1500 in the circle of Altdorfer and Wolf Huber (cf. in particular the picture by Wolf Huber in Vienna), but their isolation impeded the formation of a specific iconographic tradition.[1] In Italy the subject was even more unusual; one of the earliest examples must be a picture attributed to Bernardino Luini in the Poldi Pezzoli Museum, Milan,[2] while later in the sixteenth century Tintoretto depicted the raising of the thief's cross in the *Crucifixion* in the Scuola di S. Rocco, Venice. The earliest seventeenth-century example in Italy was painted by Rubens for the chapel of S. Helena in S. Croce in Gerusalemme, Rome (now known from a copy in Grasse). Later in the century a number of North Italian artists besides Procaccini also painted the subject, including Alessandro Tiarini (Estense Gallery, Modena)[3] and Daniele Crespi (Chiesa della Passione, Milan).[4] The subject is also found in South Italy in a picture by Mattia Preti at Sambughè.[5] Although Cardinal Federico Borromeo, Archbishop of Milan, devotes a whole chapter to the iconography of the Crucifixion in his *De Pictura Sacra*, published in 1624, he makes no reference to the depiction of the raising of the Cross.

Acquired in 1965 with an attribution to G. C. Procaccini which is absolutely convincing, and which has never been questioned. It is close in style to G. C. Procaccini's signed *Mocking of Christ* in the Graves Art Gallery, Sheffield, which has the same intense acrid colouring and strong chiaroscuro.[6] The stylistic proximity of these two pictures was particularly evident when they were exhibited together, for the first time, in Birmingham in 1974.[7] In 1970, however, Valsecchi had already suggested that they might have originally formed a pair, on the evidence of their style, common subject matter and almost identical size, and he dated them *c.* 1616–20.[8] By this date Rubens, in S. Croce in Gerusalemme, Rome, had already established an iconographical precedent in Italy for the association of these two subjects on the lateral walls of a chapel.

In the 1970 *Shorter Catalogue* attention was also drawn to a third picture by G. C. Procaccini, of the same size and with a closely comparable densely packed dramatic composition, representing the *Capture of Christ*. This undocumented picture was with Tomás Harris, London, in 1937,[9] and was subsequently exported to Spain where it was last seen in 1945.[10] Its similarity to the Edinburgh and Sheffield pictures raises the possibility that all three pictures might have formed part of a more extensive series of scenes from the Passion of Christ.[11]

In the absence of any documentary evidence this hypothesis can only be advanced with considerable caution, but it gains some strength from the surprisingly numerous references to large scale pictures of scenes from the Passion by G. C. Procaccini in England during the nineteenth century, a period when the artist was little known, even to knowledgeable collectors. In 1830 a *Crucifixion* by G. C. Procaccini was recorded in the *Literary Gazette* as in the possession of Mr Young of Craig's Court, and it is not impossible that this is an early reference to our picture.[12] In 1836 a *Deposition from the Cross* was exhibited at Davidson's Pall Mall Gallery and was also described in the *Literary Gazette;*[13] and what appears to have been the same picture was then exhibited at Manchester in 1857 as from the Abraham Darby collection.[14] Scharf, who in the same year recorded its composition and its dimensions ($84^{1}/2 \times 58$ in.), attributed it to Camillo Procaccini,[15] but at the Darby sale, Christie's 8 June 1867 (100), it reappeared under an attribution to Giulio Cesare Procaccini,[16] and was paired with a picture of *Christ Led to Calvary* (99).[17] The *Christ Led to Calvary* cannot now be identified (unless it was in fact the picture of the *Capture of Christ* described above), but the *Deposition* can be recognised from Scharf's sketch as a picture which much later was in a private collection, Milan, when it was published by Wittgens (in 1933).[18] This might be the *Deposition* by Procaccini which had been bought in at the Nathaniel W. J. Strode sale at Camden Place, Chislehurst, 12–14 June 1889 (469).[19] Meanwhile in 1853 a *Mocking of Christ of Large Size* by G. C. Procaccini is recorded in the possession of Charles O'Neill, a London picture dealer; and this could well be the picture of this subject now in Sheffield.[20] On the other hand, no specific nineteenth-century references to a *Raising of the Cross* or to a *Capture of Christ* by G. C. Procaccini have yet been found, and it therefore remains a matter of conjecture whether our picture and the ex. Tomás Harris picture were already in Britain by this date.

A picture of the *Raising of the Cross* by G. C. Procaccini is, however, recorded in the Maffei collection, Brescia, in 1760, by G. B. Carboni.[21] Bearing in mind the rarity of the subject, it does not seem impossible that this is a reference either to our picture or to a connected oil sketch. If Carboni was describing our picture, then its possible association with a series which included the Sheffield picture, the ex. Tomás Harris collection picture and the ex. Darby collection *Deposition* would have to be discounted, since there is no mention of any of them in Carboni's account.

In view of the difficulties surrounding the chronology of G. C. Procaccini's work, there has been remarkable unanimity in following Valsecchi's suggested date of *c*. 1618–20 for our picture.[22] Its compositional complexity suggests a date later than the *Circumcision* in Modena (delivered 1616). On the other hand its broad handling indicates a date distinct from, and arguably earlier than, that of the much more dryly painted *Constantine Receiving the Instruments of the Passion* in the Castello Sforzesco, Milan, (dated 1620), the *Apotheosis of S. Carlo* in Dublin, probably of *c*. 1624–5,[23] and a *Cain killing Abel*, signed and dated 1623, in the Accademia Albertina in Turin.[24]

Bought from Colnaghi's, London, 1965

1. See E. Mâle *L'Art Religieux après le Concile de Trente* Paris 1932 pp. 269 ff. W. Friedlaender *Caravaggio Studies* 1955 (New York 1972 ed. pp. 28 ff.) and G. Schiller *Iconography of Christian Art* London 1972 II p. 86 fig. 317, where the picture by W. Huber in Vienna is reproduced.

2. See F. Russoli *La Pinacoteca Poldi Pezzoli* Milan 1955 p. 181 no. 664.

3. See R. Pallucchini *I Dipinti della Galleria Estense di Modena* Rome 1945 p. 134 no. 297 fig. 99.

4. See M. Valsecchi *Il Seicento Lombardo, Catalogo dei dipinti e delle sculture*. Exhibition Catalogue, Milan 1973 p. 52 no. 128 pl. 144.

5. See A. Moir *The Italian Followers of Caravaggio* Cambridge (Mass.) 1967 II p. 93 and fig. 228.

6. Inv. 2459. Canvas 218 × 147. Signed *G.C.P.*

7. See P. Cannon-Brookes *Lombard Paintings c. 1595–1630. The Age of Federico Borromeo* Exhibition Catalogue, Birmingham 1974 pp. 185–7 where both pictures are also reproduced. For further details see also a review of the exhibition by H. Brigstocke in the *Burlington Magazine* CXVI 1974 pp. 688 ff. See also Brigstocke in *Revue de L'Art* 85, 1989, pp. 52–3.

8. M. Valsecchi in *Paragone* 243 1970 pp. 22 ff. and figs. 20 and 21.

9. Photograph in Witt Library, Courtauld Institute, London, as Tomás Harris collection 1937. The size of the picture is given as 211 × 142 cm.

10. See M. Trens *El Arte en la Pasion de Nuestro Señor* Exhibition Catalogue, Barcelona 1945 fig. 13 as private collection.

11. This possibility was also raised by N. Neilson in *Arte Lombarda* XXXVII (2) 1972 pp. 24 ff., where the ex. Tomás Harris picture is again reproduced. See further J. Bober in *Arte Lombarda* 73/75 1985, pp. 55 ff; he suggests that a *Flagellation* in the Museum of Fine Arts, Boston, might also be from the same series but offers no concrete evidence that it has a British nineteenth-century provenance. Cf. H. Brigstocke in *Revue de L'Art* 85, 1989, p. 53 n. 44. This issue has now been further complicated by a recent suggestion by L. Konečný (*Paragone* 441, November 1986 p. 60 tav. 32) that a *Baptism of Christ*, signed *GCP*, in the Slovenská Národná Galéria, Bratislava, may have been part of the same commission. From the photograph this picture appears to be a late work.

12. *Literary Gazette* 1830 p. 372: 'We have just seen a magnificent crucifixion by Giulio Cesare Proccaccini [sic] in the possession of Mr. Young of Craig's Court ...' I am indebted to Hamish Miles for this reference.

13. *Literary Gazette* 1836 p. 250: '... exhibited ... for the first time ... a most powerful and splendid Proccaccini [sic] – the subject, the "Deposition of the Cross"; ...' I am indebted to Hamish Miles for this reference.

14. Manchester *Art Treasures Exhibition* 1857 (229) as 'Procaccini *A Pietà*'.

15. See George Scharf's annotated copy of the Manchester exhibition catalogue, and his *Sketch Book* (45 p. 94), both preserved at the National Portrait Gallery, London.

16. Bought by Waters £21.

17. Bought by Cox £31-10-od.

18. F. Wittgens in *Rivista d'Arte* XV 1933 pp. 59 f. fig. 16. See further H. Brigstocke in *Revue de L'Art* 85, 1989 p. 55 ff. fig. 22.

19. There appears to be no basis for a statement, originating from Colnaghi's, that our picture was lot 469 in the Strode sale. This statement was repeated in the *Shorter Catalogue* 1970 p. 71.

20. See H. Brigstocke in *The Connoisseur* 183 May 1973 p. 16 note 6.

21. G. B. Carboni (ed. Chizzola) *Le Pitture e Sculture di Brescia ...* Brescia 1760 pp. 153 ff.: *Cristo levato di Croce con quantità di figure*. For this connection see also H. Brigstocke in *The Connoisseur* 183 May 1973 p. 17 note 40.

22. For later references cf. note 7 above.

23. For the probable date of the Dublin picture see H. Brigstocke in the *Burlington Magazine* CXVIII 1976 pp. 198–203 and in *Jahrbuch der Berliner Museen* 18 1976 pp. 90 ff. note 40. See further H. Brigstocke in *Revue de L'Art* 85, 1989, p. 56 note 75.

24. H. Brigstocke in *Revue de L'Art* 48 1980, pp. 30 ff. 3.

RAPHAEL *1483–1520*

Raffaello Santi. He was born in Urbino, son of the painter Giovanni Santi. He studied under his father and then under Perugino who, at this period, divided most of his time between Perugia and Florence. Raphael's earliest commissions were for churches in Città di Castello (including the *Crucifixion*, dedicated in 1503, now in the National Gallery, London (Inv. 3943) and the *Marriage of the Virgin*, dated 1504, now in the Brera Gallery, Milan) and in Perugia (including the *Ansidei Madonna*, in the National Gallery, London (Inv. 1171) and the *Entombment*, dated 1507, now in the Borghese Gallery, Rome). To judge from Vasari's account Raphael probably spent much of the period *c.* 1504–8 in Florence, and a strong Florentine influence is detectable in his early works which, in addition to the pictures listed above, also included many small Madonnas and some portraits. Late in 1508 or early in 1509 Raphael was summoned to Rome by Pope Julius II, and was at work on the frescoes in the Stanza della Segnatura in the Vatican from *c.* 1509–11. After the accession of Pope Leo X in 1513 Raphael continued to be employed principally in the Vatican, both as a painter and architect. Pupils in his Roman studio included Giulio Romano and G. F. Penni. He died in Rome in 1520.

Holy Family with a Palm Tree

Canvas transferred from wood: circular, diameter 101.5.

Cleaned 1988, X-rayed. (Figs. 29, 30). The outer edge of between 2 to 4 cm. is made up all round. The transfer to canvas took place at some time between 1729[1] and 1808,[2] probably when the picture was in the Orléans collection.[3] The supporting canvas has imposed a foreign texture onto the surface, most disturbingly in the head of the Virgin.

A random network of filled and retouched cracks is probably due to the shrinkage and wrinkling of the paint layer during the transfer. These fillings were removed during the 1988 cleaning. There is some abrasion in the paint of the flesh (the thinnest passage of the picture) and further losses have occurred along the line of one of the original joins in the panel where it runs through the figure of the Christ Child. Apart from these damages the picture is in good condition, notably in the painting of the heads. The landscape and the draperies are also well preserved and are remarkable for the intensity of the pigments, especially in the garments of the Virgin.

The traditional attribution to Raphael has not been seriously questioned. It is supported by the existence of a preparatory study executed in metalpoint, and also firmly attributed to Raphael, which is now in the Louvre (Fig. 31).[4] This drawing shows an early idea for the pose of the Virgin and Child, in which the Child leans away from his mother, but with both feet still balanced on her left thigh. The circular form of the painting is indicated by lines at the right. Joannides has suggested that a drapery study in black chalk (Paris, Fondation Custodia) is a preparatory study for the left profile of the Virgin's drapery in our picture.[5] Investigation of the painting with infra-red reflectography has revealed no trace of preparatory underdrawing; this may be due to the lack of the normal ground layer which was apparently removed at the time of the transfer from panel to canvas.

There is no evidence on which to date the Bridgewater House picture with precision, but writers since Ottley,[6] Passavant,[7] Waagen[8] and Crowe and Cavalcaselle[9] have been in general agreement that it was completed during Raphael's Florentine period. More recently Fischel has suggested a date c.1505[10]. Dussler placed it nearer the end of the Florentine period around 1507.[11] He was followed by Pope-Hennessy who has argued that its design might have been evolved at about the same time as the Borghese *Entombment* dated 1507, to judge from the frieze-like fashion in which the figures are arranged across the picture surface,[12] although it must be said that the impassive and tranquil attitudes of the figures in the Bridgewater House picture have little in common with the energetic and exaggerated postures adopted by many of the figures in the Borghese Gallery picture. In any case, a date of around 1507 for the Bridgewater House picture is also indicated by stylistic comparison with Raphael's *La Belle Jardinière*, dated 1507, in the Louvre, Paris.[13]

Passavant suggested the Bridgewater House picture might have been one of the two pictures mentioned by Vasari as painted for Taddeo Taddei in Florence.[14] One of these has been identified as the *Madonna del Giardino* now in Vienna, the other was described as in Raphael's *maniera prima di Pietro* [ie Perugino] and therefore cannot be the Bridgewater House picture. Most recently, Clifford[15] has argued that the picture contains many visual references which connect it with Francesco Maria della Rovere (1480-1538), Duke of Urbino. Specifically, it shows the Virgin Mary, after whom Francesco Maria was christened, juxtaposed with a palm tree, the Duke's *impresa*.[16] On the top of the sarcophagus on which the Virgin sits are oak leaves, the device of the Della Rovere. Joseph, kneeling before the Virgin, wears black and gold, Francesco Maria's heraldic colouring. Francesco Maria ascended to the Dukedom of Urbino in 1508. Raphael had returned to Urbino in October 1507 and was back in Florence by 21 April 1508, having recently supplied the Prefectess Giovanna, Francesco Maria's mother, with a Madonna which, Clifford contends, was the Bridgewater House picture, presented by Giovanna to her son on his becoming Duke of Urbino. This would, therefore, be the picture described in a 1623 inventory of the Duke of Urbino's collection as showing Christ, the Virgin Mary and Joseph and being in the form of a mirror (therefore probably circular).[17]

After the Bridgewater House picture had reached France, a copy, now lost, was painted by Philippe de Champaigne for the church of Port-Royal in Paris, at the instigation of La Marquise d'Aumont;[18] there it was paired with Philippe de Champaigne's own design of *La Samaritaine*, now in Caen, which Dorival believes to have been painted after 1648.[19] Another old French copy, in enamel, and of oval format, by P. Jean, of 1660, is in the Louvre.[20]

Coll: Possibly commissioned by Giovanna della Rovere as a present for her son, Francesco Maria della Rovere on his accession to the Dukedom of Urbino. Recorded in the Ducal Palace at Urbino in 1623. The Bridgewater House picture must almost certainly have reached France by 1656 when it was engraved (in reverse) by Gilles Rousselet.[21] According to Félibien, the French provenance was as follows:[22] Henri Hurault, Comte de Cheverny,[23] La Marquise d'Aumont[24] who sold it (probably c.1648–50) to L'Abbé de La Noue;[25] Antoine Tambonneau;[26] Monsieur de Vannolles[27] who sold it to the Régent, Philippe Duc d'Orléans. Cust, however, gave an alternative provenance and stated that after leaving the Abbé de La Noue's collection it was subsequently in the collection of the Marquis du Chatel until 1751.[28] The basis of Cust's statement is not revealed but it is demonstrably incorrect since the picture is already recorded in the Orléans collection in a 1724 inventory.[29] Sale Bryan's Gallery, London, 1798 (113) reserved for the 3rd Duke of Bridgewater;[30] thence by inheritance.[31]

Duke of Sutherland loan 1946.

---

1. Described as on wood by J. A. Crozat *Recueil d'Estampes d'après les Plus Beaux Tableaux ... en France* Paris 1729 I no. XXIII where it is engraved in reverse by Jean Raymond.

2. The earliest reference to the transfer is in Britton 1808 p. 14 no. 9. In the *Catalogue of Bridgewater House* 1926 p. 8 no. 35 it is stated that the transfer was carried out by the French restorer, Hacquin.

3. For earlier attempts to describe the condition of the picture see Passavant 1836 I pp. 122–23; Waagen 1838 II p. 43; F. Gruyer *Les Vierges de Raphael et l'iconographie de la Vierge* Paris 1869 III p. 265; J. A. Crowe and G. B. Cavalcaselle *Raphael. His life and Works* London 1882 II p. 287. A legend, reported by Crozat *loc. cit.*, and subsequently much repeated, that the picture had once been cut in half to resolve a dispute about its ownership, is demonstrably incorrect.

4. Metalpoint 225 × 152 mm. For a discussion of the Louvre drawing see O. Fischel *Raphaels Zeichnungen* Berlin 1913–41 III no. 139. See also E. Knab, E. Mitsch, K. Oberhuber *Raffaello i Disegni* Stuttgart/Florence 1983 no. 164 who also identify the earlier preparatory drawings (nos. 157, 154 and their versos, now in the Biblioteca Apostolica Vaticana, Rome) for the Bridgewater House composition.

5. P. Joannides *The Drawings of Raphael with a Complete Catalogue* Oxford 1983 p. 167 no. 138 *verso*. The drawing is Paris, Fondation Custodia I, 1952.

6. Ottley and Tomkins 1818 I no. 2.

7. Passavant 1836 I pp. 122 ff. and J. D. Passavant *Raphael d'Urbin et son père Giovanni Santi* Paris 1860 II pp. 38–9 no. 33.

8. Waagen 1838 II pp. 42–3.

9. *Op. cit.* pp. 285 ff.

10. O. Fischel (translated B. Rackham) *Raphael* London 1948 I p. 359.

11. L. Dussler (translated S. Cruft), *Raphael. A critical catalogue of his pictures, wall paintings and tapestries* London 1971 p. 23 pl. 59.

12. J. Pope-Hennessy *Raphael. The Wrightsman Lectures delivered under the auspices of the New York University Institute of Fine Arts* London 1974 p. 195 and pp. 286–7 note 39.

13. This picture is conveniently reproduced by Dussler *op. cit.* pl. 58. For a discussion of the question of the Bridgewater House picture's date see also J. D. Passavant *Raphael d'Urbin et son père Giovanni Santi* Paris 1860 II pp. 38–9.

14. Passavant 1836 I p. 124.

15. T. Clifford *The Raphael Tondo from the Sutherland loan pictures*, lecture given 5 March 1991 in the *NACF Italian Renaissance Lecture Series* at the Royal Geographical Society, London (text in Gallery files, to be published by the National Galleries of Scotland).

16. G. F. Hill *A Corpus of Italian Medals of the Renaissance before Cellini* London 1930 no. 320. On the reverse of a medal of Francesco Maria della Rovere is a palm tree with one branch depressed by a stone with a scroll around the trunk inscribed INCLINA RESVRGO.

17. G. Gronau *Documenti artistici urbinati* Florence 1936 p. 77.

18. According to Crozat *loc. cit.* La Marquise d'Aumont sold the Bridgewater House picture to the Abbé de La Noue on condition that he paid for this copy.

19. For the companion picture, now in Caen, see B. Dorival *Philippe de Champaigne 1602–1674. La vie, l'oeuvre, et le catalogue raisonné de l'oeuvre.* Paris 1976 II pp. l 33–4 no. 52 pl. 52.

20. Reproduced in *Raphael et l'art français* Exhibition Catalogue, Grand Palais, Paris 1983/4 p. 256 no. 381.

21. Nagler XV p. 267 no. 26. See also G. Pezzini, S. Massari, S. Prosperi Valenti Rodinò *Raphael Invenit. Stampe da Raffaello nelle Collezioni dell' Istituto Nazionale per la Grafica* Rome 1985, p. 186 no. 8.

22. A. Félibien *Entretiens sur les vies et sur les ouvrages des plus excellens peintres anciens et modernes* Trévoux 1725 I p. 339. And see Crozat *loc. cit.*

23. See E. Bonnaffé *Dictionnaire des Amateurs Français au XVIIe siècle* Paris 1884 (reprint Amsterdam 1966 p. 62).

24. See Bonnaffé *op. cit.* p. 11.

25. See Bonnaffé *op. cit.* p. 158.

26. See Bonnaffé *op. cit.* p. 300.

27. Unidentified.

28. Cust and Bourke 1903 no. 2.

29. See C. Stryienski *Galerie du Régent Philippe Duc d'Orléans* Paris 1913 p. 158 no. 122. Also recorded by L. F. Dubois de Saint Gelais *Description des tableaux du Palais Royal* Paris 1727 p. 432. Engraved by R. Massard in *Galerie du Palais Royal gravée* I Paris 1786.

30. For the sale of the Italian pictures in the Orléans collection see Buchanan 1824 I pp. 1–147; for the Bridgewater House picture see particularly p. 47.

31. Recorded by Britton *loc. cit.*; Ottley and Tomkins 1818 I no. 2; Passavant 1836 I pp. 122 ff.; Waagen 1838 II pp. 42–3; Jameson 1844 pp. 119–20 no. 92; Catalogue of the *Bridgewater Collection* 1851 no. 35; Waagen 1854 II pp. 26–7, Cust and Bourke *loc. cit.*; *Catalogue of Bridgewater House* 1926 no. 35.

The Bridgewater Madonna

Canvas transferred from wood: 82 × 57; painted surface 81 × 55.

It was evidently on wood up to 1729,[1] and was transferred to canvas when in the Orléans collection[2] An arched niche or window originally occupied most of the wall to the right, behind the Madonna's head, and the outlines, incised in the gesso, are clearly visible in the X-ray (Fig. 32). Cleaned and restored 1992 (Frontispiece). The removal of the discoloured varnish and old repaints has yielded spectacular dividends, revealing a picture in extremely good condition for a work of its age, and far better than modern scholars have ever supposed. There are paint losses on the Madonna's left cheek and her left shoulder, and the Infant Christ's lower left leg, but otherwise the figures are well preserved. There are indications that Raphael painted a landscape background beyond the niche on the right but then himself elected to paint it out.[3] The pale brown form in the upper right corner is probably a window-shutter. The curtain and the wall in the background of the picture are also visible.

The attribution of the Bridgewater House picture to Raphael has never been seriously questioned,[4] and is endorsed by the numerous preparatory drawings, firmly attributed to him, which are connected with its design. Fahy has observed that the overall design of the picture, and in particular the pose of the Madonna, is derived from Leonardo da Vinci's *Benois Madonna* in the Hermitage, Leningrad.[5] However, as De Tolnay first demonstrated, the diagonal posture of the Child was inspired by Michelangelo's Taddei tondo of *c*. 1504 which is now in the collection of the R.A., London; this marble probably came to Raphael's attention when he first reached Florence.[6] A pen and ink drawing, at Chatsworth, convincingly attributed to Raphael by Byam Shaw (there is also an old copy in the Louvre) is a fairly literal adaptation from the Michelangelo tondo (Fig. 33).[7] Another stage in Raphael's development of this concept is found in a study, made in pen and ink, on a sheet in the British Museum, London (Fig. 34)[8] and in a closely related study in the Albertina, Vienna, made in black lead, pen and ink (Fig. 35);[9] and these ideas were then apparently followed up by another preparatory study for the Bridgewater House picture, but in the reverse sense, made in pen and ink, on a sheet which is in the Uffizi, Florence (Fig. 36).[10] In each of these three drawings the Child is still placed astride the Madonna's knee, as in the Chatsworth drawing, but His position is reversed, so that His head is turned towards the Madonna who is shown gazing downwards.

Then at a later stage, inspired perhaps by Leonardo da Vinci's *Madonna of the Yarn-winder*, Raphael changed his idea for the pose of the Child, who in the Bridgewater House picture is shown stretched across the Madonna's lap. Two sheets of drawings for an infant Christ, made in metalpoint, which are now in the British Museum (Fig. 37),[11] and at Lille (Fig. 38),[12] and which both originally belonged to what Fischel designated Raphael's *Pink Sketchbook*, contain studies for an infant Christ strongly reminiscent of the pose of the Christ Child in the Bridgewater House picture; and both sheets also contain what are unquestionably preliminary thoughts for the Child in Raphael's *Madonna di Loreto*.[13] It seems likely, as Ruland,[14] followed by Pouncey and Gere,[15] has indicated, that these studies were made shortly before the execution of the Bridgewater House picture. In this case there would be a strong argument for dating the completion of the picture as late as 1508–9, since the *Pink Sketchbook*, which also contains a study for the *School of Athens* in the Vatican, is usually thought to have been made during Raphael's early Roman period. There is also at least a *prima facie* case for dating the *Bridgewater Madonna* at the beginning of Raphael's Roman period on the basis of the connected study in the Uffizi which is on the same sheet as his study for a figure in the Vatican fresco of the *Disputà*.

Crozat,[16] Passavant,[17] Gruyer[18] and Tempesti[19] are among those who have also lent support to the idea that the Bridgewater House picture is a Roman work. An alternative solution has been to associate the completion of the *Bridgewater Madonna* with Raphael's Florentine period and to regard the connected studies in the *Pink Sketchbook* as later elaborations of the pose of the Child in the picture. A date for the Bridgewater House picture between 1506–7 has been proposed by Ottley,[20] Waagen,[21] and Crowe and Cavalcaselle,[22] followed more recently by Shearman,[23] Freedberg[24] and Dussler.[25]

In any case Raphael's earliest thoughts for the design of the Bridgewater House picture certainly appear to originate from the time of his residence in Florence. This applies in particular to the Chatsworth study which is on the *verso* of a drawing for the *Madonna of the Meadow* of 1505, now in the Kunsthistorisches Museum, Vienna,[26] to the preparatory drawing in the Albertina, Vienna,[27] and to the pen and ink study in the

British Museum which is on the same sheet as studies for a number of other Madonnas by Raphael which probably can be dated between 1505–8.[28] On the other hand the distinctive cool colours, the draperies and the solidly rendered figures in the Bridgewater House picture (which have been revealed by its recent cleaning) appear to reinforce the idea that its execution was completed in Rome. In view of the variety and complexity of Raphael's drawings, and the substantial alterations to the background of the painting it is not at all unlikely that the preparations and execution of the Bridgewater Madonna was spread over a relatively extended period of time, perhaps spanning the artist's move from Florence to Rome.

Coll: According to Dubois de Saint Gelais it was in the collection of the Marquis de Seignelay (1651–1690).[29] Then, according to Crozat, it belonged to M. de Montarsis (sic)[30] who may be identified as the jeweller Laurent le Tessier de Montarsy.[31] It was later in the collection of the jeweller M. André Rondé[32] who in turn sold it to the Duc d'Orléans. The date of its entry into the Orléans collection is not known; according to Couché it was acquired by the Régent, Philippe Duc d'Orléans,[33] but it is not listed in the 1724 Orléans collection inventory made at the time of his death[34] and it is first catalogued in the Orléans collection by Dubois de Saint Gelais in 1727 when it belonged to Louis Duc Orléans.[35] Sale Bryan's Gallery, London, 1798 (64) reserved for the 3rd Duke of Bridgewater;[36] thence by inheritance.[37]

Duke of Sutherland loan 1946.

---

1. Described as on wood by J. A. Crozat *Recueil d'Estampes après les Plus Beaux Tableaux … en France* Paris 1729 I no. XXI where it is engraved in reverse by Nicolas de Larmessin (Fig. 39).

2. The earliest reference to the transfer is in Britton 1808 pp. 57–9 no. 46. But according to Passavant 1836 I pp. 125–26 the transfer had been carried out in France by Hacquin (who had worked on Sebastiano del Piombo's *Raising of Lazarus* now N.G., London, in 1771). For a detailed account of the picture's condition when it was in the Bridgewater Gallery see Waagen 1838 II pp. 43–4.

3. L. F. Dubois de Saint Gelais *Description des tableaux du Palais Royal* Paris 1727 p. 432 wrote: *Le fond du Tableau est brun.* However an engraving by J. Houlanger (Fig. 40), based on the design of our picture but in the reverse sense, shows a landscape background, seen through a window, in place of the niche, and on the other side a curtain. See Nagler XVI p. 394 no. 397; see further G. Pezzini, S. Massari, S. Prosperi Valenti Rodinò *Raphael Invenit. Stampe da Raffaello nelle Collezioni dell' Istituto Nazionale per la Grafica* Rome 1985, p. 186, no. 11. Little evidence of these features can be detected in the X-ray of our picture. The engraving by Nicolas de Larmessin (see note 1 above) and an engraving by A. Romanet also in reverse (in *Galerie du Palais Royal gravée* I Paris 1786) both show a plain niche without a landscape background.

4. In 1838 Waagen *loc. cit.* did cast some doubt on the attribution of the Bridgewater House picture, but he later retracted (1854 II pp. 27–8).

5. E. Fahy *The Legacy of Leonardo. Italian Renaissance Paintings from Leningrad,* Exhibition Catalogue, National Gallery, Washington 1979 p. 40.

6. C. de Tolnay *The Youth of Michelangelo* Princeton 1943 I p. 163.

7. Pen and ink 250 × 194 mm. See J. Byam Shaw *Old Master Drawings from Chatsworth. A Loan Exhibition from the Devonshire Collection* International Exhibitions Foundation 1969–70 p. 31 no. 57. For a discussion of the version in the Louvre see also O. Fischel *Raphaels Zeichnungen* Berlin 1913–41 III no. 108.

8. Pen and ink 254 × 184 mm. See Fischel *op. cit.* III no. 109. See also P. Pouncey and J. A. Gere *Italian Drawings … in the British Museum. Raphael and his circle* London 1962 pp. 15–17 no. 19 illus. as frontispiece and E. Knab, E. Mitsch, K. Oberhuber *Raffaello i Disegni* Stuttgart/Florence 1983, p. 596, no 161. For further discussion of this drawing and of the question of Raphael's development of the design of the Bridgewater House picture see J. Pope-Hennessy *Raphael. The Wrightsman Lectures delivered under the auspices of the New York University Institute of Fine Arts* London 1974 pp. 187–90.

9. Black lead, pen and ink 256 × 184 mm. See Fischel *op. cit.* III no. 111. See also Pouncey and Gere *loc. cit.;* and Knab (see note 8 above) *op. cit.*

10. Pen and ink over black chalk and lead pencil 249 × 271 mm. See Fischel *op. cit.* VIII no. 358. See also Pouncey and Gere *loc. cit.*

11. Metalpoint on pink prepared surface 168 × 119 mm. See Fischel *op. cit.* VIII no. 350. See also Pouncey and Gere *op. cit.* pp. 19–20 no. 23.

12. Metalpoint on pink prepared surface 167 × 119 mm. See Fischel *op. cit.* VIII no. 351.

13. What is almost certainly Raphael's original version of this composition has recently been identified at Chantilly. For the fullest discussion see *La Madone de Lorette*, Exhibition Catalogue, Musée Condé, Chantilly, 1979–80.

14. C. Ruland *The Works of Raphael Santi da Urbino as represented in The Raphael Collection in the Royal Library at Windsor Castle, formed by H.R.H. the Prince Consort, 1853–61 and completed by Her Majesty Queen Victoria* London 1876 p. 70.

15. *Op. cit.* pp. 19–20 no. 23 pl. 28. The evolution of O. Fischel's view on this subject is more difficult to follow. In 1898 (see *Raphaels Zeichnungen. Versuch einer Kritik der bisher veröffentlichten Blätter* Strasbourg 1898 p. 305) he followed Ruland (*loc. cit.*) in proposing a definite connection between these two sheets from the *Pink Sketchbook* and the Bridgewater House picture. In 1939 (p. 187) he connected the repeated motive of the awakening Child in the Lille drawing with the *Madonna di Loreto* but added that 'In the Child at the bottom it is amalgamated with the happy boy at play in the *Bridgewater Madonna* which was perhaps completed at the very beginning of the Roman period'. In his *Raphaels Zeichnungen* Berlin 1913–41 VIII nos. 350 and 351 he simply connected both of these sheets from the *Pink Sketchbook* with the *Madonna di Loreto*, but continued to regard the *Bridgewater Madonna* as a work from the Roman period. Finally in 1948 (see *Raphael,* translated B. Rackham, London 1948 p. 127 and pp. 359–60) he discussed the Bridgewater House picture in a chapter devoted to 'Roman Madonnas', but then, perhaps erroneously, dated it 1507 in his *Catalogue raisonné*. He then went on to refer to 'designs for the *Bridgewater Madonna*' in the *Pink Sketchbook* which he dated 1508.

16. *Loc. cit.*

17. *Loc. cit.* See also J. D. Passavant *Raphael d'Urbin et son père Giovanni Santi* Paris 1860 II pp. 119–20 no. 89.

18. F. Gruyer *Les Vierges de Raphael et l'iconographie de la Vierge* Paris 1869 III p. 82.

19. A. F. Tempesti *Raffaello. L'opera, le fonti, la fortuna* Novara 1968 II pp. 386–7.

20. Ottley and Tomkins 1818 I no. 3.

21. Waagen 1854 II pp. 27–8.

22. J. A. Crowe and G. B. Cavalcaselle *Raphael. His Life and Works* London 1882 II pp. 345 ff.

23. In the *Burlington Magazine* CVII 1965 p. 35.

24. S. Freedberg *Painting in Italy 1500–1600* London 1970 p. 30.

25. L. Dussler (translated S. Cruft) *Raphael. A critical catalogue of his pictures, wall paintings and tapestries* London 1971 p. 23 pl. 60.

26. See note 7 above.

27. See note 9 above.

28. See note 8 above.

29. *Loc. cit.* For the Marquis de Seignelay see E. Bonnaffé *Dictionnaire des Amateurs Français au XVIIe siècle* Paris 1884 (reprint Amsterdam 1966 pp. 289–90). See also C. Le Marie *Paris ancien et nouveau* Paris 1685 III p. 262 for a description of the collection and in particular for a picture by Raphael which might be the *Bridgewater Madonna: Premierement* [sic] *une Vierge de Raphael d'Urbin, qui est un tres precieux Tableau; cét* [sic] *excellent ouvrage n'est composé que d'une Vierge jusqu'aux genoux qui tient le petit JESUS.* I am indebted to Anthony Blunt for kindly transcribing this passage from his copy of the book.

30. *Loc. cit.*

31. For Montarsy see G. Brice *Description nouvelle de ce qu'il y a de plus remarquable dans la ville de Paris* Paris 1706 I p. 104. Montarsy's collection is said to have been displayed *dans la maison située à l'extrémité du cul-de-sac de S. Thomas du Louvre.* See also Bonnaffé *op. cit.* p. 223.

32. For Rondé see M. Rambaud *Documents du Minutier Central concernant l'histoire de l'art (1700–1750)* Paris 1971 II p. 271. See also C. Stryienski *Galerie du Régent Philippe Duc d'Orléans* Paris 1913 p. 14.

33. J. Couché *Galerie du Palais Royal gravée* I Paris 1786.

34. See Stryienski *op. cit.* p. 159 no. 123.

35. *Loc. cit.*

36. For the sale of the Italian pictures in the Orléans collection see Buchanan 1824 I pp. 1–147; for the Bridgewater House picture see particularly p. 46.

37. Recorded by Britton *loc. cit.*; Ottley and Tomkins *loc. cit.*; Passavant 1836 I pp. 125–26; Waagen 1838 II pp. 43–4; Jameson 1844 pp. 121–2 no. 93; *Catalogue of the Bridgewater Collection* 1851 no. 38; Waagen 1854 II p. 27; Cust and Bourke 1903 no. I; *Catalogue of Bridgewater House* 1926 no. 38.

Madonna del Passeggio

Wood: 90 × 63

Inscribed on the reverse at the top: · N.º 228 · DIRAFFEL : D'VRBINO

Cleaned 1991. X-rayed. According to Poerson, Director of the French Academy in Rome, the picture was extensively repaired in Rome in 1721.[1] A joint between the two planks out of which the panel was made had opened up; the crack runs through the Madonna's left shoulder. There is also a score in the paint surface on the left of the picture, running horizontally across the grain, just above the Baptist's right hip. Apart from losses along these two breaks, the paint surface is in very good condition. The panel would appear not to have been trimmed.

Shearman has suggested that the principal group of figures may possibly have been derived from an antique relief, now known from casts made from an old copy.[2] This relationship is arguable, although it is impossible to establish whether Raphael, who is generally credited with the design of the Bridgewater House picture, could have known of this antique prototype.

The Bridgewater House picture was considered an original work of high quality by Raphael while in the collections of the Aldobrandini family[3] and Queen Christina,[4] and also later when in the Orléans collection.[5] It was engraved as such by Jean Pesne (1639–1700).[6] It was also accepted as a work from Raphael's own hand by Ottley[7] and by Britton[8] after it had entered the Bridgewater House collection. Passavant, in 1836, was the first to cast doubt on this traditional viewpoint.[9] He suggested that the execution might be due to Penni working from a design by Raphael, and this idea has been supported by Crowe and Cavalcaselle,[10] Fischel,[11] Dussler,[12] and Pope-Hennessy.[13] The attribution to Penni depends largely on stylistic comparison with the landscape in the *Transfiguration* from the church of S. Spirito degli Incurabili, Naples, and now in the Prado, Madrid, which is widely regarded as a copy by Penni of Raphael's picture in the Vatican, Rome.[14] The landscape in the Bridgewater House picture and the relationship of the figures to the landscape background may also be compared with a *Holy Family* attributed to Penni, in Warsaw.[15] If executed by Penni, the Bridgewater House picture was probably completed between 1515–16, when he was collaborating with Raphael on the cartoons for the Vatican tapestries, and 1518–19, when he was working as an assistant on the Loggia frescoes in the Vatican.

The recent cleaning of the *Madonna del Passeggio* has revealed a work of considerable quality, in which the figures are modelled with firm assurance and the colours, the draperies and the luminous landscape glow with a remarkable intensity. These qualities together explain the high critical reputation of this picture in Queen Christina's day and it now seems appropriate to raise the possibility that this is an autograph work by

Raphael himself rather than a studio work by Penni who remains a shadowy and very secondary artistic personality.[16]

Coll: According to Olimpia Aldobrandini's annotation of Agucchi's 1603 inventory of the Aldobrandini collection (see note 3 below), the picture was given by the Aldobrandini family in 1621 to Cardinal Ludovico Ludovisi, whose uncle Gregory XV, became Pope that year. It is then recorded in Queen Christina's collection in an inventory of her possessions made in Antwerp and dated May 1656.[17] According to a subsequent inventory of the collection, made c. 1662 in the Palazzo Riario, Rome, it had been given to her by the King of Spain (Philip IV).[18] (This conflicts with a statement of Crozat, which is probably unreliable, that it was painted for the Duke of Urbino who gave it to the King of Spain who in turn gave it to Gustavus Adolphus, King of Sweden.[19] Equally, there is insufficient evidence to justify Bildt's suggestion that the Bridgewater House picture was acquired for Queen Christina by Philip IV of Spain from the Duke of Buckingham in 1654–5.[20]) At the time of Queen Christina's death the Bridgewater House picture is again recorded in an inventory of her collection dated 1689 (no. 41).[21] It next passed by inheritance first to Cardinal Dezio Azzolino (died 1689) and then to his nephew, Marchese Pompeo Azzolino, who sold it to Prince Livio Odescalchi (died 1713); then by inheritance to Prince Baldassare Odescalchi-Erba, who sold it to the Régent, Philippe Duc d'Orléans, in 1721. Recorded in a 1721 inventory (no. 7) made at the time of the sale,[22] and again in the 1724 Orléans collection inventory.[23] Sale Bryan's Gallery, London, 1798 (31) reserved for the 3rd Duke of Bridgewater;[24] thence by inheritance.[25]

Duke of Sutherland loan 1946.

1. Letter from Poerson to the Duc d'Antin dated 12 August 1721 quoted by C. Stryienski *Galerie du Régent Philippe Duc d'Orléans* Paris 1913 p. 31: *Nous sommes toujours assidus à préparer les tableaux de Son Altesse Royale, et la Belle Vierge de Raphael, a été heureusement raccommodée par le fameux seigneur Domenico, d'une manière si ingénieuse, qu'elle fait l'admiration de ceux qui l'ont vue et qui la voient à présent: et cela sans avoir employé ni pinceau, ni huile, ni couleur, mais avec du stuc d'une certaine composition dont il a rempli les trous, dont quelques-uns avaient cinq ou six lignes de profondeur.*

2. Verbal communication from John Shearman 1969. One cast is in the Akademisches Kunstmuseum of Bonn University; another cast is reproduced in *Enciclopedia dell'Arte Antica* 1958–66 III p. 431.

3. John Dick has pointed out that the number 228 on the reverse corresponds with the entry in Agucchi's 1603 inventory of the Aldobrandini collection: *228. Una Madonna in piede col Christo, che lo tiene per un braccio, e Gio. Batt. che si abbracciano con un S. Gioseffe, di mano di 'Raffaele' d'Urbino, con cornice tutta dorata.* crossed out, inscribed opposite *fù donato dell' Ecc.ma Signora al Sig. Cardinale Ludovisio l'anno 1621* and *questa donatione l'offata a istantia delli miei figli. Olimpia Aldobrandini,* see C. d'Onofrio 'Inventario dei Dipinti del cardinal Pietro Aldobrandini compilato da G. B. Agucchi nel 1603' *Palatino* 1964 p. 206.

4. See the inventory of Queen Christina's possessions in Antwerp, dated May 1656, published by J. Denucé *De Antwerpsche 'Konstkamers' Inventarissen van Kunstverzamelingen te Antwerpen in de 16e en 17e eeuwen* Amsterdam 1932 pp. 177: *Peintures: No. I. Premièrement une caisse, nombrée no primo, marquee de la marce en marge, contenante une piece de Raphaël Urbin, representant Nostre-Dame, Nostre-Seigneur et Sainct-Jehan* [sic]. See also the inventory of Queen Christina's pictures in the Palazzo Riario, Rome 1662, *Inventoria della Regina Christina,* Riksarkivet, Stockholm, Azzolinosamlingen Vol. 48 f. 56: *Una Madonna con Cristo Bambino S. Giovanni, e S. Giuseppe in Tavola, con cornice d'Ebbano, alta palmi quattro, e mezza, e Larga palmi tre e Mezzo, con La sua tendina di Taffettano rosino, con Merlettini d'Oro attorno, e suo ferretto indorato. Di Raffael D'Urbino Donato a S. M. dal Re di Spagna.* For later references see O. Granberg *La Galerie de Tableaux de la Reine Christine de Suède* Stockholm 1897 p. 32 no 12.

5. See L. F. Dubois de Saint Gelais *Description des Tableaux du Palais Royal* Paris 1727 p. 433; and J. A. Crozat *Recueil d'Estampes d'après les Plus Beaux Tableaux ... en France* Paris 1729 I no. XX where it is engraved in reverse by Nicolas de Larmessin.

6. Nagler XII p. 300 no. 95.

7. Ottley and Tomkins 1818 I no. 5.

8. Britton 1808 pp. 15 ff. no. 10.

9. Passavant 1836 I p. 126. See also J. D. Passavant *Raphael d'Urbin et son père Giovanni Santi* Paris 1860 II pp. 331–2 no. 271.

10. J. A. Crowe and G. B. Cavalcaselle *Raphael. His Life and Works* London 1882 II p. 552.

11. See Thieme-Becker XXIX 1935 p. 442.

12. L. Dussler (translated S. Cruft) *Raphael. A critical catalogue of his pictures, wall paintings and tapestries* London 1971 pp. 45–6 pl. 99.

13. J. Pope–Hennessy *Raphael. The Wrightsman Lectures delivered under the auspices of the New York University Institute of Fine Arts* London 1974 p. 221.

14. Identified as by Penni in Vasari (ed. Milanesi IV p. 646). For the identification of the Prado picture as that formerly in the church of S. Spirito degli Incurabili in Naples see *Museo del Prado, Catalogo de las Pinturas* Madrid 1963 p. 530 no.315. For the attribution to Raphael and/or Penni see further *Raphael en España*, Exhibition Catalogue, Prado, Madrid 1985 p. 139 no. 4 as Raphael.

15. See *National Museum, Warsaw, Catalogue of Paintings, Foreign Schools*, Warsaw 1970 II p. 34 no. 954.

16. An alternative view, first advanced by Waagen, has been to regard the Bridgewater House picture as an old copy by an unknown hand after a lost original picture by Raphael; but against this idea is the complete absence of any documentary reference to such a lost picture, as well as the high quality of the picture in Edinburgh. Waagen 1838 II pp. 44–5 and 1854 II pp. 28–9.

17. See note 4 above.

18. See note 4 above.

19. *Loc. cit.*

20. C. Bildt in *The Nineteenth Century* LVI December 1904 pp. 998–9.

21. See Granberg *loc. cit.* The inventory is also printed in G. Campori *Raccolta di cataloghi ed inventarii inediti* Modena 1870 pp. 336ff.

22. See Granberg *loc. cit.* For details of the negotiations prior to the sale and for a reference to the Bridgewater House picture by L'Abbé Louis de Targny who saw the picture in Rome with Pierre Crozat, see Stryienski *op. cit.* pp. 18–20.

23. See Stryienski *op. cit.* p. 159 no.125. Also recorded by Dubois de Saint Gelais *loc. cit.* Also engraved in reverse by H. Guttemberg in *Galerie du Palais Royal gravée* I Paris 1786.

24. For the sale of the Italian pictures in the Orléans collection see Buchanan 1824 I pp. 1–447; for the Bridgewater House picture see particularly p. 46.

25. Recorded by Britton *loc. cit.*; Passavant 1836 I p. 126; Waagen 1838 II pp. 44–5; Jameson 1844, pp. 122–3 no.94; *Catalogue of the Bridgewater Collection* 1851 no.37; Waagen 1854 II pp. 28–9; Cust and Bourke 1903 no.3; *Catalogue of Bridgewater House* 1926 no.37.

After RAPHAEL

Madonna with the Veil

Wood: 68.5 × 47.8

The paint surface is somewhat worn, with areas of retouching, especially in the foreground.

Also known as *La Vierge au diadème bleu*. Accepted as an autograph work of Raphael by Britton in 1808[1] and by Ottley in 1818,[2] but generally recognised, since Passavant in 1836,[3] as a relatively old copy of a Raphael design, of which the best known version is in the Louvre, Paris (Inv. 1497).[4] Although no drawing for the composition made by Raphael himself has ever come to light, it seems reasonable to suppose that he was responsible for the original idea, during his Roman period. The Louvre picture does not appear to have been executed by Raphael and was probably painted by one of his workshop assistants. In the Bridgewater House picture, the soft modelling of the flesh and the use of brown glazes in the shadows suggest a technique later than Raphael's. The oak panel might suggest this picture is of Flemish origin.

Coll: Sir Joshua Reynolds collection by 1791 when it was offered for sale in *Ralph's Exhibition* (A–56).[5] By inheritance to Sir Joshua's niece, Lady Inchiquin, in 1792. Sir Joshua Reynolds deceased sale

Christie's 17 March 1795(95) bought in.[6] According to Farington's Diary, by the 8 March 1797 it had been acquired by Michael Bryan,[7] who sold it to the 3rd Duke of Bridgewater, by 26 March 1797.[8] Recorded in 1808 by Britton in the Stafford Gallery as from the Reynolds collection;[9] thence by inheritance.[10]

Duke of Sutherland loan 1946.

---

1. Britton 1808 pp. 13–14 no.8.
2. Ottley and Tomkins 1818 I no.4, incorrectly as formerly in the Orléans collection.
3. Passavant 1836 I p. 127. See further J. D. Passavant *Raphael d'Urbin et son père Giovanni Santi* Paris 1860 II pp. 108–10 no.83. Also described as a copy by Waagen 1838 II p. 45 and 1854 II p. 29.
4. For the Louvre version see L. Dussler (translated S. Cruft) *Raphael. A critical catalogue of his pictures, wall paintings and tapestries* London 1971 pp. 28–9 pl. 74. Cf. also S. De Ricci *Description raisonné des peintures du Louvre* Paris 1913 p. 214 no. 1497 as by Raphael; and G. Gronau *Raffael* Klassiker der Kunst Stuttgart/Leipzig 1909 p. 76.
5. I am indebted to F. J. P. Brown for this reference and for his kind assistance in verifying the provenance of our picture.
6. An annotation in Viscount Ridley's copy of the 1795 Reynolds sale catalogue (preserved at the Paul Mellon Centre for Studies in British Art, London) states, with reference to our picture: 'This Picture called Raphael by Benvenuto Girsofilo (sic), was bought in at a sale at Christie's for £16 and sold to Sr. Joshua Reynolds for £150.'
7. Farington Diary (British Museum typescript) 8 March 1797 as follows: 'Bryant (sic) has at the desire of Lady Inchiquin exchanged with her the Dido for which he gave 200 guineas for a threequarter of a little girl in white kneeling and the small Holy Family by Raphael'. This quotation is published by the gracious permission of Her Majesty The Queen.
8. Farington Diary (British Museum typescript) 26 March 1797 as follows: 'Duke of Bridgewater (sic) bought … Sir Joshua's small Raphael Holy Family'. This quotation is published by the gracious permission of Her Majesty The Queen.
9. *Loc. cit.*
10. Recorded Ottley and Tomkins *loc. cit.*; Passavant 1836 I p. 27; Waagen 1838 II p. 45; Jameson 1844 pp. 123–24 no.95; *Catalogue of the Bridgewater Collection* 1851 no.36; Waagen 1854 II p. 29; Cust and Bourke 1903 no. 4; *Catalogue of Bridgewater House* 1926 no.37.

After RAPHAEL

110   S. Peter

Canvas: 83.7 × 67.7
In quite good condition. The paint surface is slightly worn.

Hitherto catalogued as Italian School and as representing S. Peter. But as Cuzin first recognised, the head, shoulders and hands of the figure are based directly on the S. Joseph in Raphael's *Madonna of Francis I* in the Louvre.[1] The copyist has made some changes in the draperies and has also inserted the symbol of a key, presumably with the intention of changing the identity of the figure to S. Peter. This feeble pastiche probably dates from the eighteenth century and was not necessarily made by an Italian artist.

Coll: R.I., Edinburgh by 1830 and exhibited for the first time at the R.I. 1831(17) as by an unknown artist, but without indication of provenance.[2] It might well have been among the pictures which Andrew Wilson acquired in Italy on behalf of the R.I., but there is no positive evidence to this effect.

Royal Institution 1830.

1. Verbal communication from Jean-Pierre Cuzin, July 1975.
2. Also exhibited R.I. 1832(17).

After RAPHAEL

854   The Madonna and Child with S. John

Wood: 29.5 × 22.3
There is an area of damage at the top right which has been repaired.

A variant of Raphael's *Aldobrandini* or *Garvagh Madonna* in the National Gallery, London.[1] It probably dates from the seventeenth century.

Presented by Mr and Mrs J. Percy Callard 1936.

1. For the National Gallery picture see C. Gould *National Gallery Catalogue. The Sixteenth Century Italian Schools* London 1975 p. 215 Inv. no.744. See further J. D. Passavant *Raphael d'Urbin et son père Giovanni Santi* Paris 1860 II pp. 107–8 no.82.

Guido RENI *1575–1642*

He was born in Bologna and trained there under Denys Calvaert. In 1595 he joined the Accademia degli Incamminati, and came under the influence of the Carracci. In 1601–14 he was in Rome, and for a brief period *c.* 1604–6 he was strongly affected by the chiaroscuro and naturalism of Caravaggio. However, as Malvasia recognised, the principal characteristic of Reni's style is a refined elegance, combined with a capacity for naturalistic expression. At the end of his career Reni developed an extremely delicate and poetic silvery manner, with a minimum of modelling and a disregard for unnecessary detail.

2375   Moses with Pharaoh's Crown

Canvas: 132.2 × 172.7
Cleaned 1978 shortly before its acquisition by the Gallery. Notwithstanding its neglected appearance in 1977, the picture was found to be in very good condition, apart from two minor horizontal tears in the centre. The mid-brown coloured ground has been left visible beneath the delicate and sketchily applied paint surface to define shadows and half tones. The transluscent quality in many areas is accentuated by the fact that the paint has become more transparent with age. The apparent sketchiness and indecisive drawing of the child's legs is accentuated by this process; the artist's preliminary thoughts and subsequent *pentimenti* now show through the paint surface. Although the unfinished appearance of the picture is largely a question of style, there are some areas where the artist may have failed to complete the picture, especially the infant's extended foot and Pharaoh's right hand.

The picture shows Moses holding Pharaoh's crown before he throws it to the ground and tramples on it (*Speculum Humanae*, ed. Lutz-Pedrizet 1909 I part 3 p. 201). The picture first came to light at Christie's, London in 1977 with the correct attribution to Guido Reni, but by then it was in a sadly neglected state. It was widely recognised as a masterpiece of Guido Reni's very late 'unfinished' or minimal style of 1640–2 and was subsequently published as such by Pepper after it had entered the Gallery's collection.[1] It may have been left in the artist's studio at the time of his death, although it cannot be positively identified in the inventory of the late artist's possessions, dated 11 October 1642 and recently published by Spike. Spike's suggestion that our picture might be the *S. Catterina con Massimo Imperatore*, recorded in the inventory, is not convincing.[2] The earliest reference to our picture may be in a 1774 document (Frick Art Reference Library) which lists the contents of some important Roman collections. Here what appears to be our picture is listed as the property of the Bolognetti, and described as a 'sketch of a woman holding a child with crown in his hand, presenting to a man'.[3]

Coll: Probably Bolognetti Collection, Rome 1774; Christie's, London 2 December 1977 (lot 3) illus. in its uncleaned state; bought Thomas Agnew and Son, London.

Purchased 1979.

1. S. Pepper in *Burlington Magazine* CXXI 1979 pp. 418 ff. fig. 16–18; S. Pepper *Guido Reni: A Complete Catalogue of his Works with an Introductory Text* Oxford 1984 p. 292 no. 213 pl. 241. See further S. Pepper in *The Age of Correggio and the Carracci* Exhibition Catalogue Washington/New York/Bologna 1986–7 pp. 523–4 no. 189.
2. J. Spike *Accademia Clementina. Atti e Memorie* Nuova Serie 22, Bologna 1988 p. 60 line 405, and footnote.
3. *Recueil de Cat. des principales collections de tableaux* 1774 I p. 38 (MS. Frick Art Reference Library, New York) cited by Pepper 1984 (see note 1 above).

Pandolfo RESCHI *c.1640–96*

Born around 1640 in Danzig as Pandolfo Resch but went to Rome at an early age where he was known by the name of Reschi.[1] There he was a pupil of Salvator Rosa and Il Borgognone. He was still in Rome in 1663 but, according to Baldinucci, he moved to Tuscany soon afterwards, and remained there for the rest of his life apart from a visit to Lombardy *c.* 1670. In Florence he was patronised by the Marchese Gerini who arranged for him to study under Livio Mehus, Antonio Giusti, and Pier Dandini. He was required to make copies of landscapes and battle pictures by Borgognone in the Gerini collection. Apart from these, the Gerini appear to have acquired six battle pictures and ten landscapes by Reschi. He also worked for a number of other Florentine families, including the Riccardi, the Corsini and the Rinuccini, as well as for Prince Ferdinando and for Cardinal Francesco de' Medici. Only a small number of Reschi's pictures have been identified. They include a *Bull Hunt* in the Doria Collection, Rome;[2] a *Landscape with Waterfall* in the Galleria Nazionale, Rome; a number of *Battle scenes* in the Pinacoteca at Lucca, in the Bardini Museum, Florence,[3] and in the Corsini collection in Florence;[4] and some pictures in the storerooms of the Uffizi and Pitti galleries, three of which were brought to light in the exhibition *Artisti alla Corte Granducale* in Florence in 1969.[5] There is still insufficient evidence to establish the chronology of Reschi's works with any precision.

70   A Battle

Canvas: 95 × 147.3
Cleaned 1977. In good condition apart from minor damages and paint losses.

Acquired as by Reschi from the Gerini collection in Florence, a family with whom the artist had a particularly close connection, after he had left Rome. There is no particular basis on which to date our picture. It is close in style to the two *Battle Scenes* in the Corsini collection, Florence, which are traditionally attributed to Reschi;[6] their date is not recorded but two further pictures, now lost, were acquired by the Corsini from Reschi in 1680.[7] *A View of Florence* painted by Reschi for the Gerini family, which appeared in 1972 on the Florentine art market, can be securely dated on topographical evidence no later than the early 1680s, and our picture might well have been commissioned by the Gerini at about the same time.[8]

Coll: Bought from the Gerini collection, Florence by Andrew Wilson on behalf of the R.I. Edinburgh, in 1831.[9] Exhibited R.I. 1832 (32). Recorded by Waagen in the collection of the R.I. 1854.[10]

Royal Institution 1831.

1. The principal source for Reschi's biography is the *Vite* by F. S. Baldinucci (Biblioteca Nazionale, Florence). See *Raccolta di Fonti per la storia dell'arte diretta da Mario Salmi, seconda serie III: 'Francesco Saverio Baldinucci Vite di artisti dei secoli XVII-XVIII'* ed. Anna Matteoli 1975 pp. 218–29. The most informative modern study is by M. Chiarini in *Pantheon* XXXI (2) 1973 pp. 154–61. See further M. Chiarini *The Twilight of the Medici* Exhibition Catalogue, Detroit/Florence 1974 (English edition p. 300).
2. Reproduced by Chiarini in *Pantheon* XXXI (2) 1973 p. 156 fig. 4.
3. See M. Gregori 70 *Pitture e Sculture del '600 e '700 Fiorentino* Exhibition Catalogue, Florence 1965 p. 55 fig. 29.
4. Reproduced (a detail only) by M. Gregori in *Paragone* 267 1972 p. 80 note 8 fig. 62.
5. See M. Chiarini *Artisti alla Corte Granducale* Exhibition Catalogue, Florence 1969 p. 62 figs. 73–5. For further pictures by Reschi in the Florentine galleries see M. Chiarini in *Paragone* 273 1972 p. 65 fig. 44.
6. See Gregori *loc. cit.*
7. See M. Chiarini in *Pantheon* XXXI (2) 1973 p. 157.
8. See M. Chiarini in *Pantheon* XXXI (2) 1973 p. 159. The *View of Florence*, together with its pendant, was sold at the *Asta degli arredi di G. Andrea dei Marchesi Gerini*, Villa di Colonnata (Sesto Fiorentino) October–November 1972 (216 and 217); it is reproduced by L. Salerno *Pittori di paesaggio del Seicento a Roma* [1977] II p. 675 no. 114.7.
9. See further *Pictures for Scotland* pp. 27 ff.
10. Waagen 1854 III p. 270.

Marco RICCI *1676–1729*

Born in Belluno. Mainly active in Venice, where he specialised in painting landscape. He also sometimes travelled with his uncle, Sebastiano Ricci, with whom he collaborated on a number of pictures. They were probably in Florence together around 1705.[1] Here, at the Grand Ducal court, they must both have come into contact with Antonio Peruzzini, an artist specialising in landscape;[2] and by 1707 Sebastiano Ricci had collaborated with Peruzzini on a picture now in the Porro collection, Milan.[3] In Florence Marco also came into contact with the Genoese artist, Alessandro Magnasco, and by 1705 they, together with Bianchi di Livorno and Nicola van Houbraken, had joined forces to complete a signed and dated picture of *Hermits in a Landscape*, formerly in the Della Gherardesca collection at Bolgheri (Leghorn).[4] Marco's style also appears to have been influenced by the works of Salvator Rosa, Gaspard Dughet, Pandolfo Reschi and Crescenzio Onofri.

Attributed to Marco RICCI

7 **Landscape with Monks**

Canvas: 95 × 127.5
In very good condition, apart from numerous minute paint losses, particularly around the left, bottom and right-hand edges.

According to Fiocco the landscape shows the Piave valley near Belluno.[5] Acquired by the R.I. Edinburgh in 1831 and exhibited in 1832 as by Bernasio,[6] presumably a misreading for Bernasco (i.e. Magnasco) to whom it was attributed in the Gerini collection, Florence, by 1825.[7] Catalogued from 1859 as by Bernazzano, who lived one hundred and fifty years too early. In the 1912 *Catalogue* the attribution was changed to Magnasco. Then in 1929 Fiocco convincingly attributed the landscape to Marco Ricci, and more contentiously suggested that the figures were by Sebastiano Ricci, imitating Magnasco.[8] According to Soprani, Sebastiano Ricci made particular efforts to imitate the figure style of the Genoese master.[9] Fiocco's view was endorsed by Arslan,[10] and was then repeated in the 1936 *Catalogue*. But Longhi, followed by Geiger in 1949, reverted to the view that the figures were painted by Magnasco, and further suggested that the landscape might be by Carlo Antonio Tavella.[11] Fiocco's attribution to the two Ricci was nevertheless retained in the 1957 *Catalogue*. Then in 1964, Gregori raised the question of Antonio Francesco Peruzzini's style as a landscape painter and, if only by implication, the possibility that he might have painted the landscape of our picture.[12] In the 1970 *Shorter Catalogue* the picture was listed under the name of Marco Ricci, with the reservation that the figures might be by Magnasco.

Since then, Chiarini has lent fresh support to Fiocco's viewpoint.[13] More specifically, he compares the figures in our picture to those in a picture of the same subject at the Fogg Museum, Cambridge (Mass.), which, following Pospisil, he attributes to Sebastiano Ricci.[14] There is certainly a close connection between the figures in our picture and those in the Fogg Museum picture, but without exhibiting them side by side it is virtually impossible to be sure that the figures in each are by the same hand. The attribution of the figures in the Fogg Museum picture to Sebastiano Ricci is, in any case, by no means secure. Indeed if, as Geiger has suggested,[15] the Fogg Museum picture was originally a companion to the signed picture by four hands, formerly in the Della Gherardesca collection, where the figures are definitely by Magnasco, then a case could be made for attributing the figures of monks in the Fogg Museum picture to Magnasco as well.

The possibility that our picture might be the work of a single hand does not seem to have been seriously entertained since the 1912 *Catalogue*. Yet the manner in which the figures are assimilated into the landscape does not necessarily suggest that we are concerned with a collaborative work. The landscape is much closer to Marco Ricci's style than to Magnasco's wild and vigorous manner, and it is perhaps not unreasonable to speculate that he, like his uncle, might also have been capable of imitating Magnasco's style of figure painting.

In conclusion, as already suggested in the 1970 *Shorter Catalogue*, it still seems most likely that the landscape is by Marco Ricci; and that the figures, in the style of Magnasco, if not by the Genoese artist himself, might well be a very successful imitation by Marco Ricci.

The date of our picture is also a matter of some dispute. Fiocco places it in the late

1720s and compares it to Sebastiano and Marco Ricci's *Moses Striking the Rock* which was originally painted for the church of SS. Cosma and Damiano, Venice (now deposited in the Cini Foundation, Venice, on loan from the Accademia).[16] This suggestion of a relatively late date has subsequently been followed by Arslan[17] and Daniels.[18] On the other hand, in the 1970 *Shorter Catalogue* a much earlier date of *c.* 1705 was proposed, on the strength of the Florentine provenance of our picture and the fact that this was the moment when Magnasco and Peruzzini and the two Riccis were all in Florence. This view has subsequently been supported by Chiarini.[19] Another version of our picture was with Victor Spark, New York 1984; it is attributed by the owner to Tavella with figures by Magnasco.[20]

Col: Marchese Gerini, Florence. Presumably Gerini sale catalogue 1825 (98) as by Cav. Bernasco.[21] Bought from the Gerini family, Florence, by Andrew Wilson on behalf of the R.I., Edinburgh, 1831.[22] Exhibited R.I. 1831 (31). Recorded by Waagen in the collection of the R.I. 1854.[23]

Royal Institution 1831.

1. The evidence for this is conveniently summarised by M. Chiarini *The Twilight of the Medici* Exhibition Catalogue, Detroit/Florence 1974 (English ed. p. 302)

2. See M. Gregori in *Paragone* 169 1964 pp. 24ff.

3. Reproduced by W. Arslan in *Studies in the History of Art dedicated to W. E. Suida* London 1959 pp. 304ff. fig. I.

4. See M. Pospisil *Alessandro Magnasco* Florence 1944 p. 75 no. 20 pl. 20. See also Gregori *op. cit.* p. 25.

5. G. Fiocco *Venetian painting of the seicento and settecento* Verona 1929 p. 63.

6. See *Catalogue of the Sixth Exhibition of Ancient Pictures* R.I. Edinburgh 1832 (31).

7. *Catalogo e stima dei quadri e bronzi esistenti nella galleria del Sig. Marchese Giovanni Gerini* Florence 1825.

8. *Loc. cit.*

9. R. Soprani *Vite de' Pittori, Scultori e Architetti Genovesi* 1674 (ed. C. Ratti, Genoa 1786 II p. 159).

10. W. Arslan in *Gazette des Beaux-Arts* XIII 1935 p. 36.

11. B. Geiger *Magnasco* Bergamo 1949 p. 85 pl. 377. Longhi's unpublished opinion is also reported by Geiger.

12. *Op. cit.* p. 25.

13. *Op. cit.* p. 302 no. 178 illus. See further A. Scarpa Sonino *Marco Ricci* Milan 1991 pp. 121–2 no. 33.

14. Chiarini *loc. cit.* The Fogg Museum picture is discussed and reproduced by Geiger *op. cit.* p. 77 fig. 371.

15. *Op. cit.* pp. 77 and 130.

16. *Loc. cit.* For the date of the *Moses Striking the Rock* see J. Daniels *Sebastiano Ricci* Hove 1976 p. 135 no. 464 figs. 318–22.

17. See note 10 above.

18. *Op. cit.* p. 26 no. 86 fig. 87.

19. *Loc. cit.*

20. Photographs in the Gallery files, together with letters from Victor Spark dated 29 May and 10 July 1984.

21. See note 7 above.

22. See further *Pictures for Scotland* pp. 27ff.

23. Waagen 1854 III p. 270.

Salvator ROSA *1615–73*

Born in Naples where he worked in the studio of Francesco Fracanzano. He was also influenced in Naples by Ribera and Aniello Falcone. In 1635 he went to Rome, where he remained for most of his life except for the period 1640–9 which he spent in Florence. His pictures included portraits, landscapes, battle scenes, as well as works reflecting his stoic philosophy. He was active as a print-maker. His series of *Figurine*, small scale figure etchings of warriors and bandits, which enjoyed a considerable success, were much copied after his death.

After Salvator ROSA

600 A Figure in Armour

Canvas: 87 × 60.2. In good condition.

600A A Figure in Armour

Canvas: 87.5 × 60.5. In good condition, apart from a damage in the bottom left corner.

Two companion pictures. Both were acquired as by Salvator Rosa and were so catalogued until 1957. The 1957 *Catalogue* suggested that although the quality is worthy of Rosa, 'the paint medium and execution' are unlike his work. In the light of more recent studies on the artist, and in particular Salerno's monograph of 1963 where our pictures are described as copies,[1] it seems much clearer that they cannot be from Rosa's hand. They are probably by a late seventeenth-century imitator, and in each case the design is derived from an etching in Rosa's *Figurine* series: see Bartsch XX 37 for our no. 600 and Bartsch XX 40 for our no. 600A.

Coll: Both pictures are inscribed on the back of the stretcher: [*Thos*] *Campbell.*[2] By inheritance to Hamilton, daughter of Walter Frederick Campbell of Shawfield and Islay, who married the 8th Lord Belhaven in 1815.

Lady Belhaven bequest 1873.

1. L. Salerno *Salvator Rosa* Milan 1963 p. 153.
2. No Thomas Campbell of Shawfield is recorded since 1735. The earlier history of the family is not known.

After Salvator ROSA

622 River Scene with Figures

Canvas: 36.2 × 89.2
Cleaned 1940. In good condition.

Acquired as by Salvator Rosa and subsequently catalogued under his name, but from the 1946 *Catalogue* onwards the attribution has been recognised as doubtful.[1] A companion to our picture is in the collection of the Royal Scottish Academy. Both pictures are unconvincing pastiches of Rosa's landscape style and appear to date from no earlier than the eighteenth century.

Bequeathed, together with its companion, to the Royal Scottish Academy by Mrs Mary Veitch (née Pitcairn) in 1875; transferred 1910.

[1]See also L. Salerno *Salvator Rosa* Milan 1963 p. 153 where it is listed under *Opere incerte o non controllate o non autografe.*

Cosimo ROSSELLI *1439–1507*

Florentine. A pupil of Neri di Bicci from 1453–6. He was also influenced by Benozzo Gozzoli and Alesso Baldovinetti. In 1481 he was summoned to Rome to help decorate the side walls of the Sistine Chapel.

030   **S. Catherine of Siena as the Spiritual Mother of the Second and Third Orders of S. Dominic**

Wood: 170 × 171.5; painted surface 157.7 × 163.5.
The paint surface is badly worn throughout, particularly around the edges of the obtrusive and wide craquelure; these abrasions may have been aggravated by the lack of an adequate protective varnish, although there are still traces of an old bleached varnish which now disfigures the paint surface. There are relatively few serious damages for a work of its age. The areas most seriously affected by old restoration are the niche behind the head of S. Catherine; S. Catherine's nose; the left sleeve and the collar of the male saint on the far left; the entire figure of the devil; the left cuff of the kneeling female figure at the extreme right; and the step in the centre foreground. Otherwise the picture is in good condition.

S. Catherine, wearing the Dominican habit, sits enthroned in the centre: with her right hand she gives a bound volume of the Rule to the kneeling members of the second Order of S. Dominic, and with her left hand she gives a paper of regulations to a kneeling group of members of the third Order, one of whom is in secular dress. At the left side of the throne stand S. Lawrence and S. Dominic; on the right-hand side stand S. Peter Martyr and S. Raphael with the young Tobias. As Kaftal has pointed out, the subject is mystical rather than historical.[1] It is close in spirit to the text of S. Catherine's sixteenth-century biographer 'Doctor Caterinus Senensis' (Lancelotto Politi, 1483–1553, Archbishop of Conza), translated in 1867 by John Fen as follows: 'And because she was the first virgin that was received into [the habit of S. Dominic], she was also accounted afterwards the head and foundress of all the other virgins that, by her example, were admitted into the same order'.[2]

Acquired with a traditional attribution to Cosimo Rosselli which had been endorsed by Berenson in 1896 (also in 1932, 1936 and 1963) and subsequently catalogued under this name. Gronau speculated that it might have been commissioned for the church of S. Domenico al Maglio, attached to the convent of S. Catherine in Florence, where three of Cosimo Rosselli's nieces received the habit in 1499.[3] The convent was not apparently opened until very shortly before this date, and on this basis our picture would have to be identified as a very late work.[4] Although in style our picture shows some affinity with relatively early works by Cosimo Rosselli, such as the *Annunciation* in the Louvre, dated 1473,[5] it is by no means impossible that it was painted as late as *c.* 1500, since Cosimo Rosselli's stylistic development does not appear to have been strictly progressive.

Coll: Acquired by Charles Butler in Florence before 1885 when he lent it to the *Exhibition of Works by the Old Masters* R.A., London (243) as by Cosimo Rosselli. Also lent to the *Exhibition of Early Italian Art* The New Gallery, London, 1893–4 (3) as by Cosimo Rosselli.

Bought at the Charles Butler sale Christie's 25 May 1911(76).[6]

1. G. Kaftal *St. Catherine in Tuscan Painting* Oxford 1949 p. 132.

2. Doctor Caterinus Senensis *The Life of the Blessed Virgin St. Catharine of Sienna* (translated into English by John Fen and re-edited by J. D. Aylward, London 1867 p. 55).

3. G. Gronau in *Thieme–Becker* XXIX p. 35. This view was followed by W. and E. Paatz *Die Kirchen von Florenz* Frankfurt 1955 II p. 6.

4. See H. Brockhaus 'Die grosse Ansicht von Florenz in Berlin' in *Mitteilungen des Kunsthistorischen Instituts in Florenz* I 1909 p. 63. See also K. Oberhuber *Early Italian Engravings from the National Gallery of Art* Washington 1973 p. 47 note 5.

5. Reproduced by R. Van Marle *The Development of the Italian Schools of Painting* The Hague 1929 XI p. 593 fig. 361.

6. Reproduced, shortly after its acquisition by the Gallery, in the 1911 *Portfolio* (no. 2) of the Arundel Club for the Publication of Reproductions of Works of Art in Private Collections and Elsewhere.

SANO DI PIETRO *1406–81*

Ansano di Pietro di Mencio. A pupil of Sassetta in Siena. Active there as a painter of frescoes, paintings and miniatures.

Workshop of SANO DI PIETRO

1565   Coronation of the Virgin

Wood: 72.7 × 43.5; painted surface (now enclosed in a modern frame) 70 × 41.5. Christ's blue robe has discoloured and is affected by heavy paint losses and subsequent restoration. The Cherub's left eye is damaged and has been completely repainted.

Acquired as by Sano di Pietro and subsequently catalogued under this name. It has also been listed as such by Van Marle in 1927[1] and by Berenson in 1932, 1936 and 1968. The overall design, as well as the individual figures of Christ and the Virgin, are clearly based on more celebrated interpretations of this subject by Sano di Pietro, such as (1) the fresco in the Palazzo Pubblico, Siena,which is signed and dated 1445;[2] (2) the triptych in the Pinacoteca, Siena, (Inv. 269)[3] where the influence of Sassetta is less pronounced than in the Palazzo Pubblico fresco and which is therefore probably somewhat later in date; (3) the picture in the sacristy of S. Girolamo, Siena, and (4) the predella for an altarpiece of the *Madonna and Child* in the Collegiata of San Quirico di Val d'Orcia. It would appear that our picture is a relatively late product of Sano di Pietro's workshop.

Bought from Durlacher's, London, 1922.

1. R. Van Marle *The Development of the Italian Schools of Painting* The Hague 1927 IX p. 528.
2. Reproduced by Van Marle *op. cit.* p. 475 fig. 299.
3. Reproduced by Van Marle *op. cit.* p. 496 fig. 315.

Andrea del SARTO *1486–1530*

Born on 16 July 1486 in Florence, the son of a tailor, Agnolo di Francesco. He is said by Vasari to have been a pupil in the workshop of Piero di Cosimo; later he shared a workshop with Franciabigio. He was admitted to the *Arte de' Medici e Speziali* on 12

December 1508. Apart from a year in 1518–9 spent in France at the court of François 1er he was mainly active in Florence.

297 **Portrait of Domenico di Jacopo di Matteo Becuccio, Bicchieraio**

Wood: 86 × 67

X-rayed at the Courtauld Institute, London, before it was acquired by the Gallery. Cleaned 1967. The head and most of the sitter's drapery, apart from a serious damage around his left shoulder, are in very good condition. But his hand and the jug he is holding, as well as the area beneath his outstretched arm (above and to the right of the bowl in the foreground) are damaged, with substantial paint losses. There are also areas of paint loss in the background, particularly at the bottom left and along the right-hand edge. Substantial *pentimenti* are still clearly visible along both sides of the sitter's body, and also to a lesser extent around his head; in these areas the paint surface is relatively thin and somewhat worn.

Traditionally described as a *Self-portrait* by Andrea del Sarto and catalogued as such in 1978. The identification of the sitter was questioned in the nineteenth century by Biagi,[1] von Reumont,[2] Waagen,[3] and Guinness,[4] but more recently it was supported by both Freedberg[5] and Shearman,[6] largely on the basis of what then appeared to be a reasonably convincing comparison with a picture on tile in the Uffizi, Florence, now unfortunately somewhat damaged, which is probably the Andrea del Sarto *Self-portrait* described by Vasari as painted *c.* 1528–9.[7] The same head as in our picture has also been recognised, less equivocally, in a small roundel portrait in the Art Institute, Chicago, (Fig. 41) which Freedberg,[8] followed by Shearman,[9] also believed to be a late self-portrait by del Sarto. However, Conti[10] has now argued persuasively that the Chicago roundels are portraits of the glassmaker Domenico di Jacopo di Matteo Becuccio and his wife which form part of the predella of an altarpiece they commissioned from del Sarto: the *Madonna and Child with Saints* which is now in the Palazzo Pitti, Florence and which was fully described by Vasari.[11] Conti believes our picture also represents Domenico di Jacopo di Matteo Becuccio. Earlier comparisons with the Andrea del Sarto *Self-portrait* in the Uffizi are now discredited.

The attribution of our picture to del Sarto is not in serious doubt. It was accepted by Biadi in 1829[12] and by Waagen in 1857;[13] and in 1965 Shearman convincingly argued that it is a late work by del Sarto dating from 1528–30.[14] This view was also accepted, without reservation, by Grossmann[15] and Nicolson,[16] and was then completely vindicated when the picture was cleaned in 1967. Freedberg is the only modern writer to have questioned this attribution. In 1963 he described it as a 'posthumous tribute to Andrea by a painter of the Sarto revival of the late sixteenth century'.[17] In 1966 he again described it as the work of an imitator, who might have used the small roundel *Self-portrait* by del Sarto, now in Chicago, as a model.[18] By 1979, however, Freedberg had revised this judgement and accepted our picture as a self-portrait by del Sarto himself.[19]

Coll: Ricci collection, Florence;[20] Galleria Dini, Piazza di S. Gaetano, Florence, by 1829;[21] bought in Florence as from the Ricci collection by the Rev. John Sanford *c.* 1832;[22] exhibited B.I., London, June 1839 (112) lent Rev. John Sanford; by descent to his daughter Anna, who in 1844 married Frederick, later 2nd Lord Methuen of Corsham Court; described in the Corsham Court collection by Waagen in

1857;[23] lent by Lord Methuen to the *Exhibition of Works by the Old Masters* R.A., London 1877 (279); Methuen sale Christie's 13 May 1899 (88) bought Waring; in the Vernon Watney collection, Cornbury Park, by 1915;[24] by descent to Oliver Watney.

Bought at the Cornbury Park sale Christie's 23 June 1967 (38).

1. L. Biadi *Notizie inedite della vita d'Andrea del Sarto raccolte da manoscritti, e documenti autentici* Florence 1829 pp. 161 and 168.

2. A. von Reumont *Andrea del Sarto* Leipzig 1835 pp. 221–2.

3. Waagen 1857 pp. 396–7.

4. H. Guinness *Andrea del Sarto* London 1899 p. 100.

5. S. J. Freedberg *Andrea del Sarto* Cambridge (Mass) 1963 II p. 221.

6. J. Shearman *Andrea del Sarto* Oxford 1965 p. 128 and pp. 282–3 no. 96.

7. Tile 49 × 36 cm. See Shearman *op. cit.* pp. 276–5 no. 87. For a woodcut based on this portrait see G. Vasari *Le Vite de' più eccellenti pittori, scultori, e architettori* ... (Florence 1568 edition V. p. 48).

8. Wood 11 cm. diameter. Published by S. J. Freedberg in *Museum Studies* I Chicago 1966 pp. 15 ff. fig. I.

9. Verbal communication from John Shearman in 1969.

10. See A. Conti *Prospettiva* 33–6, 1983–4, pp. 161–5. See also Vasari (ed. Milanesi) V p. 40: *Tornato Andrea a Firenze, lavorò a Becuccio Biccheraio da Gambassi, amicissimo suo, in una tavola una nostra donna in aria col Figliuolo in collo, ed abbasso quattro figure, San Giovanni Battista, Santa Maria Maddalena, San Bastiano e San Rocco; e nella predella ritrasse di naturale esso Becuccio e la moglie che sono vivissimi: la quale tavola è oggi a Gambassi, castello fra Volterra e Fiorenza nella Valdelsa.*

11. *Loc. cit.* It had already been engraved by G. Saunders as a work by Andrea del Sarto. This engraving was used as frontispiece to G. Molini *Pitture a fresco di Andrea del Sarto esistenti nella Compagnia dello Scalzo in Firenze* Florence 1830; it is reproduced by Freedberg 1963 (see note 5 above) fig. 167.

12. *Loc. cit.*

13. *Loc. cit.*

14. *Loc. cit.*

15. F. Grossmann *Between Renaissance and Baroque* Exhibition Catalogue, Manchester 1965 pp. 66–7 no. 210.

16. B. Nicolson in the *Burlington Magazine* CVII 1965 p. 172.

17. See note 5 above.

18. See note 8 above.

19. S. J. Freedberg *Painting in Italy 1500–1600* revised ed. London 1979 p. 235.

20. Biadi *loc. cit.* described it as formerly in the Ricci collection. An old inscription on the back of the panel reads *dalla Casa Ricci a Firenze.*

21. Biadi *loc. cit.*

22. B. Nicolson in the *Burlington Magazine* XCVII 1955 p. 214 quoting a MS. inventory of the Rev. John Sanford's pictures. This is confirmed by two manuscript letters from the Rev. J. Sanford in Florence to Tyndal Bruce at Falkland Palace, Fifeshire dated 30 January 1832 and 26 February 1833, preserved in the Scottish Record Office (ref. GD152/53/l/18/2 and GD152/53/1/18/3). In the first letter Sanford refers to pictures on public sale, including: 'Andrea del Sarto by himself, a beautiful Portrait cited in his life painted for the Ricci family ... price about £250.' In the next letter he reports: 'All the Pictures I recommended to you I have bought. For the Magnificent Portrait of Andrea del Sarto I have had two offers for it one from the King of Prussia and the other from the *Autocrat* [sic] thro' their Ministers. I have furnished myself with all the best authorities and have really made it a constant study since I have been here.'

23. *Loc. cit.*

24. *Catalogue of Pictures ... at Cornbury and 11 Berkeley Square* 1915 no. 59.

Sinibaldo SCORZA *1589–1631*

Born on 16 July 1589 at Voltaggio.[1] Worked in Genoa under Giovanni Battista Paggi *c.* 1604. In 1619 he was invited to Turin by the Duke of Savoy and remained there until 1625. He was in Rome *c.* 1625–7 and died in Genoa. He was the earliest of the Genoese specialists in naturalistic landscape in the Flemish mode, often including animals. The character and development of his style has not been studied in any detail, and few of the pictures attributed to him are signed or documented. Notable exceptions are an early *Immacolata* signed and dated 1617, now in the Oratorio di San Giovanni Battista at Voltaggio, and a signed picture of the *Piazza del Pasquino* in the Galleria Nazionale, Rome.

76   Landscape with the Story of Philemon and Baucis

Canvas: 48 × 72
Cleaned 1941. In good condition.

77   Landscape with the Story of Latona and the Peasants

Canvas: 48 × 72
Cleaned 1941. The sky is a little rubbed, with minor restorations, mainly at the top right. Otherwise the paint surface is in good condition.

For no. 76 see Ovid *Metamorphoses* VIII, lines 621–96. The two peasants are seen welcoming their guests, Jupiter and Mercury.

For no. 77 see Ovid *Metamorphoses* VI, lines 314–81. Latona, with her children Apollo and Diana, turn the Lycian peasants into frogs.

A pair of landscapes, both acquired from a branch of the Doria family, Genoa, with an attribution to Scorza, except for the figures which were then said to be by Domenico Fiasella, who, like Scorza, had been a pupil of Paggi. In the 1957 *Catalogue* Waterhouse suggested that the figures might also be by Scorza, since they do not appear to be at all characteristic of Fiasella. Both pictures were also exhibited under the name of Scorza at Birmingham in 1955,[2] and the attribution was reiterated by Waterhouse in 1962.[3] The unqualified support for the attribution to Scorza must largely be based on the fact that it originates from the time when the pictures were still in Genoa, in the collection of the Doria, for whom Scorza is known to have worked.[4] Certainly the stylistic influence of the work of North European artists, Abraham Bloemaert in the case of the *Philemon and Baucis*, Paul Bril in the case of the *Latona*, is quite consistent with our pictures having been painted by a Genoese artist in the early seventeenth century. Moreover the figures in both of our pictures show some similarities with the figures in Scorza's signed *Piazza di Pasquino* in Rome.[5] Yet these stylistic considerations are not at all conclusive and would carry little weight without the traditional association of our pictures with the relatively unfashionable name of Scorza.

Coll: Bought from the Doria family, Genoa, by Andrew Wilson, on behalf of the R.I., Edinburgh, in 1830.[6] Exhibited R.I. 1831 and 1832 (26 and 27).

Royal Institution 1830.

1. For biographical information on Scorza see R. Soprani *Vite de' Pittori, Scultori e Architetti Genovesi* 1674 (ed. C. Ratti, Genoa 1768 I pp. 214 ff.). See also *Pittori Genovesi a Genova nel '600 e nel '700* Exhibition Catalogue, Palazzo Bianco, Genoa 1969 pp. 77 ff; M. Newcome in *Paragone* 391 September 1982, pp. 25 ff.

2. *Exhibition of Italian Art from the thirteenth century to the seventeenth century* City of Birmingham Museum and Art Gallery 1955 p. 37 nos. 95 and 96.

3. E. K. Waterhouse *Italian Baroque Painting* London 1962 pp. 202–3 fig. 176.

4. See Soprani *op. cit.* I p. 217.

5. Reproduced *Pittori Genovesi del seicento e del settecento* Exhibition Catalogue, Palazzo Reale, Genoa 1938 (2nd ed. pl. 29). For a reference to the signature see *Pittori Genovesi a Genova nel '600 e nel '700* Exhibition Catalogue, Palazzo Bianco, Genoa 1969 p. 77.

6. See further *Pictures for Scotland* pp. 27 ff.

Jacopo del SELLAIO *c. 1441–93*

Jacopo di Arcangelo, son of a Florentine saddler.[1] According to Vasari, he was a pupil of Filippo Lippi; he was also clearly influenced by Sandro Botticelli. His work has not been separated from that of Filippo di Giuliano with whom he is recorded in partnership in 1473 and in 1480–1. There are three altarpieces attributed to Jacopo del Sellaio which are in some degree authenticated: an *Annunciation* of c. 1473 in S. Lucia dei Magnoli, Florence; a *Pietà* of c. 1483 from S. Frediano, Florence, which was formerly in the Berlin Museum and has been destroyed; and a *Crucifixion* from S. Frediano, Florence. Many other works of a more derivative character are also now attributed to Sellaio.

1941 **Christ as the Man of Sorrows, with S. Raphael and the Young Tobias, and S. Sebastian**

Wood: 28.8 × 43.4

The paint surface is badly damaged overall, with many old repaints. The most seriously affected features are along the line of a horizontal crack which bisects the Virgin's face and Christ's thighs. The areas of shadow have been strengthened.

Probably the central panel of a predella. The iconography derives from a panel by Fra Angelico in the Alte Pinakothek, Munich (Inv. WAF.38a). Catalogued until 1957 as by Castagno, but the attribution to Sellaio was first made by Berenson in 1909 and was repeated by Van Marle in 1931[2] and again by Berenson in 1932, 1936, and 1963. Although the rather moderate quality of the execution of our panel suggests it was painted by a workshop assistant, the style and design have definite points of contact with the better authenticated works of Jacopo del Sellaio, described in the biography above. It may also be compared with an *Entombment* in the Accademia, Florence (Inv. 8655), traditionally attributed to Jacopo del Sellaio, which is close to it in style.

Coll: W .T. Ottley sale, Foster's 30 June 1847 (75) as Pollaiuolo (this is confirmed by a note on the back of the panel which reads: 'Sold at Ottley's as Pollaiolo'). Rev. Walter Davenport-Bromley sale Christie's 12 June 1863 (124) as by Castagno. It was subsequently acquired by the Lothian family (possibly by the 9th Marquess who inherited the title in 1870), to judge from the negative evidence of its exclusion from a family inventory dated 1833, but apparently corrected until c. 1870.[3] Lent by Lord Lothian to the exhibition of *Old Masters and Scottish National Portraits* Edinburgh 1883 (512), and to the *Exhibition of the Works of the Old Masters* R.A., London 1885 (217) both as by Castagno.

11th Marquess of Lothian bequest 1941.

1. See H. Mackowsky in *Jahrbuch der Königlich Preussischen Kunstsammlungen* XX 1899 pp. 192 ff. and pp. 271 ff.; H. Horne in the *Burlington Magazine* XIII 1908 pp. 210 ff.; and M. Davies *National Gallery Catalogue, The Earlier Italian Schools* London 1961 pp. 469–70.

2. R. Van Marle *The Development of the Italian Schools of Painting* The Hague 1931 XII p. 410. Here he also incorrectly states that the picture was on loan to the Gallery from the Earl of Southesk.

3. On the other hand, most of the early Italian pictures in the Lothian collection were bought by the 8th Marquess; see *Pictures for Scotland* pp. 111 ff.

Attributed to Jacopo del SELLAIO

538 Triumphal Procession; Reception and Coronation of a Prince or Victor

Wood: 44 × 167.7; painted surface: 42 × 166

The front panel from a *cassone*. There is a margin of bare wood beyond the gesso preparation, except on the right-hand side where about 2 cm. has been lost due to damage from woodworm. The paint surface is extensively damaged and restored.

The scene is almost certainly Roman, but has not been satisfactorily identified. Borenius suggested the story might be that of David who, after the death of Saul, met the men of Judah at Hebron and was there anointed king.[1] See *Samuel* II, 1–4.

Our panel was attributed to Filippino Lippi in the Davenport-Bromley and Fuller Maitland collections, but after its acquisition by the Gallery was catalogued in 1924 as Florentine school. Since 1936 it has been catalogued under the name of Jacopo del Sellaio, following a suggestion first made by Borenius in 1926.[2] The attribution was also endorsed by both Van Marle in 1931[3] and Berenson (1932, 1936 and 1963). It is close in style to some other *cassone* panels often associated with Jacopo del Sellaio, and in particular (judging from old photographs) to a panel in Cleveland (now much damaged as the result of an accident) representing *The Entry of Tarquinius Priscus into Rome*, which has been attributed to Jacopo del Sellaio since Schubring in 1915.[4] On the other hand, our panel seems to be distinct from and inferior to other *cassone* panels, long attributed to Jacopo del Sellaio, such as the *Story of Cupid and Psyche* in the Fitzwilliam Museum, Cambridge.[5] This confused situation arises from the absence of adequate stylistic links between any of these *cassone* panels and the three altarpieces, listed in the biography above, on which our present knowledge of Jacopo del Sellaio's work depends. It is therefore largely as a matter of convention that the attribution of our panel to Jacopo del Sellaio is retained.

Coll: Rev. Walter Davenport-Bromley sale Christie's 12 June 1863 (32) as by Filippino Lippi and said there to have been formerly in the collection of Cardinal Fesch.[6] Next recorded in the catalogue of the W. Fuller Maitland collection at Stansted Hall in 1872 (p. 13) as Filippino Lippi, and in the Stansted Hall catalogue 1893 (34), again as by Filippino Lippi.

Bought from W. Fuller Maitland in 1921.

1. In *Apollo* III 1926 p. 135 illus.
2. *Loc. cit.*
3. R. Van Marle *The Development of the Italian Schools of Painting* The Hague 1931 XII p. 410.

4. P. Schubring *Cassoni, Truhen und Truhenbilder der Italienischen Frührenaissance* Leipzig 1915 p. 307 no. 368 pl. LXXXVI. See also *The Cleveland Museum of Art Catalogue of Paintings: Part One, European Paintings before 1500* Cleveland 1974 pp. 125–6 no. 44 illus. A suggestion by Federico Zeri, reported in the Cleveland catalogue, that the Edinburgh and Cleveland panels might have been companions is not justified on the available evidence, especially since the two panels do not even appear to have a common nineteenth century provenance.

5. See J. W. Goodison and G. H. Robertson *Fizwilliam Museum Cambridge. Catalogue of Paintings. Italian Schools* Cambridge 1967 p. 153 no. M.75 p. 2.

6. Although lot 32 in the Davenport-Bromley sale cannot be traced with any certainty to the Fesch sale in Rome in 1845, where Davenport-Bromley did acquire a large number of other pictures, it might possibly have been lot 1230–2389 *Une famille de souverains entrant en triomphe dans une ville* 1p. 7p. × 5p. op. [48.2 × 152.4 cm.], in spite of the discrepancy in size. It might also be the picture seen in the Davenport-Bromley collection by Waagen 1854 III p. 374, attributed to the school of Botticelli and described as follows: 'David coming to Samuel who is crowning him. Full of lively motives in the taste of Sandro Botticelli, as for instance a kicking horse and some beautiful heads'.

Giovanni SERODINE *1600–30*

Born in Ascona. Active in Rome from *c.* 1620. Influenced by the work of Caravaggio, Guercino, and Borgianni. There are also strong affinities between his work and Hendrik Terbrugghen's but the circumstances of any association between these artists is not known.[1]

1513   **The Tribute Money**

Canvas: 142.3 × 227

The picture was seriously damaged by immersion in water during transit to the Serodine exhibition at Ascona in 1950. It was then restored in Italy. The canvas has shrunk and the paint surface is therefore very uneven. Much the best preserved areas are the faces of the two men on the left. Local areas of paint loss include the cheek, nose, eye and black hat of the third man from the left, and the neck of the fourth man from the left, and some other more incidental passages. The surface has also been badly rubbed, especially in the dark areas.

For the subject see *Matthew* XXII, 17–22. The picture entered the collection as by Ribera to whom it had been attributed since 1830 and under whose name it was exhibited in Edinburgh in 1883.[2] Fiocco first identified it as by Serodine in 1929, and he pointed out its stylistic affinities with the *Almsgiving of S. Lawrence*, formerly in the church of S. Lorenzo fuori le Mura, Rome, and now at Valvisciolo.[3] In 1955 Longhi endorsed Fiocco's attribution and, on the evidence both of style and the similar measurements, suggested that it might originally have been a pendant to the *Meeting of S. Peter and S. Paul* in the Palazzo Mattei, Rome.[4] The connection between these two pictures was confirmed by the publication in 1968 of a 1631 inventory of the Mattei collection;[5] this included not only the *Meeting of S. Peter and S. Paul* but also a picture of *The Tribute Money*,[6] both listed under the name of Giovanni della Voltolina (i.e. Giovanni Serodine).[7] The final link is provided by a receipt, dated 27 January 1802, and a certificate, dated 1 February 1802, both of which were issued to William Hamilton Nisbet by Giuseppe Duca Mattei.[8] A further related painting, *Christ among the doctors*, has recently come to light and was acquired by the Louvre in 1983.[9]

All the known pictures which Serodine painted during his short lifetime can be dated *c.* 1620–30, but their precise chronology has never been established. Longhi dates our picture 1620–5,[10] Nicolson places it soon after 1625,[11] and Schönenberger has suggested 1626–8.[12]

Coll: Marchese Asdrubale Mattei, Rome, by 1631.[13] Sold from the Palazzo Mattei to William Hamilton Nisbet in 1802.[14] By inheritance to Miss Nisbet Hamilton who lent it to the exhibition of *Old Masters and Scottish National Portraits* Edinburgh 1883 (349). By inheritance to Mrs Nisbet Hamilton Ogilvy.

Mrs Nisbet Hamilton Ogilvy bequest 1921.

1. R. Longhi *Giovanni Serodine* Florence 1955 pp. 7 f. See also *Serodine. La pittura oltre Caravaggio* Exhibition Catalogue Locarno/Rome 1987 no. 7.

2. The picture was previously attributed to Rubens; the attribution to Ribera was made by a Mr Bury, on 24 January 1830, in a note preserved in the Ogilvy MSS. in the Scottish Record Office: GD 205 Portfolio 18.

3. G. Fiocco in the *Burlington Magazine* LV 1929 pp. 190 f.

4. R. Longhi *Giovanni Serodine* Florence 1955 pp. 31 nos. 7 and 8 figs. 22 and 23. But cf. M. Pompilio in the *Connoisseur* 187 1974 pp. 6 ff. for a quite unconvincing attempt to discredit the attribution of our picture to Serodine.

5. G. Panofsky-Soergel in *Römisches Jahrbuch für Kunstgeschichte der Bibliotheca Hertziana* XI 1967–8 p. 185.

6. *Un quadro de farisei, quando mostrano la moneta di Gio. della Voltolina.*

7. For the connection between these two pictures, and the significance of Giovanni Serodine's nickname see R. Longhi in *Paragone* 233 1969 pp. 59–62.

8. Preserved in the Ogilvy MS. in the Scottish Record Office (GD 205 Portfolio 18). A transcription from a contemporary copy of the certificate is also published by Panofsky-Soergel *op. cit.* p. 188. In this document our picture is described as *N.S. con gli Farisei di Rubens.* See further *Pictures for Scotland* pp. 109 ff.

9. Probably also from the Mattei collection and described in the 1631 inventory as by Anteveduto Grammatica, subsequently sold in 1802 as by Rubens. See *Serodine…* Exhibition Catalogue no. 8 and J. P. Cuzin in *Musée du Louvre Nouvelles acquisitions du Département des Peintures (1983–1986)* Paris 1987 pp. 209–10.

10. See note 4 above.

11. B. Nicolson *Hendrick Terbrugghen* London 1958 p. 11.

12. W. Schönenberger in *Basler Studien zur Kunstgeschichte* XIV 1957 pp. 59 f.

13. See note 5 above.

14. For the documents relating to the sale see note 8 above.

Elisabetta SIRANI *1638–65*

Born in Bologna on 8 January 1638, daughter of the artist Giovan Andrea Sirani. She worked in Bologna as a late follower of Guido Reni and died there on 28 August 1665.[1] Much the most important painting by her to have found its way into a British collection is the *Judith with the Head of Holofernes* in the Marquess of Exeter's collection at Burghley House, Stamford, which is signed and dated 1658, and which is recorded in Malvasia.[2]

79   The Child S. John in the Wilderness

Canvas: 75.5 × 62. The original canvas is 75.5 × 53; strips of *c.* 4.5 cm. have been added on both sides.

Signed on the stone beneath the Saint's left foot: ELISAB. SIRANI F/MDCLXIIII.
Cleaned 1935. The paint surface is discoloured by old varnish, but appears to be in good condition.

In view of the fact that our picture was formerly in the Gerini collection, Florence, it may very probably be identified as the picture of *S. John in the Wilderness*, recorded in Malvasia as painted by Elisabetta Sirani, in 1664, for a Florentine *Cavallier*.[3]

Coll: Gerini collection, Florence, by 1786, catalogued as by E. Sirani and with an engraved reproduction;[4] Gerini sale catalogue 1825 (106).[5] Bought from the Gerini family in Florence by Andrew Wilson on behalf of the R.I., Edinburgh, 1831.[6] Exhibited R.I. 1832 (38). Recorded by Waagen in the collection of the R.I. 1854.[7]

Royal Insitution 1831.

---

1. For biographical notes see A. Emiliani in *Maestri della Pittura del Seicento Emiliano* Exhibition Catalogue, Bologna 1959 pp. 140 f.

2. The Burghley House canvas, for which there are two preparatory drawings at Windsor (see O. Kurz *Bolognese Drawings of the XVII and XVIII Centuries in the collection of Her Majesty the Queen at Windsor Castle* London 1955 p. 134 nos. 493 and 494 figs. 91 and 92, where the connection with the picture is overlooked), can be identified as the picture described in C. Malvasia *Felsina Pittrice. Vite de' Pittori Bolognesi* 1678 (ed. Bologna 1841 II p. 394) as painted in 1658 for *il sig. Cattalini*.

3. Described in C. Malvasia *Felsina Pittrice. Vite de' Pittori Bolognesi* 1678 (ed. Bologna 1841 II p. 398) as follows: *Un S. Giovannino nel deserto, che con la destra mano coglie dell'acqua in una scotella, e la sinistra tiene appoggiata sopra la testa dell'agnellino per un Cavallier Fiorentino.*

4. *Raccolta di ottanta stampe rappresentanti i quadri più scelti de' Signori Marchesi Gerini* Florence 1786. The size of the picture is given as *Pal rom.* 3 × P.3. The engraving is inscribed *Lorenzo Lorenzi dis. Violante Vanni incise.*

5. *Catalogo e stima dei quadri e bronzi esistenti nella galleria del Sig. Marchese Giovanni Gerini* Florence 1825.

6. See further *Pictures for Scotland* pp. 27 ff.

7. Waagen 1854 III p. 270.

Pietro TESTA *1612–50*

He was born in Lucca in 1612 and moved to Rome *c.* 1630. He studied there, first with Domenichino and then with Pietro da Cortona.[1] He was also employed by Cassiano dal Pozzo to copy sculpture and classical remains for his 'paper museum' (*Museum Chartaceum*). Testa's fame rests chiefly on his graphic works, and less than thirty of his paintings have been securely identified. In particular his early style as a painter has never been satisfactorily defined. A fresco on the theme of *Liberty and Justice*, commissioned for the Cortile degli Svizzeri, Lucca, probably in 1632, is now so badly damaged as to be virtually invisible. Testa's work from the mid-1630s, which shows the clear influence of Nicolas Poussin, includes a painting of *Venus* and *Adonis*, now in Vienna, and two paintings now in Potsdam, first recorded in an inventory of the Giustiniani collection, Rome, in 1638. There is documentary evidence for dating an altarpiece in S. Romano, Lucca, *c.* 1636–7.[2] An altarpiece of the *Vision of S. Angelo* in S. Martino ai Monti, Rome, was paid for between October 1645 and January 1646. Testa died in Rome in 1650, probably by suicide, following the rejection *c.* 1647 of his designs for decorating the apse of S. Martino ai Monti, Rome, and the poor reception, earlier in the 1640s, of his frescoes (now destroyed) for S. Maria dell' Anima, Rome. Other late works include the *Alexander the Great saved from the River Cydnus* (Metropolitan Museum, New York), *The Birth and Infancy of Achilles* (Sotheby's, London 5 July 1989 (lot 8)); and *Aeneas on the Bank of the River Styx* (Private Collection, on loan to the Metropolitan Museum, New York).[3]

325 Adoration of the Shepherds

Canvas: 88.3 × 125.5
X-rayed (Fig. 42). There are a number of severe damages which unfortunately affect the head of the Child and the heads of the cherubs; and there is a patch, replacing another damaged area, which includes the head of the crouching shepherd, in the left fore-ground, and the right arm of the shepherdess immediately above. Otherwise, the paint surface is in reasonably good condition.

The main subject of the Adoration of the Shepherds is combined here with the subsidi-ary subject of the Annunciation to the Shepherds which is shown in the background on the left. The two separate incidents are brought into relationship with each other by showing, in the middle ground of the composition, the approach of the shepherds to the Nativity scene. This combination of subjects was unusual in early seventeenth-century Italian painting, and here Testa may have been influenced both by Nicolas Poussin's *Adoration of the Shepherds*, now in the National Gallery, London, which was probably completed by the mid 1630s,[4] and by a design of Polidoro da Caravaggio.[5]

Our picture first came to light at Christie's in 1958, attributed to Pietro Testa,[6] and it was acquired by the Gallery in 1973 under this attribution. Although the picture was overlooked in the fundamental articles defining Testa's authentic paintings, published by Sutherland Harris in 1967, and Schleier in 1970, the attribution is not in doubt,[7] and is supported by numerous drawings by Testa which are preparatory studies for the composition.[8] A connected sheet in the Ashmolean Museum, Oxford,[9] made in pen and ink and black chalk, consists of two independent studies later joined together. The left-hand drawing is an early idea for the principal figures in a composition of the *Adoration of the Shepherds* which Testa then worked out in greater detail in another pen drawing, formerly in the Aschaffenburg collection, Germany,[10] where an architectural and land-scape background is added, and subsidiary figures are introduced. This composition was then followed quite closely by Testa for our picture, except that the monumental columns of a classical temple replace the rudimentary background of the Aschaffenburg drawing. Testa also made individual studies in red chalk for each of the two shepherd-esses at the left of the picture and for the shepherd with arms raised at the right; these studies are bound into the artist's manuscript *Treatise*, which is now preserved in Düsseldorf.[11] A further study, in red chalk, for the three small angels, was sold at Christie's, London 11–13 December 1985 (lot 169).

Testa also made another series of compositional drawings related to the subject of the *Adoration of the Shepherds*; these are in the reverse sense to our picture but almost certainly represent an alternative discarded idea for it. An early stage of this alternative design is seen in the right-hand drawing of the Ashmolean sheet: it is a study for a group of shepherds and shepherdesses. Then, in a pen and ink drawing in the Pierpont Morgan Library, New York,[12] and in another drawing, known only from a reproductive engraving (probably in the reverse sense) attributed to Collignon, the principal figures of Mary and Joseph and the Child are added, together with a landscape and some rustic architecture.[13] In some respects this series of drawings is closer than either the ex. Aschaffenburg drawing or our picture to the design of Nicolas Poussin's *Adoration*; this is evident in the greater emphasis on the figures of the shepherdesses with their baskets of fruit and flowers, and also in the position of S. Joseph who is placed standing behind the Virgin and Child rather than seated in the foreground.

The date of our picture cannot be established with any precision. Its schematic, well ordered design, suggests it is more advanced than the *Venus and Adonis* in Vienna, the two pictures from the Giustiniani Collection and the *Vision of St Dominic of Soriano* in Lucca (see biography above) all of which date from before 1638.[14] It is probably more or less contemporary with the *Massacre of the Innocents* in the Spada Gallery, Rome and the etching of *Sinorix Carried from the Temple of Artemis* for which Testa made an unusually elaborate sequence of preparatory drawings. These works may date from around 1639–42.[15] Elizabeth Cropper has compared one of the preparatory drawings for our picture (in the Pierpont Morgan Library) with compositional studies Testa made for a sarcophagus relief in the Raimondi Chapel in San Pietro in Montorio, Rome representing Carnival, Ash Wednesday and Death. In each of these drawings one finds very similar elongated necks and feet and an almost grotesque delineation of facial expressions. On this basis, she too favours a date for our picture *c.* 1639–42.[16]

Hartmann has suggested that our picture might be the *Nativity* (*presepio*) by Testa recorded in an eighteenth-century inventory of the Buonvisi collection, Lucca.[17] This certainly seems more probable than Marabottini's idea that a picture of the *Adoration of the Magi*, in the Musée Fabre, Montpellier, which follows Testa's print (Bartsch XX 3), in the same sense, might be the ex. Buonvisi collection picture.[18]

Coll: Our picture cannot be traced with certainty beyond a Christie's sale 25 July 1958 (101) bought Oppé.

Bought from Miss Armide Oppé, with help from the N.A.C.F., 1973.

---

1. The fundamental pioneering account of Testa's life and works, with a summary of earlier literature, is by A. Sutherland Harris in *Paragone* 213 1967 pp. 35 ff., where Testa's death certificate is also published. The year of his birth was later established by A. Boschetto in *Paragone* 217 1968 pp. 65 ff. In 1970 K. Hartmann presented a Ph.D. thesis on Testa, at the Courtauld Institute, University of London, which remains unpublished but which she kindly made available for consultation. Further discussions of Testa's paintings from a stylistic point of view have since been published by E. Schleier in the *Burlington Magazine* CXII 1970 pp. 665 ff., by H. Brigstocke in *Paragone* 321 1976 pp. 15 ff. and in *Münchner Jahrbuch der bildenden Kunst* XXIX 1978 pp. 117 ff. Above all, however, see E. Cropper *Pietro Testa 1612–50. Prints and Drawings* Exhibition Catalogue, Philadelphia Museum of Art 1988.

2. E. Cropper in *Grafica Grafica* Vol. 1 no. 4, December 1977 pp. 88–107

3. E. Cropper 1988 (see note 1 above) p. 258 no. 117 and p. 271, no. 127. See further H. Brigstocke *Poussin et ses amis en Italie*. Lecture at symposium *La Peinture italienne du XVII Siècle et la France*. Ecole du Louvre, Paris 14 October 1988 (1990 pp. 215–29 figs. 3 and 6).

4. Inv. 6277.

5. Cf. for instance a drawing of this subject in Madrid published by A. Marabottini *Polidoro da Caravaggio* Rome 1969 I p. 303 no. 23 and II pl. LXV.

6. Christie's 25 July 1958 (101) bought Oppé.

7. The attribution to Testa is also accepted by Hartmann (see note 1 above). See further I. van

Regteren Altena and P. Ward-Jackson *Drawings from the Teyler Museum, Haarlem* Exhibition Catalogue, V. and A. Museum, London 1970 pp. 67–8.

8. These drawings are reproduced by H. Brigstocke in *Paragone* 21 1976 pp. 65 ff. figs. 25–31.

9. Inv. 957. Pen and ink and black chalk 161 × 383 mm. See K. T. Parker *Catalogue of the Collection of Drawings in the Ashmolean Museum* Oxford 1956 II pp. 481–2. The connection of this drawing with our picture is first noted in the 1958 Christie's sale catalogue (see note 6 above).

10. Pen and brown ink 184 × 241 mm. The drawing was engraved in reverse by F. Collignon. The connection of the drawing with our picture is first noted in the 1958 Christie's sale catalogue (see note 6 above).

11. For Testa's *Treatise*, now in Düsseldorf, see E. Cropper in *Journal of the Warburg and Courtauld Institutes* XXXIV 1971 pp. 262 ff.; and E. Cropper *The Ideal of Painting: Pietro Testa's Düsseldorf Notebook* Princeton 1984 p. 190 fig. II; p. 219 figs. XV and XVI and p. 266, figs. XXVII and XXVIII. The drawings connected with our picture are Folio 2 *recto*, and Folio 25 *recto* and *verso*. These are noted by Hartmann (see note 1 above) but she confuses Folio 28 *recto* and *verso* with Folio 25 *recto* and *verso*. Hartmann further suggests, but less persuasively, that Folio 10 *recto* and *verso* may also be regarded as preparatory studies for our picture.

12. Inv. IV.180.C Pen and brown ink 194 × 260 mm. See Cropper (note 1 above) 1988 p. 95 no. 49.

13. The engraving is reproduced by H. Brigstocke in *Paragone* 321 1976 pp. 65 ff. fig. 31.

14. For an earlier discussion of the probable date of both our picture and the picture in Leningrad cf. H. Brigstocke in *Paragone* 321 1976 pp. 65 ff. Here it was suggested that our picture might date from just after the altarpiece in S. Romano, Lucca, anticipating Testa's relatively late paintings of the mid 1640s, 'with their strong chiaroscuro, and a rather severe classicism …'. Then in the 1978 edition of this catalogue I suggested a date 1636–7, possibly just before the S. Romano altarpiece.

15. E. Cropper 1984 (see note 11 above) pp. 43 ff and E. Cropper 1988 (see note 1 above) pp. 97–117 nos. 50–58. See also H. Brigstocke in *Burlington Magazine* CXXXI February 1989 pp. 175–8.

16. E. Cropper 1988 (see note 1 above) pp. 92–3 nos. 47 and 48.

17. Hartmann (see note 1 above).

18. For this suggestion and for a description of the eighteenth-century inventory of the Buonvisi collection see A. Marabottini in *Commentari* V 1954 p. 117 note 4 and p. 134 note 20.

After Pietro TESTA

326   The Triumph of Painting

Canvas: 85 × 106.8

Executed in grisaille. There are damages along the bottom and left sides and in the top right-hand corner. The paint surface is badly worn and the abraded inscription on the cartouche, lower right, is illegible.

Testa, in his *Treatise*, writes frequently of the parallels between the sister arts of Poetry and Painting; he wished to establish the place of Painting on the heights of Parnassus along with Poetry.[1] This preoccupation is also reflected in his etching (Fig. 43) of the *Triumph of Painting* (Bartsch XX 35) dedicated to Girolamo Buonvisi; in a preparatory drawing for it at Frankfurt;[2] and in our picture which is a precise copy after the print except that the relative proportions have been slightly altered with a reduction in the horizontal, and an extension of the vertical dimensions. The idea of Poetry and Painting as sister arts was familiar to the writers of antiquity, including Aristotle, Plutarch, and Horace who coined the well-known simile *ut pictura poesis*. The particular interest of Testa's composition is that it emphasises the struggle of the artist. Painting must represent the emotions, yet must overcome the entanglement of passion and theory, before arriving at Parnassus and achieving immortality. The left-hand part of the composition shows the bound souls weighed down by their passions. In the centre,

Poetry, holding a quill pen, sits beside Painting, who is crowned by three graces. Two putti collect colours from a pot at the end of the rainbow which also serves as a triumphal arch. Above, Iris clings to the rainbow and protects her eyes from the light of inspiration which comes from above the temple of Mount Helicon. Poets, the muses, a river god, and Pegasus (symbol of fame or virtue) preside over Mount Helicon at the top right of the composition.

In a detailed analysis of Testa's original design, Elizabeth Cropper has pointed out that the colours of the spectrum of the rainbow bestowed upon Painting express Testa's understanding that colour in painting is an effect of light.[3] However Testa, in his *Notebook* or *Treatise* (published by Cropper in 1984)[4] also expresses his understanding that Painting does not triumph through colour alone, but through the power of drawing and chiaroscuro. As Cropper explains: 'In his *Notebook* Testa records an imaginary conversation on Parnassus in which Giulio Romano defended his devotion to drawing, claiming that because Painting was feminine and Drawing masculine their frequent union exhausted them both. He attacks those who had sought to delight the senses through colour and had thereby made drawing the slave of 'that despicable little woman they call Painting'. Raphael, in Testa's debate, silenced Giulio by showing that Painting and Drawing could always be united: without the other each was dead, and to this statement, writes Testa, Painting gave her assent. In the preparatory drawing now in Frankfurt the piebald horses who draw Painting's chariot are identified as *chiaro* and *oschuro*. They are bridled only by delicate ribbons held by another little love. Testa thus here represents Painting's triumph in accordance with Raphael's instructions for the harmonious union of chiaroscuro and colour.'[5]

Although the technique of our monochrome picture, with its vigorous execution and animated use of chiaroscuro, reflects a clear understanding of Testa's original ideas as well as confident familiarity with his design, it has been classified as an anonymous copy by Hartmann in 1970[6] and was acquired as a copy by the Gallery, a view that was also followed by the present writer in the first edition of this catalogue. Doubts about the attribution are based on the fluid manner of the picture's execution, distinct from the style of Testa's more securely identified paintings, and on the apparent absence of any further paintings by the artist in a grisaille technique. As Julien Stock has observed, it is similar in spirit to Jan der Bisschop's copies of earlier drawings.

A painting, formerly in the Jandolo collection, Rome, but now lost, which is also based on Testa's *Triumph of Painting*, but in the reverse sense, has been attributed to Testa by Lopresti,[7] followed by Sutherland Harris and Lord.[8] On the other hand Schleier, from the evidence of a photograph, prefers to regard it as a weak derivation from the print.[9] Other copies after Testa's design include a drawing in the Uffizi[10] and a drawing at Windsor,[11] both in the same sense as the print. A reproductive print, inscribed only *P. Testa fecit*, in the British Museum, and another reproductive print by Georg A. Wolfgang (Nagler XXV 38) are in the reverse sense to Bartsch XXV 38.

Coll: Sotheby's 9 March 1966 (143) as Poussin *The Triumph of the Arts.*

Presented by Miss Armide Oppé through the N.A.C.F. 1973.

1. For Testa's *Treatise* now in Düsseldorf, see E. Cropper in *Journal of the Warburg and Courtauld Institutes* XXXIV 1971 pp. 262 ff. See further E. Cropper *The Ideal of Painting: Pietro Testa's Düsseldorf Notebook*, Princeton 1984 pp. 41 (note 175), 43 (note 192), 45–6, 97. For Testa's ideas on chiaroscuro see further p. 129.

2. Inv. 4405. Pen and ink 394 × 705 mm. For a detailed discussion of the iconography of the composition see A. Sutherland Harris and C. Lord in the *Burlington Magazine* CXII 1970 pp. 14 ff. where Testa's print and the Frankfurt drawing are both reproduced figs. 18 and 19. They suggest a date of *c*. 1644 for Bartsch XX 35.

3. E. Cropper in *Pietro Testa 1612–1650 Prints and Drawings* Exhibition Catalogue, Philadelphia Museum of Art 1988 no. 73.

4. See note 1 above.

5. See note 3 above.

6. K. Hartmann, PhD thesis on Testa (unpublished) Courtauld Institute, University of London, 1970.

7. L. Lopresti in *L'Arte* XXIV 1921 p. 75 fig. 10.

8. *Op. cit.* (see note 2 above) p. 19 note 28.

9. E. Schleier in the *Burlington Magazine* CXII 1970 p. 668.

10. Inv. 15747 F. Unpublished.

11. Inv. 5947 and 5948. See A. Blunt and H. Cooke *Roman drawings of the XVII and XVIII Centuries in the collection of Her Majesty the Queen at Windsor Castle*, London 1960 p. 116 no. 990 and no. 991.

Giovanni Battista TIEPOLO *1696–1770*

Baptised in Venice on 16 April 1696. He studied under Gregorio Lazzarini and was influenced by Sebastiano Ricci and Giovanni Battista Piazzetta. His earliest documented picture is the *Sacrifice of Isaac* in the Ospedaletto, Venice, of *c*. 1715–16. His fame rests largely on his achievements as a fresco painter, and he decorated numerous palaces and churches in Venice, Udine, Bergamo, Milan and elsewhere in Italy. From 1750–3 he was employed at Würzburg in Germany. In 1762 he went to Spain and was active in Madrid until his death there in 1770.

91   The Meeting of Antony and Cleopatra

Canvas: 66.8 × 38.4
Cleaned 1942. In very good condition.

Our picture probably represents Antony and Cleopatra meeting in Cilicia, a province of Asia Minor in 41 B.C. The figures are dressed in sixteenth-century costumes based on pictures by Paolo Veronese.

Our picture was acquired as by G. B. Tiepolo. Morassi, in 1943, was the first to recognise it as a preparatory sketch for the central section of the fresco of the same subject in the principal room of the Palazzo Labia, Venice (see Fig. 44).[1] G. B. Tiepolo also painted a fresco of the *Banquet of Antony and Cleopatra* on the opposite wall, and an oil sketch in Stockholm University is generally recognised as a preparatory sketch for it.[2] The Stockholm picture is of the same format as our picture and they are similar in style. The date of G. B. Tiepolo's frescoes in the Palazzo Labia cannot be firmly established, although Knox and Thiem have speculated that they were executed during the summer of 1744,[3] and Levey has conclusively shown that at least part of the decoration, an allegorical group above the *Banquet*, had been completed by 1746–7 when it was copied by Franz Kuen.[4] A date in the mid-1740s for these frescoes is also indicated by the style of the pair of sketches in Edinburgh and Stockholm. Both sketches are remarkably close in handling to sketches in the National Museum, Stockholm, and in a private collection, Milan, which were made by G. B. Tiepolo for his frescoes at Montecchio Maggiore, dating from 1743.[5]

The earliest evidence of Tiepolo's obsessive interest during the 1740s in the story of Antony and Cleopatra is a large painting of the *Banquet of Antony and Cleopatra*, now in Melbourne, which was described by Algarotti on 31 January 1744 after he had ordered it for King Augustus of Saxony. Apparently it had been commissioned some time before for another patron who had subsequently withdrawn, and Tiepolo was now prepared to finish it for the King of Saxony. The Labia frescoes are probably a direct continuation of the same theme, but this commission involved a matching scene of the *Meeting of Antony and Cleopatra*.[6]

The main difference between the design of our sketch and the connected fresco in Venice is that, whereas in our picture Antony is showing kissing Cleopatra's hand, in the Labia fresco he is leading her towards a flight of painted steps (not shown in the sketch) as if they were about to join the spectator in the actual Salone of the Palazzo Labia.

Two further sketches on the same theme as the frescoes, the *Meeting of Antony and Cleopatra* (Wrightsman Collection, New York, Fig. 45)[7] and the *Banquet* (National Gallery, London),[8] both of horizontal format, may represent an earlier stage in Tiepolo's preparation for this commission, before Mengozzi-Colonna had designed the architectural framework for the Palazzo Labia decorations. As Levey perceptively pointed out, the Palazzo Labia decorations are in essence oblong compositions, each divided into three portions by the painted architecture, with the central section framed in a high pillared arch which disguises the horizontal axis of the original design.[9] Although this is immediately apparent when the frescoes are studied *in situ*, it is not so readily appreciated from photographs.

The necessity of breaking up the horizontal axis of his original design forced Tiepolo to devise more concentrated compositions, especially for the scene of the *Meeting of Antony and Cleopatra*. In the New York sketch, the encounter takes place against a coastal setting with a pyramid and a palm tree in the background. In our sketch the pyramid and the seashore are suppressed and the scene is set in a harbour. In both sketches, and in a preparatory pen and wash drawing in the Metropolitan Museum, New York (Inv. 37.165.10), which may have been made at an intermediate stage between the two *bozzetti*, Antony is shown kissing Cleopatra's hand.[10] Yet in the fresco, as Cleopatra advances towards us, she scarcely glances at Antony who supports her arm.

The same scenes are repeated again in two large-scale oil paintings at the former Youssoupov Villa at Archangelskoye, near Moscow, one of which is dated 1747.[11] These pictures probably date from the end of the sequence, after the Labia frescoes, and in the *Meeting* Cleopatra is again led forward by Antony as in the fresco. However, the obvious compositional link between these two paintings and Tiepolo's two oil sketches of horizontal format, in London and New York, has prompted many writers to argue for a direct connection, and to regard the London and New York pictures as preparatory *bozzetti* for the large pictures in Russia.[12] Although one cannot exclude the possibility that Tiepolo was working simultaneously on two parallel projects, a pair of vertical sketches (Edinburgh and Stockholm) for the Labia frescoes, and a pair of horizontal sketches for the Russian pictures, equally there is no escaping both the close stylistic links between the New York sketch of the *Meeting of Antony and Cleopatra* and our sketch,[13] and the close compositional association between each of these two sketches and the Labia fresco on the same theme.

Coll: Acquired in Venice in 1845 by Alexander Christie, Manager of the Trustees Academy, on behalf of the R.I., Edinburgh.[14] Recorded by Waagen in the collection of the R.I. in 1854.[15]

Royal Institution 1845.

1. A. Morassi *G. B. Tiepolo* Milan/Bergamo/Rome 1943 p. 29 fig. 78. The Palazzo Labia frescoes are reproduced by A. Pallucchini *L'opera completa di Giambattista Tiepolo* Milan 1968 p. 113 no. 187. Earlier Waagen 1854 III p. 271 had described our picture as *The landing of Pharaoh's daughter*.

2. For further details see A. Morassi *A Complete Catalogue of the Paintings of G. B. Tiepolo* London 1962 p. 49 where the measurements are given as canvas 67 × 41 cm. The Stockholm picture is conveniently reproduced by A. Morassi *G. B. Tiepolo, His Life and Work* London 1955 fig. 32, and by A. Rizzi *Mostra del Tiepolo, Catalogo dei dipini*, Villa Manin di Passariano, Udine 1971 p. 100 no. 53.

3. G. Knox and C. Thiem *Drawings by Giambattista, Domenico and Lorenzo Tiepolo* International Exhibitions Foundation 1971 pp. 13 and 152.

4. M. Levey *Banquet of Cleopatra* Charlton Lecture, Newcastle-on-Tyne 1965 (unpaginated) where the Kuen drawing is illustrated fig. 3.

5. For this argument see Levey *loc. cit.* The Stockholm sketch is conveniently reproduced by Morassi 1955 (see note 2 above) pl. 29. The Milan sketch is reproduced by Rizzi op. *cit.* p. 90 no. 43.

6. M. Levey *Giambattista Tiepolo* New Haven and London 1986 pp. 130 ff.

7. See E. Fahy *The Wrightsman Collection. Paintings, Drawings* New York 1973 pp. 218 ff. no. 24. Canvas 45 × 65.5 cm.

8. Inv. 6409. Reproduced by Fahy *op. cit.* p. 228 and by A. Smith in the *Burlington Magazine* CXIV 1972 p. 632 fig. 52.

9. See Levey note 6 above.

10. See J. Bean and F. Stampfle *Drawings from New York Collections III. The Eighteenth Century in Italy* Exhibition Catalogue, Metropolitan Museum of Art, New York 1971 p. 54 no. 110.

11. Reproduced and discussed by Morassi 1962 (see note 2 above) p. 2 figs. 311 and 313. Morassi gives the size of each as canvas 338 × 600 cm.

12. For this argument see, for instance, I. Grabar in *Iskusstvo* X March/April 1947 pp. 63–81 (summarised by Fahy *op. cit.* p. 227); F. Watson in *Italian Art and Britain* Exhibition Catalogue, R.A., London 1960 pp. 171–72 no. 415; R. Pallucchini in *Acropoli, Rivista d'Arte* II 1961–2 p. 110; Morassi 1962 (see note 2 above) p. 11; J. Bean *100 European Drawings in The Metropolitan Museum of Art* New York 1964 pl. 43; Pallucchini 1968 (see note 1 above) p. 112 nos. 176 and 177; J. Bean and F. Stampfle *Drawings from New York Collections III. The Eighteenth Century in Italy* Exhibition Catalogue, Metropolitan Museum, New York 1971 p. 54 no. 110. Cf. also G. Lorenzetti *Mostra del Tiepolo* Venice 1951 (2nd ed.) pp. 89–91 no. 66 where the New York sketch is compared with the Archangel picture.

13. See Fahy (note 7 above) *loc. cit.*

14. See further *Pictures for Scotland* p. 39.

15. Waagen 1854 III p. 271.

92   The Finding of Moses

Canvas: 202 × 342

Cleaned 1950. In good condition apart from a small damage to Moses' left hand and a few other minor damages, mainly in the sky. A piece *c.* 205 × 132 cm. depicting a *Halberdier with a Dog* was cut from the right-hand side of the original canvas, probably shortly before 1830 and in any case before 1845; this fragment was in the Lord Blantyre sale, Christie's 19 April 1912 (60),[1] and was in a private collection in Turin in 1968.[2] Comparison with a reduced copy for the entire composition in Stuttgart (Inv. 575)[3] indicates that both our picture and the fragment with the halberdier were slightly cut down along the bottom edge.

The connection between our picture and the halberdier fragment was first recognised by Willis in 1913, from the evidence of the Stuttgart copy.[4] By this time, however, the halberdier fragment had been altered to give the figure a more central position within the picture-frame; to achieve this effect, part of the landscape, which was originally on the left of the figure of the halberdier, was removed and then was joined instead to the right-hand edge and repainted. By 1914 the halberdier fragment had been restored to its original format, and the result of this operation was published by Hénard.[5] Our picture and the halberdier fragment were subsequently exhibited together at the R.A., London in 1930.[6] (For a reconstruction photograph showing the original appearance of the complete picture, see Fig. 46).

The scene is an illustration of *Exodus*, II 5. The figures, however, are dressed in sixteenth-century costume, and the wooded mountain landscape is consciously remote from the Nile. Most of the individual figures in the composition are derived from Paolo Veronese's picture of the same subject in Dresden (Inv. 229); the Dresden picture was in Venice, in the Casa Grimani, until 1747.[7]

Our picture was acquired as by G. B. Tiepolo, and to judge from its style is clearly by him. Among the first to endorse the attribution were Waagen in 1854,[8] Berenson in 1907, and Molmenti in 1909.[9] It has never been disputed since. The 1957 *Catalogue* refers to a connected drawing in the Albertina, Vienna, but this statement seems to be incorrect.

Our picture was for long regarded as a mature work. This view, first expressed by Sack in 1910,[10] was followed by Morassi in 1943 who suggested a date in the late 1750s,[11] and was also accepted in the 1957 *Catalogue*. Then in 1963, when the picture's full provenance had still not been discovered, Levey,[12] reviewing Morassi (1962),[13] pointed out that it could not be dated plausibly much later than 1740, and that in any case it could not possibly date from after Tiepolo's visit to Würzburg in 1750–3. More specifically, Levey compared the handling and the 'brilliant but undramatic colouring' in our picture with the two large pictures at Verolanuova representing the *Gathering of the Manna* and the *Sacrifice of Melchisedek* which can probably be dated no later than 1742 and which may even date from a little earlier.[14] Levey also speculated on the possibility that our picture might have been intended to accompany the Verolanuova pictures. In spite of the fact that all three works depict scenes from the life of Moses, there is no evidence to support this idea. In 1968 Pallucchini followed Levey in dating our picture *c.* 1740.[15]

It is possible that our picture dates from even earlier than *c.* 1740. Its asymmetrical composition, with the strong emphasis on the landscape to the right of the main group of figures, seems to develop from the design of G. B. Tiepolo's *Ulysses discovering Achilles among the Daughters of Lycomedes*, formerly in the Palazzo Sandi, Venice, and now in the collection of the Conti Da Schio, Castelgomberto.[16] Whereas the *Ulysses* ..., which can probably be dated *c.* 1725, still shows the young artist's debt to Piazzetta, our picture is smoother in handling and more opulent in style and must be a little more advanced in date. On the other hand, it is more subdued in colour and less decorative in design than the frieze of the *Brazen Serpent*, originally in the church of SS. Cosma e Damiano, Venice, and now in the Accademia, which can probably be dated 1733–5.[17] The composition of our picture has a more classical quality, similar to that of G. B. Tiepolo's three frescoes of *Scenes from the Life of S. John the Baptist* in the Colleoni Chapel, Bergamo, which are dated 1733.[18] These stylistic comparisons together suggest that our picture might well date from the first half of the 1730s.

A small painting of the *Finding of Moses* in the National Gallery, London (Inv. 3542), which was attributed to G. B. Tiepolo by Berenson, and which is in some respects apparently dependant on the original design of our picture, is now ascribed to Francesco Zugno, a follower of G. B. Tiepolo.[19] Sack's view that it was conceived as a preparatory sketch for our picture can no longer be sustained.[20]

Coll: Andrea Antonio Giuseppe Corner Collection at the Palazzo Corner della Regina, Venice and first recorded there in an inventory of 1744; sold after his death (in 1742) by his sister-in-law Cecilia Mocenigo *c.* 1745/6 but the buyer is not recorded;[21] bought in Venice by Sir James Wright for the 3rd Earl of Bute in 1769, with an attribution to Veronese;[22] seen at Luton Park, Bedfordshire (Bute Collection) by the 9th Earl of Exeter in 1776;[23] recorded in the Luton catalogue of 1799 (43) as by Carletto Cagliaro (or Teniers), and in the Luton catalogue 1822 (28) as by Cagliari otherwise Paul Veronese;[24] 2nd Marquis of Bute sale (from Luton Park) Christie's 7 June 1822 (lot 50) described as 'Cagliari *The Finding of Moses* a Gallery Picture by Tiepolo, in the manner of – very spirited' bought Emerson £25.4s.;[25] presented to the R.I., Edinburgh by Robert Clouston 1845.[26] Recorded by Waagen in the collection of the R.I. in 1854.[27]

Royal Institution 1845.

---

1. In the sale catalogue the size is given as 79 × 59 1/2 in. (200.6 × 151 cm.). The pictures sold then had apparently been collected by Robert Walter Stewart (11th Lord Blantyre) who died in 1830, two years after Erskine House, Renfrewshire, was built. (Information from Sir David Baird; letter, in Gallery files, dated 21 September 1970). This evidence indicates that the original picture by Tiepolo was cut up before 1830; it conflicts with Giles Robertson's unconvincing suggestion (in the *Burlington Magazine* XCI 1949 pp. 99 ff.) that the picture was probably cut in two in Scotland after the Hamlet sale at Christie's 22 May 1841, but before 1845 when the principal section was acquired by the Royal Institution, Edinburgh. There is no reference to the figure of the halberdier in the very full description of the picture in the Hamlet sale catalogue: 'Tiepolo, The Finding of Moses. The daughter of Pharoah is standing on the bank of the river surrounded by her attendants, two of whom are bringing the infant in the cradle to her; a rich landscape forms the background; a *gorgeous specimen ...*'

2. See A. Pallucchini *L'opera completa di Giambattista Tiepolo* Milan 1968 p. 105 no. 131 illus. See also A. Morassi *A Complete Catalogue of the Paintings of G. B. Tiepolo* London 1962 p. 20 fig. 20 as ex. M. Tree collection, London.

3. Canvas 71.6 × 148 cm. The connection with the Stuttgart copy was first recognised by E. Sack *G. B. und D. Tiepolo* Hamburg 1910 p. 128 and p. 195 fig. 190, who regarded it as a preparatory sketch for our picture. Morassi 1962 (see note 2 above) p. 50 described it as an excellent old copy, probably by Domenico Tiepolo. Although the picture is clearly an old copy there is no real basis for an attribution to Domenico Tiepolo. See also *Katalog der Staatsgalerie Stuttgart* Stuttgart 1957 p. 291.

4. See G. C. Willis in *Der Cicerone* February 1913 pp. 139–40.

5. R. Hénard in *L'Art* 2 1914 pp. 218 ff., illustrating the picture in its altered format (p. 220) and restored to its original format (p. 221). The alterations to the fragment's original form presumably took place before the picture was acquired for Erskine House (see note 1 above).

6. Our picture was exhibited as no. 178; the *Halberdier* was no. 179 and its size was given as 80³/₄ × 52 in. (205 × 132 cm.).

7. See F. C. Willis *loc. cit.* See also G. Robertson in the *Burlington Magazine* XCI 1949 pp. 99 ff. where

the Dresden picture is reproduced as fig. 8. For the provenance of the Dresden picture see H. Posse *Die Staatliche Gemäldegalerie zu Dresden* Dresden/Berlin 1929 pp. 124–25 no. 229.

8. Waagen 1854 III p. 271.

9. P. Molmenti *G. B. Tiepolo* Milan 1909 p. 263.

10. Sack *op. cit.* p. 128.

11. A. Morassi *G. B. Tiepolo* Milan/Bergamo/Rome 1943 p. 35 fig. 106.

12. M. Levey in the *Art Bulletin* XLV 1963 p. 294. See further M. Levey *Giambattista Tiepolo. His Life and Art* New Haven/London 1986 pp. 77–80 as late 1730s.

13. Morassi 1962 (see note 2 above) p. 11, as circa 1755–60.

14. Both pictures are on canvas 1000 × 525 cm. For these measurements and a discussion of the evidence for dating the Verolanuova pictures see A. Rizzi *Mostra del Tiepolo, Catalogo dei dipinti* Villa Manin di Passariano, Udine 1971 pp. 64–5 nos. 33 and 34.

15. Pallucchini *op. cit.* p. 105 no. 131.

16. Canvas 270 × 520 cm. For the measurements and a discussion of the probable date of this picture, see Rizzi *op. cit.* p. 32 no. 11 illus.

17. Canvas 164 × 1356 cm. For the measurements and a discussion of the probable date of this picture, see Morassi 1962 (see note 2 above) p. 54 fig. 15.

18. See Morassi 1962 (see note 2 above) pp. 3–4 and figs. 42–4.

19. Canvas 53.7 × 80.7 cm. For full details see M. Levey *National Gallery Catalogue, The Seventeenth and Eighteenth Century Italian Schools* London 1971 p. 247.

20. Sack *op. cit.* p. 195 and p. 223 no. 526.

21. Information from C. Douglas Lewis (letters in Gallery files of 22 January 1979 and 15 May 1979).

22. Information from Francis Russell (letter in Gallery files 17 May 1988), according to whom there is a reference to our picture in a letter from Sir James Wright to the 3rd Earl of Bute dated 6 July 1769 (Bute papers 7/150/3–4) as follows: 'The Great Benedetto Cagliari of yours I have had much difficulty of packing, being painted in varnish, it would not bear rolling, I therefore had it plac'd on a cimi cir(cl)e of bords, to which it was nailed and then the circle cased up by this Meens I hope it will come safe.'

23. Lord Exeter's MS. notes are now among the Bute archives; there is a photocopy in the Gallery files.

24. Transcriptions of these inventories, kindly provided by Catherine Armet, are in the Gallery files.

25. I am indebted to Lady Dorothy Lygon of Christie's who first drew my attention to this reference.

26. For Clouston see *Pictures for Scotland* p. 39.

27. Waagen 1854 III p. 271.

Jacopo TINTORETTO *1518–94*

Jacopo Robusti, nicknamed Tintoretto from his father's trade of dyer (*tintore*). He is said by Ridolfi to have trained under Titian. According to his contemporary, Raffaello Borghini, he aimed at a synthesis of Michelangelo's drawing with Titian's colouring. Active almost exclusively in Venice, where he ran a large workshop with the assistance of his sons, Domenico and Marco, and his daughter Marietta. Although several of his works are datable, ranging from the *Last Supper* of 1547 in S. Marcuola onwards, the evolution of his style is difficult to follow.

Portrait of a Venetian

Canvas: 74.5 × 61.8

The canvas has been cut along the left, right and bottom edges and it has been folded over the present stretcher; to judge from the complete absence of the characteristic pulling of threads to be found near an original edge, the reduction may have been quite substantial. Swagging threads in the canvas along the top edge show that this is an original edge or virtually so. The paint surface is in good condition, but with some rubbing in the shadows.

Attributed to Jacopo Tintoretto since 1849 when it came to light in the Coningham collection.[1] The attribution has been accepted by Berenson in 1932, 1936 and 1957, and by Rossi in 1969.[2] Berenson considered it to be an early work; Rossi also suggests a relatively early date *c.* 1549–50. In view of the fact that the Bridgewater House picture appears to have been reduced, the possibility that it was originally part of a much larger group portrait deserves consideration, especially since the head lacks the psychological intensity of many of Tintoretto's portraits of single figures. This hypothesis might also account for the indeterminate nature of the background in the Bridgewater House picture.

Coll: William Coningham sale Christie's 9 June 1849 (8) bought Farrer; 1st Earl of Ellesmere collection by 1854 when it was noted by Waagen;[3] thence by inheritance.[4]

Duke of Sutherland loan 1946.

1. On Coningham see F. Haskell in the *Burlington Magazine* CXXXIII October 1991 pp. 676 ff.

2. P. Rossi in *Arte Veneta XXIII* 1969 p. 268 and also *Jacopo Tintoretto I Ritratti* Venice 1974 p. 105 fig. 41.

3. Recorded in *Catalogue of the Bridgewater Collection* 1851 (7th edition no. 15). See also Waagen 1854 II p. 33.

4. Recorded by Cust and Bourke 1903 no. 12, but erroneously illustrated under no. 13; *Catalogue of Bridgewater House* 1926 no. 15.

689 Male Head

Canvas: 36 × 27.2

The four corners have been trimmed, leaving the original canvas octagonal in shape; the present corners are later additions. The paint surface is in good condition, apart from some losses on the man's beard.

Hitherto described as the *Head of a Venetian Nobleman.* Acquired as by Jacopo Tintoretto and subsequently catalogued under his name. This attribution, which seems quite convincing, has been accepted by Berenson (1932, 1936 and 1957), Von der Bercken,[1] and Rossi[2] who suggests a date *c.* 1549–50.

Mary, Lady Ruthven bequest 1885.

1. E. Von der Bercken *Die Gemälde des Jacopo Tintoretto* Munich 1942 p. 108.

2. P. Rossi in *Arte Veneta XXIII* 1969 p. 268, and P. Rossi *Jacopo Tintoretto. I Ritratti* Venice 1974 p. 104 fig. 34.

2161 A Venetian Family presented to the Madonna by S. Lawrence and a Bishop Saint

Original canvas: 233.7 × 173.2

X-rayed (top half of picture only) (Fig. 47). There is a vertical seam in the canvas about 58 cm. from the right-hand edge. The figures of the Madonna and Child are badly damaged, with paint losses over a wide area covering most of the Child, including his face and hands, and the Madonna's breast, neck and left hand. The book she is holding and the area of clouds immediately below it are also affected. The paint surface throughout the upper part of the picture is generally thin and worn. In the lower half the face of S. Lawrence is damaged and extensively repainted. The patterns on the draperies of S. Lawrence and of the Bishop Saint have been strengthened. The paint surface in the area of the two male children is worn. The head of the girl on the outside edge of the top row of children on the left was apparently painted over by a restorer soon after 1929 but had probably been uncovered again by 1942.[1]

The X-rays reveal an earlier design for the figures of the Madonna and Child beneath the present Madonna and Child: they are arranged in a quite different and more symmetrical composition and do not have the diagonal axis of the figures in the final solution. The Madonna, whose head is less tilted than that of the present Madonna, is surrounded by a glory, and the Child is cradled in a horizontal position. The original Child's right hand can still be seen with the naked eye, just below the present Infant Christ's left leg. The original Madonna's foreshortened left hand (not holding a book) can also still be seen with the naked eye alongside the draperies surrounding the present Madonna's thigh. In the lower part of the picture, there are several *pentimenti* around the head of S. Lawrence.

Acquired as by Jacopo Tintoretto and subsequently catalogued under his name, although in the 1970 *Shorter Catalogue* it was pointed out that the quality of the execution of parts of the painting, and in particular the portraits of the children, is suggestive of studio work. Berenson however, in 1957, had accepted it as a largely autograph work by Jacopo Tintoretto. There is no evidence on which to date it with any precision, but it certainly appears to be fairly late. Von der Bercken suggested a date c. 1584–8.[2] Pallucchini believes this may be a little too late,[3] and is followed by Rossi who has placed it c. 1570–5.[4]

The children portrayed in our picture were traditionally identified as members of the Cornaro family. In the 1957 *Catalogue* some doubt was cast on this identification, on the grounds that there is no mention of the name Cornaro in an inventory reference to our picture dating from the 1770s.[5] This identification can however be traced back as far as 1798 in another inventory which has only recently come to light;[6] but since this document throws no light on the earlier provenance of our picture, the question of the children's identity must still be regarded as unresolved.

Coll: Probably bought by the 1st Lord Clive by 1771 (a Tintoretto *Assumption of the Virgin* listed in two 1771 inventories of Lord Clive's collection at Powis Castle is identified by a later family annotation as the picture subsequently sold at the July 1929 Walcot sale, for which see below).[7] Definitely in the collection of Lord Clive's son, 1st Earl of Powis by 1798 when listed as no. 40 in a family inventory.[8] By inheritance to the 4th Earl of Powis and Viscount Clive at Walcot. Walcot sale by Harrods 24 July 1929 (753) illus. bought Tomás Harris.[9] Exhibited Munich (J. Böhler) 1931;[10] London (Tomás Harris Gallery) 1932;[11] National Gallery of Canada, Ottawa 1934;[12] Toronto Art Gallery 1935;[13] New York's World Fair *Masterpieces of Art* 1940. Noted by von der Bercken in 1942 as on Lucerne Art Market (F. Steinmeyer).[14]

Bought from Tomás Harris 1952.[15]

1. The picture was restored between 1929 and 1932; see T. Borenius in the *Burlington Magazine* LXI 1932 p. 44. Tomás Harris mentions one of the heads having been painted over in a letter to Eric Brown at the National Gallery of Canada, dated 19 March 1936 (a copy of this letter, kindly provided by Myron Laskin Jr. is in the Gallery files). The head is clearly visible in a photograph of the picture published by E. Von der Bercken *Die Gemälde des Jacopo Tintoretto* Munich 1942 pp. 87 and 114 pl. 211.

2. *Loc. cit.*

3. R. Pallucchini in *Arte Veneta* VIII 1954 p. 232.

4. P. Rossi *Jacopo Tintoretto. I Ritratti* Venice 1974 p. 105 fig. 173. See also her article in *Arte Veneta* XXIII 1969 pp. 268–69. See further R. Pallucchini and P. Rossi *Tintoretto Le opere sacre e profane* 1982 I p. 196 no. 313.

5. The inventory is at Powis Castle (a copy made in 1947 is in the Gallery files, and was kindly provided by Sir Ellis Waterhouse). The picture described there as 'Tintoretto *Assumption of the Virgin*' has been identified as our picture on the basis of an annotation to the inventory, connecting this entry with the picture sold at the Walcot sale in 1929, for which see under *Coll* above.

6. According to Lord Powis (letter in Gallery files, dated 19 July 1975) there is an inventory of pictures at Powis Castle, dated September 1798, including under no. 40 'The Carnaro Family [*sic*] by Tintoret'. The 1798 inventory contains no other pictures attributed to Tintoretto.

7. See note 5 above.

8. See note 6 above.

9. Described in the sale catalogue as: 'The Madonna and Child in glory with attendant cherubims [*sic*]; on the left a Bishop in full canonicals and a group of children, to the right St. Lawrence with the emblem of his matryrdom and a portrait group of the Cornaro Family 68 × 100 in.'. There was no other picture attributed to Tintoretto in the sale. The sale catalogue entry was kindly transcribed by Sir Ellis Waterhouse (letter in Gallery files dated 9 August 1975).

10. See Von der Bercken *op. cit.* p. 114 no. 182.

11. *Exhibition of Venetian Artists* Tomás Harris Gallery, London, June 1932 (19). See also Borenius *loc. cit.*

12. See *Great Master Paintings* Exhibitions Catalogue, Ottawa 1934 p. 3

13. Exhibited in Toronto as *Picture of the month* in Oct. 1935.

14. *Loc. cit.* The picture may have been in Lucerne as early as 1934. See the 1957 *Catalogue* p. 270, where is is also stated that the picture was in Montreal in 1935.

15. Bought as part of a package deal in which the main objective was the El Greco *The Saviour of the World* (NG 2160).

2419 The Deposition of Christ

Canvas: 164 × 127.5

Cleaned 1984–5. X-rayed (Fig. 48). The canvas originally had an arched top and the design included the figure of a flying angel. This section was left behind when our picture was cut down and removed from its original location in S. Francesco della Vigna, Venice, probably between 1602 and 1631 (see below); however, the angel's foot was exposed at the top of the surviving picture, during recent restoration. A strip of painted canvas added along the top edge, probably during the seventeenth century, and four further strips, added on all sides during the eighteenth century, were all removed during the recent restoration.[1] The original canvas, painted with a thin gesso ground, appears to have suffered from the effects of damp, possibly while it was still in its original Venetian location. Cleaning, which involved the removal of a deeply discoloured varnish, has exposed substantial paint losses (already apparent in X-rays) affecting the figures of Mary at the extreme left and the legs of the Virgin in the centre. There are three areas along the bottom edge where the original canvas has been repaired with patches: one at the centre, triangular in shape, and extending deeply into the painting, and two others at the extreme left and right corners. However, most of the paint surface is still in excellent condition, and it includes a wide range of crimson glazes. The blue stripe of Nicodemus's robe has been enlivened by a criss-crossed pattern inscribed in the wet paint surface with a sharp edged instrument, possibly the handle of a paint brush. A similar technique is apparent in the headdress of the figure of Mary on the right. The dark foreground and landscape, painted largely with a bright green copper resinate, has become severely discoloured with age and exposure to light; and similar discolouration due to chemical change affects the dense foliage on the cliff at the top right.[2]

X-rays show a number of substantial alterations to the original design of the picture, which may be summarised as follows:

1. The figure of Nicodemus was originally placed lower in the composition, which accounts both for a leg visible in the X-ray below Christ's right arm, and also for the pair of hands under Christ's armpits, which can still be seen in the picture and which cannot relate to the present figure of Nicodemus. The head of the turbaned man, to the left of the present design, now fills some of the space taken up by the original figure of Nicodemus.

2. Christ's right arm was originally shown hanging loosely downwards across the arm of the turbaned man.

3. Christ's legs were originally placed a little lower. This suggests that the standing male figure, supporting Christ's legs on his shoulder, was only inserted at a relatively late stage.

4. There are substantial alterations around the head of the female figure who supports the swooning Virgin Mary, in the lower right corner.

5. The X-ray throws no light on the unresolved question of how the weight of Christ's loins is supported. The (pink patterned) drapery beneath Christ's right thigh does not apparently relate to the standing male figure who supports Christ's left arm.

Our picture was originally conceived as the altarpiece for the Basso Chapel in S. Franceso della Vigna, Venice where it was described by Vasari.[3] The original appearance is reproduced in engravings by J. Matham, dated 1594 (Bartsch III, 191) and by L. Kilian (in reverse) who was in Venice in 1602–3,[4] as well as in a copy drawing in Liverpool (Figs. 49, 50).[5] The mutilation, first described by Ridolfi in 1648,[6] and later by Boschini in 1674,[7] probably took place between 1602, when Kilian saw it, and 1631 by which date our picture had been replaced with another by Giovanni Laudis who died in that year.[8] A copy drawing in the Uffizi shows the picture after the top had been removed.[9] The original setting in which our picture was displayed in S. Francesco della Vigna has been disturbed by later restoration in the church. Howard has pointed out that it must originally have been shown in an altar frame very similar to that which still survives in the Dandolo Chapel in the same church (see Fig. 51 for a photomontage showing Matham's engraving inserted into the altar frame of the Dandolo Chapel).[10]

Pallucchini has pointed out that the design of the lower half of our picture is derived from Daniele da Volterra's *Deposition* painted in 1541 for S. Trinità dei Monti, Rome.[11]

Our picture has always been accepted as an entirely autograph work by Tintoretto and most scholars have dated it, on stylistic evidence, in the 1560s.[12] However, this conclusion now needs to be seriously reconsidered, following the cleaning of the paint surface and recent research by Howard into the circumstances surrounding the original commission.[13] Howard has shown that the Basso Chapel was conceded to Zuanne and Zuan' Alberto dal Basso on 25 August 1548. According to the terms of the agreement the two brothers promised to pay 300 ducats in return for which the monastery undertook to have the chapel built. In addition, the dal Basso were also responsible for paying all 'expenses regarding the completion and decoration of the said chapel, the floor, the seats or benches, the iron work and glass of the windows, the altar and the altarpiece, and the rest of the decoration of the said altar and chapel.' This confirms that the dal Basso family were the patrons who commissioned Tintoretto's altarpiece, since they retained their right to the chapel throughout the artist's lifetime. The dal Basso Chapel must have been structurally complete by 1558 when the monastery acknowledged receipt of the final payment due from the two brothers, and as Howard has argued, 'it is not inconceivable that the altarpiece and its architectural frame may have been commissioned even earlier, since the form of the chapel was standard and predictable.' A revised date for our picture in the second half of the 1550s also has the support of Paul Hills. He points out that the strong influence of Schiavone apparent in our picture, above all in the treatment of the body of Christ and his bearers, rarely occurs in Tintoretto's work after 1560.[14]

***

Coll: Almost certainly the altarpiece in the dal Basso (now Sagredo) family chapel of S. Francesco della Vigna, Venice, which was noted there by Vasari (1568)[15] and Sansovino (1581);[16] removed from the church by 1648, and probably by 1631[17]. According to Stryienski, the Bridgewater House picture was acquired in Spain by the Duc d'Orléans in 1707–8,[18] and although there is no evidence to confirm this Dubois de Saint Gelais (1727) also describes it as *de Madrid*.[19] Not listed in the 1724 Orléans collection inventory,[20] but catalogued in the Orléans collection by Dubois de Saint Gelais in 1727 when it belonged to Louis Duc d'Orléans.[21] Sale Lyceum, London, 1798 (208) reserved for the 3rd Duke of Bridgewater;[22] thence by inheritance.[23]

***

Purchased by Private Treaty from the Ellesmere Trustees with a grant from the National Heritage Memorial Fund 1984.

***

1. For a full description of the removal of all the additional strips, and an account of the condition of the paint surface following the recent cleaning, see J. Dick in the *Burlington Magazine* CXXVII August 1985 pp. 511–2.

2. For a report on the materials and technique of the picture see J. Plesters in the *Burlington Magazine* CXXVII August 1985 p. 512.

3. Vasari (ed. Milanesi VI p. 592).

4. Reproduced by R. Pallucchini *La Giovinezza del Tintoretto* Milan 1950 pl. 27.

5. Inventory 5109. Pen and wash and black chalk on grey paper; 406 × 257 mm.

6. C. Ridolfi *Le Maraviglie dell'Arte* 1648 (ed. von Hadeln, Berlin 1914–24 II p. 40).

7. M. Boschini *Le ricche minere della pittura veneziana* (Venice 1674 ed. p. 400).

8. H. Macandrew in the *Burlington Magazine* CXXVII August 1985 p. 502.

9. Uffizi 728E. Engraved by Andrea Scacciati in *Disegni Originali d'Eccellenti Pittori, esistenti nella R. Galleria di Firenze* Florence 1776, pl. 2. Phillip Pouncey and Marco Chiarini believe the drawing to be Italian and suggest the method of applying the white heightening might indicate it was intended as a design for a woodcut. See H. Macandrew in the *Burlington Magazine* CXXVII August 1985 p. 502–6.

10. D. Howard in the *Burlington Magazine* CXXVII August 1985 pp. 505–11 fig. 3.

11. R. Pallucchini *La Giovinezza del Tintoretto* Milan 1950 p. 98; the Daniele da Volterra *Deposition* is reproduced pl. 26. Colin Thompson (note in Gallery files) has observed that a drawing of *The Entombment* in Chicago (for which see *Master Drawings from the Art Institute of Chicago* Exhibition Catalogue, Wildenstein, New York 1963 no. 7 pl. IV convincingly attributed to Palma Giovane) is in some respects close to the original design of our picture, as shown in the X-rays.

12. H. Tietze *Tintoretto* London 1948, p. 353; P. De Vecchi *L'opera completa del Tintoretto* Milan 1970, p. 107, no. 164; R. Pallucchini and P. Rossi *Tintoretto. Le opere sacre e profane* I Milan 1982 pp. 191–2 no. 292.

13. Howard (see note 10 above).

14. Letters in the Gallery files from Dr Paul Hills dated 5 September 1988 and 26 June 1989.

15. Vasari *loc. cit.* (see note 3 above).

16. F. Sansovino *Venetia Città nobilissima* 1581 (ed. G. Martinioni, Venice 1663 p. 48).

17. See Macandrew *loc. cit.* (note 8 above).

18. C. Stryienski *Galerie du Régent Philippe Duc d'Orléans* Paris 1913 p. 153 no. 68, and see also p. 12.

19. L. F. Dubois de Saint Gelais *Description des tableaux du Palais Royal* Paris 1727 pp. 220–21.

20. Stryienski *loc. cit.*

21. *Loc. cit.* Also engraved by L. Croutelle in *Galerie du Palais Royal gravée* II Paris 1808.

22. For the sale of the Italian pictures in the Orléans collection see Buchanan 1824 I pp. 1–147; for our picture see particularly p. 133.

23. Recorded by Britton 1808 p. 33 no. 23; Ottley and Tomkins 1818 II no. 21; Passavant 1836 I p. 130; Waagen 1834 II p. 51; Jameson 1844 p. 127 no. 112; *Catalogue of the Bridgewater Collection* 1851 no. 40; Waagen 1854 II p. 33; Cust and Bourke 1903 no. 10; *Catalogue of Bridgewater House* 1926 no. 40.

Studio of Jacopo TINTORETTO

99 Portrait of a Man

Canvas: 85 × 73.5

The head is in good condition apart form a damage above the sitter's left eye. The background has suffered from quite extensive paint loss and restoration.

Acquired as by Jacopo Tintoretto and hitherto catalogued under his name. The attribution has also been accepted by Berenson (1932, 1936 and 1957), Von der Bercken[1] and De Vecchi.[2] The rather moderate quality of the execution, however, suggests that it was largely left to studio assistants. Rossi, in 1969[3] and again in 1974,[4] suggested, that it might be by Domenico Tintoretto who worked as an assistant in his father's studio; but Domenico's individual artistic personality cannot be defined with any precision.

Coll: Thomas Duncan R.S.A. sale, Fraser's Edinburgh 21 June 1845 (420) bought for the R.I., Edinburgh. Recorded by Waagen in the collection of the R.I. in 1854.[5]

Royal Institution 1845.

1. E. Von der Bercken *Die Gemälde des Jacopo Tintoretto* Munich 1942 p. 108.

2. P. de Vecchi *L'opera completa del Tintoretto* Milan 1970 p. 128 no. 264.

3. P. Rossi in *Arte Veneta* XXIII 1969 p. 269.

4. Waagen 1854 III p. 271, where he describes it under Tintoretto as 'genuine, but commonplace'.

Follower of Jacopo TINTORETTO

96 Summer

Canvas: 116 × 95.5

The canvas is damaged along the edges, especially at the bottom right, and the paint surface has suffered from numerous small losses and abrasions.

97 Spring

Canvas: 116 × 95.5

There are filled nail holes down the right-hand side, 9 cm. from the edge, but the paint to the right of the holes appears to be original. Two rectangular patches have been added at the right edge. The canvas may have been trimmed slightly along the left-hand edge, to judge from the less accentuated swagging threads, pulled towards the nails, on this side of the picture. There are paint losses along all four edges. Otherwise the paint surface is in reasonably good condition.

98 Winter

Canvas: 115.5 × 95.5

Cleaned 1941. In better condition than nos. 96 and 97 above, and with less damage along the edges.

No. 96 has hitherto been catalogued as *Autumn,* but was identified by Suida Manning as a representation of Ceres, allegory of Summer, who crowns herself with a wreath of wheat.[1] No. 97 has hitherto been catalogued as *Summer,* but was identified by Suida Manning as a representation of Flora, the Goddess of Spring. The old man in no. 98 may be identified as Hiems, allegory of Winter.

Acquired as three companion pictures of *The Seasons* and generally regarded as such, with the proviso that there was probably originally a fourth, of which there is now no trace, to complete the series. Suida Manning suggested they all may originally have formed part of the decoration of a room, perhaps being set into the corners of a ceiling, surrounding a central medallion. Clearly no. 97 was not designed as an easel picture as we now see it. The eccentric placing of the principal figure and the wisps of foliage coming in from the right-hand edge suggest strongly that the canvas belonged to some decorative scheme and was later adapted to make an easel picture. This is confirmed by the nail holes in the canvas towards the right and the two rectangular pieces that are missing from that side. No. 96 and 97 clearly have a common origin, but Thompson has argued that no. 98, which follows a rather different pictorial convention, was not necessarily originally associated with them, although he concedes that its coarse canvas is similar.[2]

Our three pictures were acquired with an attribution to Jacopo Tintoretto, and have subsequently been catalogued under his name. This traditional attribution has also been followed by Von der Bercken and Mayer,[3] and by Suida Manning.[4] Berenson listed no. 96 and 97 under the name of Tintoretto in 1932 and 1936, and then in 1957 described all three pictures as Tintoretto studio works. However, in the 1957 *Catalogue* it was convincingly pointed out that our pictures, although profoundly Tintorettesque in invention, might be by a Flemish artist, such as Pauwels Franck (known in Venice as Paolo Fiammingo), who worked in Venice from 1573–96, at first as a landscape assistant to Tintoretto and later as an independent painter. The style of each of our three pictures is arguably even closer to the work of another Flemish artist, Ludovico Pozzoserrato, who also worked in Venice from *c.* 1573 and was in Tintoretto's studio by 1577. For instance, the figure of Flora in no. 97 is similar in design to a female figure, painted in fresco, on the façade of the Casa degli Zignoli in Calmaggiore (Treviso) which has been attributed to Pozzoserrato since the time of Ridolfi.[5] One also finds many parallels in

Pozzoserrato's work for the rather heavy handling of the landscape, and especially the foliage, in our pictures. According to Ridolfi, Pozzoserrato decorated a room in the Casa Onigo, Treviso, with representations of the Four Seasons; but there is absolutely no evidence to connect any of our pictures with this commission.[6] An attribution to a Flemish follower of Tintoretto is supported by Pallucchini and Rossi.[7]

An early copy of *Winter* was last recorded in 1950 in the U.S.A. in the collection of Dr and Mrs Emerson Crosby Kelly of Albany (N.Y.).[8]

Coll: Bought from the Cambiaso family at Genoa by Andrew Wilson, on behalf of the R.I., Edinburgh, in 1830.[9] Exhibited R.I. 1831 and 1832 (21–3 incl.). Recorded by Waagen in the collection of the R.I. 1854.[10]

Royal Institution 1830.

1. B. Suida Manning *Two 'Seasons' by Jacopo Tintoretto in Studies in the History of Art dedicated to W. E. Suida* London 1959 pp. 255 ff.

2. Verbal communication 1977 from Colin Thompson to whom I am indebted for a most helpful discussion on the relationship of the three pictures.

3. E. Von der Bercken and A. Mayer *Jacopo Tintoretto* Munich 1923 I p. 252.

4. *Loc. cit.*

5. See L. Menegazzi *Il Pozzoserrato* Venice 1958 pp. 34 ff. fig. 42.

6. C. Ridolfi *Le Maraviglie dell' Arte 1648.* (ed. von Hadeln, Berlin 1914–24 II p. 94).

7. R. Palucchini and P. Rossi *Tintoretto. Le Opere sacre e profane* 1982 I pp. 243–4, nos. A33–5 figs 660–2.

8. Information from John Maxon, Director of Museum of Art, University of Kansas; letter, dated 20 September 1950, and photograph in Gallery files.

9. See further *Pictures for Scotland* pp. 27 ff.

10. Waagen 1854 III p. 209 where he describes them as 'interesting as showing the free and slight treatment and gaudy colouring of this master in his total degeneracy'.

TITIAN *c. 1473/90–1576*

Tiziano Vecellio. Born in Cadore. The limits for his birthdate, as given in the written sources, range from *c.* 1473–90. Titian's earliest paintings were probably the frescoes (now destroyed) of the Fondaco dei Tedeschi, Venice, which were painted in collaboration with Giorgione, and for his share of which Giorgione received a payment in 1508. Then in 1511 Titian is documented as having painted frescoes in the Scuola del Santo, Padua. Apart from further local commissions in and around Venice, including the celebrated *Assunta* in the church of S. Maria dei Frari, Titian also worked as a painter of portraits, religious subjects and mythologies for the leading Italian families outside Venice, as well as for King Francis I of France, the Emperor Charles V, and above all King Philip II of Spain. Titian's style developed considerably during his long career. In his early years he appears to have been influenced by both Giovanni Bellini and Giorgione; by the end, according to Boschini (quoting a statement by Titian's contemporary, Palma Giovane) he was painting more with his hands than his brush.

The Holy Family with S. John the Baptist

Canvas transferred from wood: 62.7 × 93

Cleaned, probably in the early 1930s. X-rayed (detail of the Child, head and arms of the

Virgin, S. Joseph) (see Fig. 52). The picture still had a wooden support when described by Dubois de Saint Gelais in 1727 and the transfer probably took place while the picture was still in the Orléans collection.[1] The transfer accounts for many of the paint losses which now affect the paint surface; see the X-ray. The present condition of the picture is difficult to assess with any precision.[2] The abrupt transitions of tone are presumably due to lost glazes.

The earliest reference to the Bridgewater House picture is by Dubois de Saint Gelais who, in 1727, catalogued it under the name of Palma Vecchio.[3] It was still attributed to Palma Vecchio at the Orléans sale in 1798;[4] and the traditional attribution was later followed by Britton in 1808[5] and by Passavant in 1836.[6] It was first questioned by Waagen both in 1838 and then again in 1854;[7] and in 1871 Crowe and Cavalcaselle suggested that its style was reminiscent of Licinio and Polidoro da Lanciano.[8] Morelli, in 1892, was the first to suggest it might be by Titian,[9] and this view has been accepted by many subsequent writers including Berenson,[10] Phillips,[11] Cust,[12] Gronau,[13] Fischel,[14] Ricketts,[15] Borenius,[16] Mayer,[17] Suida,[18] Valcanover,[19] Wethey,[20] and Hope[21] who all regarded it as a relatively early work. Titian's early style has not however been satisfactorily defined and this makes any certain judgement about the Bridgewater House picture impossible, especially in view of its present condition. Nevertheless, an attribution to Titian is not unconvincing and the picture shows some clear similarities in style with Titian's documented frescoes of 1511 in the Scuola del Santo, Padua where there are the same rather voluminous draperies and somewhat wooden gestures.[22] This view of the Bridgewater House picture pre-supposes that the picture of Christ and the Adulteress in Glasgow, which also has some stylistic affinity with Titian's Padua frescoes and which is sometimes regarded as an early work by Titian, is not by him; for it does not appear to be by the same hand as the Bridgewater House picture.[23]

A variant of the design of the Bridgewater House picture was engraved as after Titian by V. Lefebre in 1680 (see Fig. 53).[24] The exact source of the print is not known but it relates closely to a weakly executed picture in Glasgow of the Madonna and Child with S. Dorothy and S. Jerome (Inv. 192) which appears to be by a follower or imitator of Titian.[25]

Coll: Acquired from the collection of the Prince de Condé by the Duc d'Orléans before 1727, when catalogued by Dubois de Saint Gelais,[26] but not listed in the 1724 Orléans collection inventory.[27] Sale Bryan's Gallery, London, 1798 (112) reserved for the 3rd Duke of Bridgewater;[28] thence by inheritance.[29]

Duke of Sutherland loan 1946.

---

1. L. F. Dubois de Saint Gelais Description des tableaux du Palais Royal Paris 1727 p. 209.

2. The Virgin's feet and hands and the foot of the Infant Christ are undamaged; and the area of grass in the foreground is also in good condition. On the other hand, the face and hair of all the figures are clearly affected by old repaints..

3. Loc. cit.

4. Bryan's Gallery, London, 1798 (112). Wethey's suggestion that it was lot 226 at the Lyceum 1798 as Giorgione is surely incorrect; see Titian. The Religious Paintings London 1969 p. 94 no. 42.

5. Britton 1808 p. 103 no. 98.

6. Passavant 1836 I pp. 129–30.

7. Waagen 1838 II p. 51 and also in 1854 II p. 33.

8. J. A. Crowe and G. B. Cavalcaselle *History of Painting in North Italy* 1871 (ed. T. Borenius, London 1912 III pp. 381–82).

9. G. Morelli *Italian Painters. Critical Studies* London 1892 I p. 47.

10. Berenson 1894, 1932 and 1957, all as early Titian.

11. C. Phillips *The Earlier Works of Titian* London 1897 p. 54.

12. Cust and Bourke 1903 no. 6.

13. G. Gronau (translated A. Todd) *Titian* London 1904 p. 281 as *c.* 1510–12.

14. O. Fischel *Tizian* Klassiker der Kunst III Stuttgart 1907 p. 16 as *c.* 1510–12.

15. C. Ricketts *Titian* London 1910 p. 41 as *c.* 1511–13.

16. In J. A. Crowe and G. B. Cavalcaselle *History of Painting in North Italy* 1871 (ed. T. Borenius, London 1912 III pp. 381–2).

17. A. L. Mayer in *Gazette des Beaux-Arts* XVIII 1937 p. 306 as early, before 1510–12.

18. W. Suida in *Arte Veneta* XIII-XIV 1959–60 pp. 62 ff. as *c.* 1512.

19. F. Valcanover *L'opera completa di Tiziano* Milan 1969 p. 96 no. 48 as *c.* 1514.

20. *Op. cit.* p. 94 no. 42 pl. 6.

21. C. Hope *Titian* London 1980 p. 40 n. 19 where he suggests a date of *c.* 1507–08.

22. See Wethey *op. cit.* nos. 93–95 pp. 128–29 pls. 139–143.

23. For a summary of published opinions on the Glasgow picture see T. Pignatti *Giorgione* Venice 1969 p. 120 tav. 168. See further Hope *loc. cit.* (see note 21 above); and F. Richardson in *The Genius of Venice 1500–1600*, Exhibition Catalogue, ed. J. Martineau and C. Hope, RA, London 1983 pp. 169–70 no. 35.

24. V. Lefebre *Opera selectiora quae Titianus Vecellius Cadubriensis et Paulus Calliari Veronensis inventarunt, ac pinxerunt quae que Valentinus Lefebre Bruxellensis delineavit et sculpsit* Venice 1680–82.

25. See Wethey *op. cit.* p. 175 no. X 21. The design of the Lefebre print is in the reverse sense to the Glasgow picture.

26. *Loc. cit.* For the Princes de Condé see E. Bonnaffé *Dictionnaire des Amateurs Français au XVIIe siècle* Paris 1884 (reprint Amsterdam 1966 pp. 70f.).

27. C. Stryienski *Galerie du Régent Philippe Duc d'Orléans* Paris 1913 no. 46.

28. For the sale of the Italian pictures in the Orléans collection see Buchanan 1824 I pp. 1–147; for the Bridgewater House picture see particularly p. 137.

29. Recorded by Britton *loc. cit.*; Ottley and Tomkins 1818 II no. 18; Passavant *loc. cit.*; Waagen 1838 II p. 51; Jameson 1844 p. 110 no. 68 as Palma Vecchio; Catalogue of the Bridgewater Collection 1851 no. 29 as Palma Vecchio; Waagen 1854 II p. 33; Cust *loc. cit.*; Catalogue of Bridgewater House 1926 no. 29 as Palma Vecchio.

The Three Ages of Man

Canvas: 90 × 150.7

X-rayed (Fig. 54).[1] The picture area is enclosed in a grey border and although it is superimposed on the original paint surface there is no reason to suppose it too is not original. A black painted border of a similar kind also surrounds Titian's *Sacred and Profane Love* in the Borghese Gallery, Rome; again, it appears to be painted over the original paint surface, and may well have been added by the artist.[2] A grey border also runs along the sides and the top of Titian's *Aretino* in the Frick Collection, New York, and along the bottom and sides of Titian's *Portrait of a Man in a Red Cap* which is also in the Frick Collection.[3] Wilde's suggestion that the Bridgewater House picture has been cut down was based on the evidence of eighteenth-century engravings, and is not convincing.[4] The picture was cleaned in 1966, without removing entirely all of the old repaints: those which remain are principally in the sky and on the body and hair of the young shepherd. The condition of the paint surface is good, although the abrupt transition in the landscape to the distant blue hills is suggestive of some wear in this area.

The X-rays show a number of substantial alterations in the design, as follows:

1. The head of the young girl, who has been painted over the landscape background, was originally turned slightly towards the spectator and there are numerous changes in the position of her left hand and of the recorder which she holds in it.

2. The head of the youth was originally placed closer to the girl.

3. There are extensive alterations in the background: originally there were additional buildings to the left of the church.

4. A quiver or some similar object, which was attached to the top of the dead tree on the right, was later painted out by the artist.

5. Two additional skulls were originally placed at the feet of the old man; examination of the present paint surface suggests that the subsequent painting out of these skulls was done by the artist.

6. A broadly curving form, visible in the X-ray behind the head of the further of the two sleeping babies in the right foreground, may have been intended as a wing, but there is no indication of a matching wing on the right shoulder of the same figure.

The picture's present title is traditional and can be traced back to 1675 when Sandrart described it.[5] A similar title was also attached to a picture, attributed to Giorgione, in the Renieri collection, Venice, by the seventeenth century.[6]

As Panofsky has pointed out, the girl offers her partner a pipe so that they may play a love duet; the old man meditates about death, but unusually he is shown not with one but with two deaths heads (defunct lovers). Even infancy is represented by a pair of lovers. A winged amorino holds off the fig tree of Death.[7] Hope interprets the subject as the transience not only of human life but also of physical love.[8] Most recently, Joannides has suggested the Bridgewater House picture depicts the central love scene in Longus's pastoral romance *Daphnis and Chloe*.[9]

Murano and Rosand, followed by Hope, have suggested that the male figure is derived from a figure in the foreground of the lost Michelangelo *Battle of Cascina*.[10] Tietze has suggested that the two sleeping putti might be derived from Mantegna's *Bacchanalian Group with a Vat* (Bartsch XIII 19).[11]

The identification of the Bridgewater House picture as a relatively early work by Titian is beyond doubt and has never been seriously questioned. Most writers have dated it, on stylistic evidence, *c.* 1510–5.[12] It is almost certainly later than the *Gipsy Madonna* in the Kunsthistorisches Museum, Vienna, which probably dates from *c.* 1510 and, as Wilde has pointed out, is apparently influenced by a picture by Giovanni Bellini in Detroit, dated 1509.[13] The Bridgewater House picture also appears to be more advanced in style than Titian's documented frescoes in the Scuola del Santo, Padua, painted in 1511, where the articulation of the figures is stiff and heavy.[14] The modelling of the young man in the Bridgewater House picture appears softer and more assured than the not dissimilar figure of S. Sebastian in the altarpiece of *S. Mark Enthroned*, in the church of the Salute, Venice, which was probably painted after the cessation of the plague in 1510–11.[15] It seems likely that the Bridgewater House picture dates from a little later, from the period of the *Sacred and Profane Love* in the Borghese Gallery, Rome, to which it is particularly close both in mood and handling. Wethey has recently published new evidence, based on his identification of an escutcheon on the picture, which strongly suggests that the *Sacred and Profane Love* was commissioned by Niccolo Aurelio in celebration of his marriage in 1514 to Laura Bagarotto of Padua.[16] On this basis the Bridgewater House picture may also be dated around 1514.

An engraving by V. Lefebre of 1680 (Fig 55) shows a variant of the design of the Bridgewater House picture, and raises the question whether Titian himself painted more than one version.[17] The print omits the old man holding the skulls but shows extra buildings in the background, as well as a T-shaped object on the tree behind the putti, a second of whom also has wings. The shepherdess has no pipe in her left hand, and her face is turned fractionally in the direction of the spectator. The X-rays of the Bridgewater House picture, described above, show there was some authentic basis for Lefebre's buildings, T-shaped object, and the extra winged putto, which suggest that he was working either from some record of an earlier stage of the design of the Bridgewater House picture, or else from an even earlier painting by Titian. Robertson has lent support to the idea that there was an earlier painting, mainly on the strength of the inscription below Lefebre's print: TITIANVS VECELLIVS CAD. INVENT. & PINXIT.[18] But since Lefebre is known to have used sixteenth-century drawings and prints in some cases, the evidence of the print's inscription is not conclusive. On the other hand, Vasari's description of what must either be the Bridgewater House picture, or another autograph version, in the collection of Giovanni da Castel Bolognese (1494–1553) in Faenza, might be regarded as suggestive of there having been another picture closer to the design of the Lefebre print, since his account omits any mention of the old man with skulls, and refers simply to a young girl offering pipes to a shepherd so that he may play them.[19] However any argument based on such negative evidence must be conjectural.

A further variant of the design is known from a late sixteenth-century or early seventeenth-century copy in the Doria collection, Rome. The figures are arranged exactly as in the Bridgewater House picture, but there are substantial changes in the background.[20] The church has been removed and replaced by a clump of trees, and some houses have been added at the extreme right. The old man is shown with the two additional skulls which are visible in the X-ray of the Bridgewater House picture. Robertson has raised the possibility that the Doria picture might be based on a third original by Titian which is also lost,[21] but there is no particularly good reason why Titian himself should have initiated the apparently insignificant changes found in this version of the design. The Doria picture may have been the source for a later copy in the Borghese Gallery, Rome, traditionally attributed to Sassoferrato;[22] alternatively they may both be based on a common prototype which is now lost. Another old version of the Bridgewater House picture, said to have been formerly in the Manfrini collection, Venice, was sold at Sotheby's 25 April 1956 (170).[23]

A pen drawing at Christ Church, Oxford, showing a pair of lovers playing music in a landscape, has a certain affinity, both in subject and mood, with the Bridgewater House picture. Byam Shaw has catalogued it as by a follower of Giorgione,[24] but since then Oberhuber has raised the possibility that it might be based on a lost preparatory study made by Titian for the Bridgewater House picture.[25]

Coll: The Bridgewater House picture, or another version, was owned by Giovanni da Castel Bolognese (1494–1553) in Faenza, where it was recorded by Vasari.[26] The earliest reference to what is certainly the Bridgewater House picture is by Sandrart in 1675 who states that it had been in the collection of Cardinal Otto Truchsess von Waldburg, Bishop of Augsburg (1514–73);[27] but one cannot exclude the possibility that, on one of his visits to Italy, von Waldburg had acquired the picture belonging to Giovanni da Castel Bolognese. When Sandrart saw the Bridgewater House picture in Augsburg, on his way to Venice in 1628, it was in the house of Matthäus Hopfer, and he states that it was subsequently sold by 'von Walberg' (who was presumably a member of Cardinal von Waldburg's family) to Queen Christina of Sweden. The picture is not listed in the 1656 Antwerp inventory of Queen Christina's collection,[28] but it is recorded in her collection in the Palazzo Riario, Rome, c. 1662.[29] This rules out the suggestion, first advanced by Della Pergola, that Queen Christina acquired her picture of the *Three Ages of Man* from the Aldobrandini collection, Rome, in 1682.[30] The Bridgewater House picture is recorded again in an inventory of Queen Christina's collection made at the time of her death in 1689 (no. 44).[31] It next passed by inheritance first to Cardinal Dezio Azzolino (died 1689), and then to his nephew, Marchese Pompeo Azzolino, who sold it to Prince Livio Odescalchi (died 1713); then by inheritance to Prince Baldassare Odescalchi-Erba, who sold it to the Regent, Philippe Duc d'Orléans, in 1721; recorded in a 1721 inventory (no. 19) made at the time of the sale,[32] and again in the 1724 Orléans collection inventory.[33] Sale Lyceum, London, 1798 (278) reserved for the 3rd Duke of Bridgewater;[34] thence by inheritance.[35]

Duke of Sutherland loan 1946.

---

1. The X-ray is reproduced and discussed in detail by G. Robertson in the *Burlington Magazine* CXIII 1971 pp. 721 ff. figs. 24 and 25. See also the *Shorter Catalogue* 1970 p. 98.

2. But cf. H. Wethey *Titian. The Mythological and Historical Paintings* London 1975 p. 175 no. 33, who suggests the border was added 'to accommodate a modern frame'.

3. For the Aretino see T*he Frick Collection, An illustrated catalogue. Paintings. French, Italian and Spanish* New York 1968 II pp. 256 ff. According to Everett Fahy (letter in Gallery files dated 17 November 1975) the original dark grey border was at one time strengthened with black oil glazes which came off with the old varnish when the picture was cleaned in 1952. For the *Portrait of a Man in a Red Cap* see the Frick Collection catalogue *op. cit.* II pp. 251 ff. the light grey border around the picture was discovered when it was cleaned in 1974. Until then, only the border across the bottom was visible, and this was usually read as a parapet. According to Everett Fahy (letter in Gallery files dated 17 November 1975): 'The cleaning revealed nail holes and extensive paint losses on the sides and top, resulting from the painting's having once been attached to a smaller stretcher. Sufficient evidence remained to suggest that the bottom border originally continued up the sides. It was impossible to tell if it went across the top, though I would assume it did.' I am also indebted to Everett Fahy for detail photographs of the edges of the picture; these are in the Gallery files.

4. J. Wilde in *Jahrbuch der Kunsthistorischen Sammlungen in Wien* N.F. VII 1933 p. 106. His view is based on the proportions of an engraving, in reverse, by S. F. Ravenet (see J. A. Crozat *Recueil d'Estampes d'après les Plus Beaux Tableaux ... en France* Paris 1/42 II no. VIII) and another engraving, also in reverse, by R. De Launay (see *Galerie du Palais Royal gravée* II Paris 1808). But Robertson *op. cit.* p. 725 note 12 has demonstrated the unreliability of these prints by the fact that the dimensions of the painting given on the Ravenet engraving are practically identical with those of the present canvas.

5. J. von Sandrart *Academie der Bau-, und Mahlerey-Künste* 1975 (ed. A. Peltzer, Munich 1925 pp. 25 and 272).

6. Described as *l'età dell' huomo* by F. Sansovino *Venetia Città Nobilissima ... Descritta* (ed. G. Martinioni, Venice 1663 p. 377).

7. E. Panofsky *Problems in Titian, mostly iconographic* London 1969 pp. 94–6.

8. C. Hope *Titian* London 1980 pp. 22–3.

9. See P. Joannides in *Apollo* June 1991 pp. 374 ff. Joannides's quotation from the central passage in Longus's text reveals a telling correspondence with the main group of young lovers in Titian's picture. However, there are also sufficient divergences between text and image (most particularly the X-ray evidence of there originally being four skulls) for Joannides's identification to be classed as speculative.

10. M. Murano and D. Rosand *Tiziano e la silografia veneziana del cinquecento* Vicenza 1976, p. 82. See also Hope *loc. cit.*

11. H. Tietze *Titian* Vienna 1936 I p. 94.

12. J. A. Crowe and G. B. Cavalcaselle *The Life and Times of Titian* London 1877 I pp. 204–06; C. Phillips *The Earlier Works of Titian* London 1897 pp. 33 ff.; G. Gronau (translated A. Todd), *Titian* London 1904 p. 281 as *c.* 1510–12; O. Fischel *Tizian* Klassiker der Kunst III 1907 p. 20 as *c.* 1510–12; C. Ricketts *Titian* London 1910 p. 41 as 1511–13; Tietze *op. cit.* II p. 292 pl. 25 as *c.* 1515; A. L. Mayer in *Gazette des Beaux-Arts* XVIII 1937 pp. 305–6 as no later than 1512; F. Valcanover *L'opera completa di Tiziano* Milan 1969 p. 95 no. 39 as *c.* 1512; H. Wethey *Titian. The Mythological and Historical Paintings* London 1975 p. 182 no. 36 as *c.* 1512–5. But cf. Hope *loc. cit.* as painted *c.* 1509 before the *Gypsy Madonna*.

13. J. Wilde *Venetian Art from Bellini to Titian* Oxford 1974 pp. 113 f. pl. 95.

14. See H. Wethey *Titian. The Religious Paintings* London 1969 pp. 128–9 nos. 93–5 pls. 139–43.

15. See H. Wethey *Titian. The Religious Paintings* London 1969 p. 143 no. 119 pls. 147–8.

16. H. Wethey *Titian. The Mythological and Historical Paintings* London 1975 pp. 175 ff. no. 33 pls. 17–25.

17. V. Lefebre *Opera selectiora quae Titianus Vecellius Cadubriensis et Paulus Calliari Veronensis inventarunt, ac pinxerunt quae que Valentinus Lefebre Bruxellensis delineavit et sculpsit* Venice 1680–2. Reference should also be made to a copy of this early stage/version of the design by Jan de Bisschop (whereabouts unknown) published by J. G. van Gelder in *Oud Holland* LXCXXVI 1971, fig. 52. Cf also another drawing after the lovers in the *Three Ages* by Jan de Bisschop, recently acquired for the Print Room of the Rijksmuseum, Amsterdam, which shows the girl holding two pipes, i.e. nearer to the later stage/version of Titian's design.

18. *Op. cit.* p. 725.

19. Vasari (ed. Milanesi VII p. 435).

20. See H. Wethey *Titian. The Mythological and Historical Paintings* London 1975 p. 183 pl. 175.

21. *Op. cit.* p. 726.

22. See P. Della Pergola *Galleria Borghese. I Dipinti*. Rome 1955 I p. 133. no. 237 illus.

23. For an earlier reference see *Art Prices Current* XXXV London 1949 no. 2828 (Sotheby's 5 February 1947).

24. J. Byam Shaw *Drawings by Old Masters at Christ Church, Oxford* Oxford 1976 I p. 195 no. 717 and II pl. 408.

25. K. Oberhuber *Disegni di Tiziano e della sua cerchia* Exhibition Catalogue, Fondazione Giorgio Cini, Venice 1976 pp. 71 ff. no. 21 illus.

26. *Loc. cit.*

27. *Loc. cit.*

28. For the inventory of Queen Christina's possessions in Antwerp, dated 7 May 1656, see J. Denucé *De Antwerpsche 'Konstkamers' Inventarissen van Kunstverzamelingen te Antwerpen in de 16eand 17e eeuven* Amsterdam 1932 pp.176 ff.

29. *Inventoria della Regina Christina*, Riksarkivet, Stockholm, Azzolinosamlingen Vol. 48 f. 45; *L'Età dell'Uomo rappresentata in un Pastore, che siede sul terreno, e guarda una Pastorella, che guardandolo con Amore, tiene insepmano dui flauti. Poco lontano dui Puttini a dormire, sopra li quali saliscie un Amorino senza destarli. Più lontano un vecchio à sedere, che guarda due Teste di Morti in atto di Contemplatione, con bellissimo Paese, figure di circa cinque palmi, ò poco Meno in Tela a giacere con cornice Liscia lndorata alta palmi cinque, a Larga palmi sei e tre quarti – Di Titiano.*

30. *Loc. cit.*

31. See O. Granberg *La Galerie de Tableaux de la Reine Christine de Suède* Stockholm 1897 p. 34 no. 28. The inventory is also printed by G. Campori *Raccolta di cataloghi ed inventarii inediti* Modena 1870 pp. 336 ff.

32. Granberg *loc. cit.*

33. See C. Stryienski *Galerie du Régent Philippe Duc d'Orléans* Paris 1913 p. 150 no. 24. Also recorded by L. F. Dubois de Saint Gelais *Description des tableaux du Palais Royal* Paris 1727 p. 469.

34. For the sale of the Italian pictures in the Orléans collection see Buchanan 1824 I pp. 1–147; for the Bridgewater House picture see particularly p. 114.

35. Recorded by Britton 1808 p. 34 no. 24; Ottley and Tomkins 1818 II no. 8; Passavant 1836 I p. 128; Waagen 1838 II pp. 47–8; Jameson 1844 pp. 128–9 no. 113; *Catalogue of the Bridgewater Collection*

1851 no. 77; Waagen 1854 II p. 30; Cust and Bourke 1903 no. 5; *Catalogue of Bridgewater House* 1926 no. 77.

Venus Anadyomene

Canvas: 75.8 × 57.6 (visible painted surface; the edges of the painted surface are masked by a waxed canvas border added in the process of lining in 1932).
Kennedy North who cleaned and X-rayed the painting in 1931–2 described the condition of the paint surface as good, except on the face.[1] This judgement still seems correct. The facial features have been strengthened, especially in the shadows; and there is also some damage and repainting in the hair.

The X-rays show that originally the head of the Venus was turned to the left instead of the right. In this form the figure would have closely resembled a marble relief of the same subject by Antonio Lombardo (1448–c. 1516) in the Victoria and Albert Museum, London (Fig. 56). It seems very likely that both works are derived from an (unidentified) antique prototype. Kennedy has suggested that Titian may have been inspired by Pliny's account of the fate of the *Venus Anadyomene* of Apelles.[2]

Although the Bridgewater House picture was never described as a work by Titian in early documents, its attribution to him has never been seriously doubted. There is no evidence on which to date it with any precision, and earlier suggestions have ranged from c. 1517–30. Gronau had dated it c. 1517 in the belief, which has not found general support, that it might be the picture referred to as a *bagno* mentioned in a letter from Titian to Alfonso d'Este in that year.[3] Mayer, who dated it as late as 1530[4] (following Richter[5]), suggested that it is close in style to the *Madonna and Child with S. John the Baptist and S. Catherine of Alexandria* in the National Gallery, London, which Gould now dates in the second half of the 1530s.[6] Valconover's suggestion that the Bridgewater House picture is close in style to the *Andrians* in the Prado, Madrid, is much more convincing.[7] He dates the *Andrians* c. 1520, but Gould[8] and Hope[9] have advanced good arguments for placing this picture after Titian's *Bacchus and Ariadne* in the National Gallery, London, and for dating it between c. 1523 and 1524/25. On this basis it is arguable that the Bridgewater House picture might also date from the first half of the 1520s.

Coll: Listed in Queen Christina's collection in the Palazzo Riario, Rome, c. 1662.[10] Recorded again in an inventory of Queen Christina's collection made at the time of her death in 1689 (no. 23).[11] It passed by inheritance first to Cardinal Dezio Azzolino (died 1689), and then to his nephew, Marchese Pompeo Azzolino, who sold it to Prince Livio Odescalchi (died 1713); then by inheritance to Prince Baldassare Odescalchi-Erba, who sold it to the Régent, Philippe Duc d'Orléans, in 1721. Recorded in a 1721 inventory (no. 41) made at the time of sale,[12] and again in the 1724 Orléans collection inventory.[13] Sale Bryan's Gallery, London, 1798(49) reserved for the 3rd Duke of Bridgewater;[14] thence by inheritance.[15]

Duke of Sutherland loan 1946.

1. S. Kennedy North in the *Burlington Magazine* LXX 1932 pp. 158–63, where an X-ray of the top half of the picture is reproduced pl. IIb. But cf. J. A. Crowe and G. B. Cavalcaselle *The Life and Times of Titian* London 1877 I p. 277 where it is incorrectly stated that the picture has been 'ruthlessly' overcleaned; and also C. Phillips *The Later Works of Titian* London 1898 p. 29 who described it equally unjustifiably, as 'terribly ruined'.

2. R. W. Kennedy *Apelles Redivivus* in *Essays in Memory of Karl Lehmann* ed. L. F. Sandler, New York 1964 p. 162. See further H. Wethey *Titian. The Mythological and Historical Paintings* London 1975 p. 27 figs. 21 and 23, for a suggestion that Titian's immediate source was a Roman statue, one of a prevalent type in which the goddess wrings or arranges her hair nonchalantly.

3. G. Gronau (translated A. Todd) *Titian* London 1904 p. 53.

4. A. L. Mayer in *Gazette des Beaux-Arts* XVIII 1937 p. 307.

5. G. M. Richter in the *Burlington Magazine* LIX 1931 p. 53.

6. C. Gould *National Gallery Catalogue* London 1975 pp. 278 II. Inv. no. 635.

7. F. Valcanover *L'opera completa di Tiziano* Milan 1969 p. 101 no. 98.

8. C. Gould *The Studio of Alfonso d'Este and Titian's Bacchus and Ariadne* London 1969 pp. 12ff.

9. C. Hope in the *Burlington Magazine* CXIII 1971 p. 717.

10. *Inventoria della Regina Christina* Riksarkivet, Stockholm, Azzolinosamlingen Vol. 48 f. 45 where it is described as: *Un Quadro d'una Venere Nuda in Mare, Mezza figura, alta palmi quattro, e larga palmi tre, e tre quarti di Tiziano, con Sud Cornice indorata.* See further *Christina Queen of Sweden*, Exhibition Catalogue, National Museum, Stockholm 1966 p. 481.

11. See O. Granberg *La Galerie de Tableaux de la Reine Christine de Suède* Stockholm 1897 p. 34 no. 27. The inventory is also printed in G. Campori *Raccolta di cataloghi ed inventarii inediti* Modena 1870 pp. 336ff. See also H Wethey *Titian. The Mythological and Historical Paintings* London 1975 pp. 187–8 no. 39.

12. See Granberg *loc. cit.* For details of the negotiations prior to the sale see C. Stryienski *Galerie du Régent Philippe Duc d'Orléans* Paris 1913 pp. 18ff; see p. 22 for a reference by Pierre Crozat to the Duke of Orléans' special interest in acquiring this particular picture. See further C. Bildt in *The Nineteenth Century* LVI December 1904 p. 995.

13. See Stryienski *op. cit.* p. 150 no. 25. Also recorded by L. F. Dubois de Saint Gelais *Description des tableaux du Palais Royal* Paris 1727 p. 470. Engraved in reverse by Augustin de Saint-Aubin (see H. Dieckmann in *Harvard Library Bulletin* VII 1952 p. 72) and also engraved by Benoist in *Galerie du Palais Royal gravée* II Paris 1808.

14. For the sale of the Italian pictures in the Orléans collection see Buchanan 1824 I pp. 1–147; for the Bridgewater House picture see particularly p. 115.

15. Recorded by Britton 1808 pp. 97–8 no. 94; Ottley and Tomkins 1818 II no. 12; Passavant 1836 I p. 129; Waagen 1838 II pp. 48–9; Jameson 1844 p. 130 no. 116; *Catalogue of the Bridgewater Collection* 1951 no. 19; Waagen 1854 II p. 31; Cust and Bourke 1903 no. 7; *Catalogue of Bridgewater House* 1926 no. 19.

Diana and Actaeon

Canvas: 184.5 × 202.2 (visible painted surface; the edges of the painted surface are masked by a waxed canvas border, added in the process of lining in 1932).

Painted on a white gesso ground. There is a vertical seam down the centre of the canvas. Kennedy North who cleaned and X-rayed the painting in 1932 stated in his report that he had stripped the paint surface of all repaints, among them a 'signature' on the plinth which he found to be an eighteenth-century addition. He subsequently added 'no painting, glazing or scumbling of any kind'.[1] This absence of retouchings in areas of paint loss has left the bare canvas visible in some areas and has provoked over-pessimistic statements by Wethey about Kennedy North's treatment and about the picture's present condition.[2] In effect the picture is displayed in stripped condition. The uneven surface is due to the relining process, and some areas of deep shadow are worn, but the picture is fundamentally in good condition. The greyish appearance of the paint surface is probably due to Kennedy North's use of paraffin wax as an adhesive and as a protective coating to the cleaned paint surface.

X-rays (Fig. 57) show substantial alterations in the design of the picture.[3] Many of these were clearly intended to increase the illusion of depth and to give greater prominence to the principal figures of Diana and Actaeon, thereby intensifying the picture's impact. The principal changes were as follows:

1. Actaeon has been moved slightly nearer the spectator; his right foot was originally placed on a higher level and further to the left.

2. The recumbent nymph at Actaeon's feet was originally covered with additional draperies, and she looked in the direction of Actaeon rather than Diana.

3. Diana was originally shown in profile, but in the picture as we now see it she is shown, apparently deliberately, in two overlapping silhouettes, one showing her figure in profile, and another in which her entire back is half turned towards the picture plane. The position of her right leg and foot was also changed several times, probably as a direct consequence of the anatomical difficulties resulting from the double silhouette.

4. Diana's black attendant was painted over a white nymph, and with slight altera-tions to the original position of the head. Her left arm was originally placed much higher, in a protective gesture, across Diana's abdomen.

5. The red curtain was painted over the landscape and was therefore a relatively late addition; on the other hand, it was apparently painted before Actaeon's head.

6. Several *pentimenti* in the structure of the arch suggest it may originally have been placed nearer the foreground.

7. The square pillar, in the middle ground and to the right, which was originally round in shape and might even have been a tree, was painted over the landscape background. The position of the nymph, half hidden behind the pillar, was altered when the pillar assumed its final form; and her original right hand is still visible with the naked eye at the top right of the pillar.

8. The edge of the bath in the foreground was originally designed to be higher. The slab beneath the feet of the seated nymph was added at a later stage.

Actaeon, while out hunting, surprises Diana in the grotto at Gargaphia. Titian himself described the picture in a letter of 19 June 1559 as *Diana at the fountain surprised by Actaeon*.[4] The scene shown in the Bridgewater House picture is fully described by Ovid in the *Metamorphoses* III lines 138–253, except for the striking architecture to which there is no specific reference. Panofsky believed this architectural feature to be connected with the 'sylvan cave, not produced by any art' mentioned in Ovid's account.[5] But more recently Ginzburg has pointed out that the architecture shown in the Bridgewater House picture is described in great detail in a vernacular version of the *Metamorphoses*, published in Venice in 1555 by Giovanni Andrea dell'Anguillara, to which Titian must certainly have had access.[6] An alternative sugges-tion by Tanner that Titian may have relied on the particular account of the story given by Nonnus in *Dionysiaca* (V, lines 287ff.), that the architecture is an allusion to the dwelling place of Fortune, that Diana can be equated with Fortuna, and that the negro attendant represents the dark aspects of Diana, seems somewhat fanciful.[7]

Most of the figures have been identified, but not always conclusively, as derivations from antique prototypes. Gould has suggested that the figure of Actaeon may have been inspired by the *Apollo Belvedere* in the Vatican Museum, Rome,[8] and that the nymph at his feet derives from the *Ariadne* (sometimes called *Cleopatra*) also in the Vatican

Museum.[9] Brendel, on the other hand, has associated this reclining nymph with the *Falling Gaul* in the Museo Archeologico, Venice,[10] while Smart believes that her form was inspired by the figure of Laodamia in a Roman sarcophagus relief in the Vatican Museum.[11] Gould has also drawn attention to a possible connection between the seated nymph in the centre of the picture and the *Crouching Venus* in the Louvre, Paris.[12] And although Hetzer has suggested convincingly that the standing nymph seen from the rear is derived from a remarkably similar figure in a chiaroscuro woodcut attributed to Ugo da Carpi (Bartsch XII 22) which is after a drawing by Parmigianino in the Uffizi, Florence (Inv. 751 E),[13] Gould maintains that these similarities might equally well be explained by a common antique source which has yet to be identified.[14]

The Bridgewater House picture is one of a series of seven *poesie* documented as painted by Titian for Philip II of Spain, at least six of which were definitely completed between *c*. 1550 and *c*. 1562. The other pictures in the series are *Diana and Callisto* (also in Edinburgh) *Danaë* and *Venus and Adonis* (both in the Prado Museum, Madrid), *Perseus and Andromeda* (Wallace Collection, London), *Rape of Europa* (Gardner Museum, Boston) and *The Death of Actaeon* (National Gallery, London). To judge from Titian's correspondence with Philip II, published by Crowe and Cavalcaselle,[15] and recently re-studied by Cloulas,[16] the series proceeded on an entirely *ad hoc* basis, rather than in accordance with any preconceived iconographic or decorative scheme, and the ultimate location of the pictures was not apparently known to the artist. Titian's first principle seems to have been to present the pictures as pairs showing the figures from different viewpoints, but the intended pairings were apparently changed as the series progressed.

By 1556 Titian had begun work on *Diana and Actaeon* as well as on *Diana and Callisto*.[17] Then, on 19 June 1559, he reported to Philip that they were both ready;[18] but they were not in fact finally completed until September 1559.[19] Skarsgård has speculated that it may have been during the period June to September 1559 that Titian made the alterations to the figure of Diana, visible in the X-ray and described above.[20] This interrupted progress is consistent with the technique of Titian's late paintings, by which he very gradually built up the paint surface with layers of pigment and glazes, always allowing the paint to dry thoroughly between each application.[21]

Since the *Diana and Actaeon* is invariably coupled with *Diana and Callisto* in Titian's letters to Philip II, it seems likely that the artist always conceived them as a pair. There is no evidence that the *Death of Actaeon*, now in London, which illustrates the sequel to the event represented in the *Diana and Actaeon*, was ever intended as a companion to the latter.[22] It is mentioned only once in Titian's correspondence, on 19 June 1559, when he described it as already begun; and by this date the two Bridgewater House pictures were virtually finished. The London picture may well have been finished (as we see it now) during the 1560s, to judge from its style which is close to that of Titian's *Annunciation* in S. Salvador, Venice; but there is no documentary evidence of its having ever left Titian's studio.[23]

A seventeenth-century copy of our picture, reduced in scale, is now in the Prado, Madrid; its traditional attribution to Mazo is not convincing.[24]

Coll: Despatched by Titian from Venice to Genoa in accordance with Philip II's instructions[25] and with the help of the Spanish Ambassador, García Hernández, in early October 1559.[26] Then, on 11 August

1560, Philip II, writing from Toledo, informed García Hernández that the consignment from Genoa had reached Cartagena and that the pictures were expected to arrive in Toledo shortly.[27] The subsequent Spanish loctaion of the *Diana and Actaeon* and the *Diana and Callisto* by Titian is not recorded until 1623 when they were both in the Alcázar at Madrid. In the same year *Diana and Actaeon*, together with *Diana and Callisto*, was packed up as a wedding gift to Charles I of England, in anticipation of his marriage to the Spanish Infanta; but the marriage negotiations collapsed and the gift was withheld. The *Diana and Actaeon* was listed subsequently in the Alcázar inventories of 1636, 1666 (no. 696), 1686 (no. 869) and 1700 (no. 491).[28] Presented by Philip V to the French Ambassador, Antoine 4th Duc de Gramont (1641–1720), in 1704.[20] and subsequently given by him to the French Régent, Philippe Duc d'Orléans. Recorded in the Orléans collection in a 1724 inventory.[30] Sale Lyceum, London, 1798 (240) reserved for the 3rd Duke of Bridgewater;[31] thence by inheritance.[32]

Duke of Sutherland loan 1946.

---

1. S. Kennedy North in the *Burlington Magazine* LXII 1933 pp. 10ff. describes a late eighteenth-century restoration and the state of the picture after he had himself cleaned it. See further J. Plesters' unpublished MS report *Titian's Poesie: a note on the condition of some of the pictures* July 1981 and see H. Lank in the *Burlington Magazine* CXXIV July 1982, pp. 400 ff where he describes the technique and restoration of Titian's *Perseus and Andromeda* (Wallace Collection, London) from the same series.

2. See H. Wethey *Titian. The Mythological and Historical Paintings* London 1975 pp. 138–9 no. 9.

3. For a description of the X-rays see Kennedy North *loc. cit.* See also L. Skarsgård *Research and Reasoning* Göteborg 1968 pp. 53ff. and pls. 4a, 5a and 6a where the X-rays are reproduced and analysed in some detail.

4. See J. A. Crowe and G. B. Cavalcaselle *The Life and Times of Titian* London 1877 II pp. 512–13; and A. Cloulas *Documents concernant Titien conservés aux Archives de Simancas* in *Mélanges de la Casa de Velázquez* Madrid III 1967 pp. 233–4.

5. E. Panofsky *Problems in Titian, mostly iconographic* London 1969 pp. 157ff.

6. G. Ginzburg in *Paragone* 339, May 1978, pp. 14–15. The relevant text from *Delle metamorfosi d'Ovidio libri III … di Giovanni Andrea dell' Anguillara*, in Vinegia, nella bottega d'Erasmo, appresso Vincenzo Valgrisi, 1555, cc. 36 r & v. reads as follows:

Detta Gargafia è quella nobil parte
di cui tenea la dea silvestre cura:
non è la grotta fabricata ad arte,
ma ben l'arte imitato ha la natura.
Un navito arco quell'antro comparte,
ch'in mezo è posto a le native mura;
tutta d'un fragil tufo è la caverna,
la fronte e i lati, e ancor la volta interna.

Goccia per tutto intorno la spelonca,
e un chiaro fonte fa dal destro lato,
dove più basso a guisa d'una conca
la natura quel tufo havea cavato.
Una goccia da l'altra vien giù tronca,
né stillamento v'è continuato,
ma per più gocce sparse un ruscel cresce,
ch'empie quel vaso e poi trabocca e n'esce.

De l'antro il ciel, che natura compose,
da le gocce e dal gel diviso e rotto,
v'ha mille varie forme e capricciose,
ch'esser mostran d'artefice ben dotto.
Tronchi, ovati e piramidi spugnose
vi pendon, ch'al gocciar fanno aquedotto;
compartimento ha tal, che lo scarpello
no'l poria far più vago, né più bello.

And cf. E. K. Waterhouse *Titian's Diana and Actaeon* Charlton Lecture, King's College, Newcastle-on-Tyne 1952 p. 3 for an earlier suggestion that Titian might have relied on an Italian translation of Boccaccio's *Genealogia Deorum*.

7. M. Tanner in the *Art Bulletin* LVI 1974 pp. 535–50. A further iconographical interpretation has been published by J. C. Nash *Veiled Images Titian's Mythological Paintings for Philip II* Philadelphia 1985 pp. 39–50.

8. C. Gould in *Apollo* XCV 1972 pp. 464ff fig. 3.

9. *Op. cit.* pp. 464ff fig. 4.

10. O. Brendel in the *Art Bulletin* XXXVII 1955 p. 122 fig. 24.

11. A. Smart in *Apollo* LXXXV 1967 pp. 427–8 figs. 14 and 15.

12. *Op. cit.* p. 464 fig. 5.

13. T. Hetzer *Tizian. Geschichte seiner Farbe* Frankfurt 1948 p. 148. For the Uffizi drawing see A. E. Popham in *Master Drawings* I 1963 pp. 3ff. pl. 6. For further discussion of this possible source see R. Kennedy *Novelty and Tradition in Titian's Art*. The Katherine Asher Engel Lectures, Smith College, Northampton (Mass.) 1963 p. 25 note 76;and Panofsky *op. cit.* pp. 156ff.

14. Gould *loc. cit.*

15. *Op. cit.* II pp. 275ff. and pp. 512ff.

16. *Op. cit.* pp. 233ff.

17. This statement is based on a letter from Titian to Philip, said by Crowe and Cavalcaselle (*op. cit.* II pp. 515–17) to date from 27 September 1559 and by Cloulas, who is probably correct, to date from 22 September 1559 (*op. cit.* pp. 238–40). In his letter Titian states that the work had begun three years earlier.

18. See Titian's letter of this date published by Crowe and Cavalcaselle *op. cit.* II pp. 512–13 and by Cloulas *op. cit.* pp. 233–34.

19. See note 17 above.

20. *Loc. cit.*

21. Cf. Lank *loc. cit.* (see note 1 above)

22. For the *Death of Actaeon* in London see Wethey *op. cit.* pp. 136ff no. 8 pls 151–3; C. Gould *National Gallery Catalogue The Sixteenth Century Italian Schools* London 1975 pp. 292ff. Inv. no. 6420, and C. Hope *Titian* London 1980 p. 134.

23. For the S. Salvador *Annunciation*, datable between 1550 and 1566, see H. Wethey *Titian, The Religious Paintings* London 1969 pp. 71–2 no. II pls. 61 and 62, and also *Titian, The Mythological and Historical Paintings* London 1975 p. 257. For the stylistic similarities between the London *Death of Actaeon* and the S. Salvador *Annunciation* see Gould (*op. cit.* p. 293) who suggests that the bulk of work on the London picture might also have been completed by the mid-1560s. Recent arguments advanced by R. Marchio in *Arte Veneta* XXIX 1975 pp. 178–82 for dating the completion of the S. Salvador picture as early as 1559–60 are not conclusive.

24. Inv. 423. Canvas 96 × 107cm. See Wethey *op. cit.* p. 140.

25. For Philip's letter instructing Titian, dated 13 July 1559, see Cloulas *op. cit.*p. 236. On the same day Philip also sent additional instructions to García Hernández: the pictures were to be delivered to the Spanish ambassador, Figueroa, at Genoa, and then shipped to the Spanish port of Cartagena. For this letter see Cloulas *op. cit.* p. 237.

26. In his letter to Philip, dated 22 or 27 September 1559 (see note 17 above), Titian states his intention of at once sending off the two pictures of Diana and other items. Then, on 11 October 1559, García Hernández wrote to inform Philip that the two pictures of Diana and other items had been sent off eight days earlier; this letter is published by Cloulas *op. cit.* p. 242.

27. See Wethey *op. cit.* p. 139.

28. The picture's history in Spain is extensively documented by Wethey *op. cit.* p. 139–40.

29. See *Boletín de la Sociedad española de excursiones* XXXV 1927 p. 116. See also J. Bottineau *L'Art de Cour dans l'Espagne de Philippe V 1700–1746* Bordeaux 1960 pp. 233–34.

30. See C. Stryienski *Galerie du Régent Philippe Duc d'Orléans* Paris 1913 p. 150, no. 21. Also recorded by L. F. Dubois de Saint Gelais *Description des tableaux du Palais Royal* Paris 1727 pp. 465–66. Also engraved in reverse by Duclos and De Longueille in *Galerie du Palais Royal gravée* II Paris 1808.

31. For the sale of the Italian pictures in the Orléans collection see Buchanan 1824 I pp. 1–147; for the Bridgewater House picture see particularly pp. 112–13.

32. Recorded by Britton 1808 pp. 88ff. no. 84; Ottley and Tomkins 1818 II no. 10; Passavant 1836 I p. 129; Waagen 1838 II p. 49; Jameson 1844 p. 129 no. 114; *Catalogue of the Bridgewater Collection* 1851 no. 17; Waagen 1854 II pp. 31–2; Cust and Bourke 1903 no. 8; *Catalogue of Bridgewater House* 1926 no. 17.

Diana and Callisto

Canvas: 187 × 204,5 (visible painted surface; the edges of the painted surface are masked by a waxed canvas border, added in the process of lining in 1932).

Signed on the plinth: TITIANUS F.

Painted on a white gesso ground. There is a vertical seam down the centre of the canvas. The weave of the canvas is much finer than that of *Diana and Actaeon*. Kennedy North who cleaned and X-rayed the painting in 1932 (Fig. 58) stated in his report that he had stripped the paint surface of nearly all repaints; only Diana's extensively restored right hand and wrist were left untouched. He subsequently added 'no painting, glazing or scumbling of any kind'.[1] The paint surface appears to be more worn than that of *Diana and Actaeon*. Bare canvas is now visible in some areas of the cliff behind Diana, the left side of Diana's body, and parts of the two nymphs at her feet; also Callisto's abdomen, the base of the statue, the hair of the attendant holding a spear and the dog at the bottom right of the picture.[2] There is no apparent basis for Wethey's statement that Diana's head is nearly destroyed and that the noses of some of the nymphs have been 'repaired'.[3] The uneven surface is probably due to Kennedy North's use of paraffin wax as an adhesive and as a protective coating for the cleaned paint surface.

The scene in which Diana discovers Callisto's pregnancy and banishes her is fully described by Ovid in the *Metamorphoses* II, lines 457–65.

Various sources have been suggested for the figure of Diana: Brendel indicates a derivation from an ancient *Nereid*;[4] Smart has pointed to an alternative source in the figure of one of Niobe's daughters in the *Niobid* sarcophagus at Wilton House, Salisbury and formerly in the façade of a house near the Capitol in Rome.[5] Kennedy has claimed, but unconvincingly, to see a connection with the figure of Venus in Giulio Romano's *Marriage Feast of Cupid and Psyche* in the Palazzo del Té in Mantua,[6] and Panofsky has suggested that the pose of the upper part of Diana's figure and the gesture of her hand reveal the influence of Hellenistic 'relief pictures' such as the *Paris and Oenone* relief in the Palazzo Spada, Rome.[7] Panofsky has claimed to recognise a classical source for the violent gesture of the nymph with raised arm on the extreme left.[8] Brendel's persuasive argument that the putto with an urn is inspired by antique fountains such as that in the Museo dei Conservatori, Rome,[9] has been followed by Panofsky[10] and Wethey.[11]

Companion to *Diana and Actaeon* and, like it, painted by Titian between 1556 and September 1559 when it was sent to Spain. There is another variant version in the Kunsthistorisches Museum, Vienna (Fig. 59) usually attributed to Titian and workshop,[12] which is almost certainly later in date, since the under-drawing (visible from a photograph of the back of the canvas taken when it was relined in 1912) follows the design of the Bridgewater House picture almost exactly, although later, in the course of the picture's execution ,a number of substantial alterations were made.[13] These changes, visible in X-rays of the Vienna picture (Fig. 60), mainly affect the two attendants above and to the left of Callisto and the female figure standing immediately behind Diana, as well as the entire background, including the fountain and also the curtain which has been reduced in size. Callisto herself is shown covered with draperies, whereas in the Bridgewater House picture these had already been taken off by her attendants. The female figure, kneeling at Diana's feet, and the large dog, in the centre foreground of the Bridgewater House picture, were both completely removed from the Vienna version; instead a small puppy was added and the pool of water widened. Consequently it was then also necessary to alter the arrangement and position of the legs of the female figure in the foreground. Like Callisto, this figure is also covered with a drapery for which there is no precedent in the Bridgewater House picture. The stone on which she rests her right hand was originally a quiver, as in the Bridgewater House picture. The figure of Diana is virtually the same in both versions, except that in the Vienna picture her left hand is disengaged from the figure originally supporting her, and is used instead to clasp a spear.

These variations in the Vienna picture were all worked out on the canvas and they may well have been executed by Titian himself; on the other hand, the more routine work, such as the under-drawing and those parts of the final picture which also directly copy the earlier design of the Bridgewater House picture, may have been left to studio assistants. This supposition is based on the markedly superior handling, to which Wilde has already drawn attention, of precisely those areas of the picture where the design has been changed.[14] The evidence of the X-ray of the Vienna picture reinforces this view. The areas most affected by alterations, which are mainly in the left-hand part of the picture, are loosely handled in a manner similar to that shown in X-rays of relatively late works unquestionably from Titian's own hand, such as the *Diana and Actaeon* (Fig. 57) and *Diana and Callisto* in Edinburgh and the *Perseus and Andromeda* in the Wallace Collection, London, all from the original series of *poesie*, and also the *Tarquin and Lucretia* in the Fitzwilliam Museum, Cambridge. On the other hand the figure of Diana, which was not much altered, is executed with a quite different technique and with hard outlines which are uncharacteristic of Titian's late style.[15]

An alternative view has been advanced by Panofsky who doubts whether Titian himself executed the alterations to the design of the Vienna picture, but who nevertheless accepts that they must have been carried out under his immediate supervision.[16]

A further complication arises from a print of the subject made in 1566 by Cornelius Cort after a design attributed to Titian (Fig. 61).[17] The immediate basis of Cort's print is not recorded, but it was produced long after the Bridgewater House picture had been sent off to Spain. In any case, except for the inclusion of a quiver in the foreground, as in the Bridgewater House picture, the print is much closer to the design adopted in the Vienna version. To suggest that the print might represent an intermediate stage between the Bridgewater House picture and the completion of the Vienna picture, based perhaps on a drawing in Titian's studio, would be to ignore the very exploratory nature of the brushwork in those parts of the Vienna version where the original design was changed. It therefore seems most logical to regard Cort's print as a later variant after the Vienna picture rather than as the basis for its design.[18] This would indicate a date before 1566 for the Vienna picture.

The belief that these developments from the original design of the Bridgewater House picture were based on Titian's own ideas raises the question whether Titian had become dissatisfied with the composition of the Bridgewater House picture to which he no longer had access. It is of course possible that his purpose was simply to transform the design from one element in a pair of *poesie* into a single and self-sufficient entity, although this would conflict with the traditional but unsubstantiated view of the Vienna painting as one of the series of seven mythologial paintings offered by Titian to the Emperor Maximilian II in 1568.[19] An alternative explanation might lie in Titian's preoccupation, in his pictures of this period, with the illusion of movement and three-dimensional space, a preoccupation which is already evident in the Bridgewater House picture and which he may have wished to develop further in the Vienna version.

A copy of the Bridgewater House picture by Rubens of almost exactly the same size, which is now in the collection of the Earl of Derby at Knowsley, Lancashire, might date from soon after Rubens' return from Spain in 1628.[20] Another seventeenth-century copy of the Bridgewater House picture, reduced in scale, is now in the Seville museum; its traditional attribution to Mazo is not convincing.[21]

Coll: See above under *Diana and Actaeon* for history from 1559–1636. Described subsequently in the Alcázar inventories of 1636, 1666 (no. 694), 1686 (no. 867), 1700 (no. 489).[22] Presented by Philip V to the French Ambassador, Antoine 4th Duc de Gramont (1641–1720), in 1704,[23] and subsequently given by him to the French Régent, Philippe Duc d'Orléans. Recorded in the Orléans collection in a 1724 inventory.[24] Sale Lyceum, London 1798 (249) reserved for the 3rd Duke of Bridgewater;[25] thence by inheritance.[26]

Duke of Sutherland loan 1946.

1. S. Kennedy North in the *Burlington Magazine* LXII 1933 pp. 10ff. describes a later eighteeenth-century restoration and the state of the picture after he had himself cleaned it.

2. See further J. Plesters unpublished MS report *Titian's Poesie: a note on the condition of some of the pictures* 10 July 1981 (copy in Gallery files).

3. H. Wethey *Titian. The Mythological and Historical Paintings* London 1975 p. 139.

4. O. Brendel in the *Art Bulletin* XXXVII 1955 p. 122.

5. A. Smart in *Apollo* LXXXV 1967 pp. 428ff.and note 52 fig. 18.

6. R. Kennedy *Novelty and Tradition in Titian's Art* The Katharine Asher Engel Lectures, Smith College, Northampton (Mass.) 1963 p. 25 note *11*. But cf. E. Panofsky *Problems in Titian, mostly iconographic* London 1969 p. 159 note 50.

7. Panofsky *op. cit.* p. 159.

8. Panofsky *loc. cit.* On the other hand, M. Kemp has suggested that for this figure Titian drew from Dürer's *Nemesis* (Bartsch VII 77); see *Dürer and Italy* Exhibition Catalogue, Glasgow University Print Room, 1971 no. 51.

9. Brendel *op. cit.* p. 119 fig. 16.

10. Panofsky *loc. cit.*

11. Wethey *op. cit.* p. 75.

12. Canvas: 183 × 200cm. For a summary of earlier opinion on its attribution see Wethey *op. cit.* pp. 75–6 and pp. 142–3 no. II pl. 154.

13. For the under-drawing see A. Stix in *Jahrbuch der Kunsthistorischen Sammlungen des Allerhöchsten Kaiserhauses* XXXI 1914 pp. 335ff. illus.

14. J. Wilde *Venetian Art from Bellini to Titian* Oxford 1974 pp. 185ff.

15. I am indebted to my former colleague Colin Thompson, and to Stephen Rees Jones of the Courtauld Institute, for their valuable advice on the interpretation of the X-rays of the Vienna picture.In this connection Thompson first pointed out that the technique of the figure of Diana was quite uncharacteristic of late Titian. Rees Jones agreed with this observation but, on the strength of the

X-ray evidence alone, was more hesitant about rejecting the possiblity of Titian's original involvement in executing this figure; he pointed out that the figure might originally have been only thinly painted (especially in view of the fact that only minor alterations to the original prototype were required) and it might then have been seriously affected by unsympathetic restoration at a later date. Rees Jones also agreed that those areas of the picture most affected by *pentimenti* were entirely typical of Titian's late technique, and, for purposes of close comparison, kindly made available to me his X-rays of the *Perseus and Andromeda* in the Wallace Collection, London and of the *Tarquin and Lucretia* in the Fitzwilliam Museum, Cambridge.

16. Panofsky *op. cit.* p. 161.

17. For Cort's print see Stix *op. cit.* pp. 338 ff. fig. 2; it is also reproduced by Wethey *op. cit.* pl. 216.

18. Stix *op. cit.* pp. 335ff. went so far as to suggest that the Vienna picture had already left Titian's workshop by 1566 and that Cort's engraving was subsequently executed on the basis of a preparatory drawing for it.

19. See H. von Voltelini in *Jahrbuch der Kunsthistorischen Sammlungen des Allerhöchsten Kaiserhauses* XIII 1892 II pp. XLVII ff. See also Wethey *op. cit.* pp. 142–3

20. Canvas 186 × 198cm. slightly trimmed in the course of old relining. Published by M. Jaffé in *Jahrbuch der Hamburger Kunstsammlungen* XVI 1971 pp. 39ff. illus. For further discussion of its possible date see Wethey *op. cit.* p. 142.

21. Seville, Museo de Bellas Artes; on permanent loan from the Prado Museum, Madrid, no. 424. Canvas 98 × 107. See also Wethey *loc. cit.*

22. The picture's history in Spain is extensively documented by Wethey *op. cit.* pp. 139ff. no. 10.

23. See *Boletín de la Sociedad española de excursiones* XXXV 1927 p. 116. See also I. Bottineau *L'Art de Cour dans l'Espagne de Philippe V* 1700–46 Bordeaux 1960 pp. 233–4.

24. See C. Stryienski *Galerie du Régent Philippe Duc d'Orléans* Paris 1913 p. 150 no. 22. Also recorded by L. F. Dubois de Saint Gelais *Description des tableaux du Palais Royal* Paris 1727 pp. 465–66. Also engraved in reverse by Duclos and Aliamet in *Galerie du Palais Royal gravée* II Paris 1808.

25. For the sale of the Italian pictures in the Orléans collection see Buchanan 1824 I pp. 1–147; for the Bridgewater House picture see particularly pp. 112–13.

26. Recorded by Britton 1808 pp. 108–09 no. 104; Ottley and Tomkins 1818 II no. II. Passavant 1836 I p. 129; Waagen 1838 II pp. 49–50. Jameson 1844 p. 129 no. 115. *Catalogue of the Bridgewater Collection* 1851 no. 18; Waagen 1854 II p. 32; Cust and Bourke 1903 no. 9; *Catalogue of Bridgewater House* 1926 no. 18.

After TITIAN

103   **Bacchanal: the Andrians**

Canvas: 168 × 218.5

Painted strips have been added to both sides of the original canvas which is 183cm wide. Cleaned 1941. There is a large right-angled tear in the centre foreground which affects the reclining male figure. The paint surface is worn, especially at the top in the area of the trees. The added strips at the sides are affected by bitumen.

The scene is based on Philostratus' description in *Imagines* I section 25, but Titian treated the text very freely.[1] The Andrians are shown enjoying the pleasures of wine and song, but Bacchus and his attendants are absent.

Our picture is an old copy of the picture painted by Titian for Alfonso of Ferrara and now in the Prado Museum, Madrid.[2] It follows the original closely, except for an addition to Ariadne's drapery and the disproportionate enlargement of the picture's horizontal dimension. It is not clear why the sides of the picture were extended. Since the new strips, and especially the one to the left, include features from the original composition it is possible that the edges of the old canvas may have been damaged. On

the other hand, the new strips also add some empty ground between the picture frame
and the figures which is not found in Titian's picture. The suggestion made in the 1859
Catalogue, that Etty, who had owned the picture, made the additions because 'it differed
from the Madrid picture, which is six inches wider on each side'; fails to take account of
the fact that our copy is now 15.5cm. wider than the original. Nevertheless, the added
strips could well have been painted by Etty.

Our picture was regarded by Grautoff as a copy by N. Poussin,[3] but this unacceptable
attribution may have been the result of confusion with no. 458. Grautoff's attribution
has been rejected by Mahon (also quoting Blunt) in 1946,[4] by Walker in 1956,[5] in the
1957 *Catalogue*, and again by Blunt in 1966.[6]

Coll: William Etty.

Bought by the Royal Scottish Academy from the trustees of William Etty in 1853; transferred 1910.

---

1. See E. Panofsky *Problems in Titian, mostly iconographic* London 1969 p. 100.
2. Canvas 175 × 193cm; for this picture see H. Wethey *Titian. The Mythological and Historical Paintings* London 1975 pp. 151ff. no. 15 pls. 57–64. Wethey also gives a list of copies, including our picture. Cf. also J. Walker *Bellini and Titian at Ferrara* London 1956 p. 115 fig. 61 where our picture is reproduced and described as by an unknown seventeenth-century artist.
3. O. Grautoff *Nicolas Poussin Sein Werk und Sein Leben* Munich/Leipzig 1914 II p. 42 no. 22.
4. D. Mahon in the *Burlington Magazine* LXXXVIII 1946 p. 38 note 2.
5. Walker *loc. cit.*
6. A. Blunt *The Paintings of Nicolas Poussin. A Critical Catalogue* London 1966 p. 178 no. R 118.

Imitator of TITIAN

104 ## Portrait of a Man

Wood: 71 × 57.7
There is a margin of bare wood beyond the paint surface at the top, bottom and right
edges. On the left side a margin of prepared ground has been left unpainted. There are
very extensive paint losses due to flaking. The preparation of the ground seems quite
uncharacteristic of a sixteenth-century picture.

Acquired as by Titian and subsequently catalogued under his name. The paint surface is
now too seriously damaged for any reliable consideration of the picture from a stylistic
viewpoint, but there is nothing to suggest it is by any sixteenth-century Venetian artist
in Titian's immediate circle, while the technique raises the serious possibility that it is a
much later pastiche.

Coll: Bought from the Duke of Vivaldi Pasqua, Genoa, by Andrew Wilson, on behalf of the R.I.
Edinburgh, in 1830.[1] Exhibited R.I. 1831 and 1832(6). Recorded by Waagen in the collection of the
R.I. in 1854.[2]

Royal Institution 1830.

---

1. See further *Pictures for Scotland* pp. 27ff.
2. Waagen 1854 III p. 269 where he describes it as: 'Titian – A portrait; too feeble in drawing and too
cold in colour, for him'.

Giovanni TOSCANI *active in the 1420s died 1430*

Toscani's date of birth is unknown but his burial is recorded as having taken place on 2 May 1430 in Florence, where he had been active as a painter.[1] Payments to him for frescoes in S. Trinità, Florence, are recorded in 1423 and 1424. He is also recorded as a painter of *cassoni*. Bellosi has argued convincingly that Toscani probably painted the works isolated by Offner in 1933[2] as by the Master of the Griggs Crucifixion (a picture now in the Metropolitan Museum, New York, Inv. 43.98.5), a group to which Pudelko (in 1938)[3] and Longhi (in 1940)[4] made further additions. Berenson did not include either Giovanni Toscani or the Master of the Griggs Crucifixion in his Lists (1963), and he divided many of the works attributed to this hand between Rossello di Jacopo Franchi and Arcangelo di Cola da Camerino.

Workshop of Giovanni TOSCANI

1738   Cassone, with Scenes from Boccaccio's Decameron

The chest: 82 high × 182 × 60. The front painted panel with cusped border: 41.9 × 142.

Cleaned 1943. The chest is a nineteenth-century reconstruction. The main feature is the front panel which, on stylistic evidence, appears to date from *c.* 1420–5; its cusped border is very unusual but might possibly be original. The coats of arms have been extensively repainted. There is no evidence as to whether the decorated back panel originates from the same chest; its painted pattern is also found on a mid-fourteenth-century *cassone* in the Victoria and Albert Museum, London (Inv. 317–1894). The remainder of the present chest is of later date, probably nineteenth-century. The lid is of a type originating in the 1460s or 1470s; the freely painted pattern on the inside is copied from a stencil pattern which, according to Callmann, originated in the workshop of Apollonio di Giovanni and may have still been used in the workshop after his death.[5] The hinges on the lid of our *cassone* are not older than late nineteenth-century and there are no signs whatsoever of any earlier set of hinges.

The painted panel illustrates the story of Lady Ginevra, wife of Bernabò of Genoa, and Ambrogiuolo, the young man who introduced himself into her house in a chest (Giornata II, Nov. 9). In the left-hand scene of the front painted panel, Bernabò bets Ambrogiuolo that Ginevra will not surrender her virtue to him within three months. In the central scene, Ambrogiuolo, recognising that his efforts will not succeed, bribes an old woman to have him conveyed into Ginevra's bedroom concealed inside a chest. On the right, Ambrogiuolo is seen inside the bedroom where he looks for circumstantial evidence to convince Bernabò that his mission had been successful; he discovers a mole under the lady's left breast.

The earliest surviving illustrations of the *Decameron* are the drawings in an Italian manuscript, written by Giovanni d'Agnolo Capponi who died in 1392 (Paris, Bibliothèque Nationale, MS. Ital. 482), but this work does not include a representation of the scenes shown in our panel.[6] Between *c.* 1414–9, a French translation of the *Decameron* by Laurent de Premierfait (Vatican, Rome, Pal. lat. 1989) was fully illustrated by a French illustrator, identified by Meiss as the Cité des Dames Master.[7] This does include a representation of part of the story depicted on our panel, in which, on the left, Ambrogiuolo is brought into Ginevra's house, hidden in the chest, and, on the right, the Sultan offers a gold vessel to Bernabò after Ambrogiuolo's trick has been exposed.[8] The scene is also represented in a similar manner in two slightly later French manuscripts dating from c. 1420–30 (Paris, Bibliothèque Nationale, MS. français 12421 fol. 97 verso,[9] and Vienna, Österreichische Nationalbibliothek, MS. 2561 fol. 90 verso).[10] A later Italian manuscript, written by Ludovico Ceffini in 1427 (Paris, Bibliothèque Nationale, MS. Ital. 63), also reproduces an incident from the same story when Ambrogiuolo finds Ginevra asleep in bed.[11] Nevertheless, by the time our panel was painted, probably in Florence in c. 1425–30, there was still no strong representative tradition to guide the artist, and it seems unlikely that he had direct access to any of the earlier pictorial models described above.

Our panel was acquired as Florentine School c. 1425. In 1948 Antal tentatively proposed an attribution to Rossello di Jacopo Franchi,[12] and this was followed, but with similar reservations, in the 1957 Catalogue. In style our panel is extremely close to two other cassone panels which were published by Schubring in 1915.[13] Schubring classified these two panels as Sienese c. 1450, but Pudelko[14] and Longhi[15] both attributed them to the Master of the Griggs Crucifixion, and they were subsequently claimed by Bellosi for Giovanni Toscani.[16] Bellosi also includes our picture in a group of cassone panels attributed to Toscani, but with understandable reservations because of the mediocre quality of its execution. It is likely that our panel, but not the chest to which it is attached, originates from Toscani's workshop.

Coll: Captain G. Pitt-Rivers sale Christie's 2 May 1929 (80).

Presented by Dr John Warrack 1929.

1. For Giovanni Toscani see L. Bellosi in Paragone 193 1966 pp. 44 ff.

2. R. Offner in the Burlington Magazine LXIII 1933 pp. 172–73 note 17.

3. G. Pudelko in Art in America XXVI 1938 p. 63.

4. R. Longhi Critica d'Arte V 1940 (II) p. 185 note 22.

5. F. Callmann Apollonio di Giovanni Oxford 1974 p. 29 note 21 pl. 219. The pattern is also found inside the lids of the following cassoni: Boston, Museum of Fine Arts (Inv. 06.2441); Brussels, Musée du Cinquantenaire; Cincinatti Art Museum (Inv. 1933.9); Courtauld Institute Galleries, London (Cat. No. 26); N.G., London (Inv. 3826); and Metropolitan Museum, New York (Inv. 14–49).

6. See M. Meiss Essays in the history of art presented to Rudolf Wittkower London 1967 pp. 56 ff. See further B. Degenhart and A. Schmitt Corpus der Italienischen Zeichnungen 1300–1450 Teil I: Süd-und Mittelitalien Berlin 1968 I pp. 134–6 no. 65; V. Branca Boccaccio medievale Florence 1970 pp. 315 ff.; F. Callu and F. Avril Bocace en France Exhibition Catalogue, Bibliothèque Nationale, Paris 1975 pp. 35–6 no. 63.

7. Meiss loc. cit. See further Callu and Avril op. cit. pp. 58–9 no. 106.

8. The illustration of this scene in the MS. has never been published, and I am indebted to François Avril for kindly providing me with the necessary descriptive details, in a letter, dated 19 March 1975, now in the Gallery files.

9. Reproduced in Boccaccio Decameron (ed V. Branca, Florence 1966 I p. 206).

10. Reproduced in Boccaccio Decameron (ed. V. Branca, Florence 1966 I p. 199).

11. Reproduced in Boccaccio Decameron (ed. V. Branca, Florence 1966 I p. 202). See also Callu and Avril op. cit. p. 37 no. 64.

12. F. Antal Florentine painting and its social background London 1948 p. 367.

13. P. Schubring Cassoni, Truhen und Truhenbilder der Italienischen Frührenaissance Leipzig 1915 nos. 427–28 pl. C. For Schubring no. 428 (now at University of Wisconsin) see F. Rusk Shapley

Paintings from the Samuel H. Kress Collection, Italian Schools XIII-XV century London 1966 pp. 99–100 K. 170 fig. 270.

14. *Loc. cit.*

15. *Loc. cit.*

16. *Op. cit.* p. 52–3.

TUSCAN mid-fourteenth-century

1958   **A Triptych: The Madonna enthroned, with Four Kneeling Angels, and (left) S. Vincent and a Bishop who Offers the Child a Rose, (right) a Deacon and S. Benedict. Left wing: The Adoration of the Kings; (above), the Archangel Gabriel. Right wing: Christ on the Cross with the Virgin, S. John and the Magdalen Kneeling; (above) the Virgin of the Annunciation.**

Wood: (inside mouldings) centre 47.5 × 22.8; wings, left 51.3 × 12, right 51.3 × 11.2; overall measurement of the triptych with the shutters closed 71 × 31.

In reasonably good condition for a work of its age. The features of the figures, including the Madonna, appear to have been slightly strengthened but there are no major repaints or repairs, and a statement by Boskovits that the Madonna's face is 'distorted by restoration' is misleading.[1] The unusual and elaborate stamped decoration is authentic.

Acquired as by Jacopo di Cione, and hitherto catalogued under this name. This attribution had first been suggested to the previous owner by Berenson in 1938,[2] and he later published this view in 1963. But Berenson's attribution is not entirely convincing, and has been questioned by Zeri[3] and Boskovits.[4] Offner had believed our picture to be by the Master of the S. Lucchese Altarpiece (q.v.),[5] but it can hardly be by the same hand as our nos. 1539 A and B which he also, more acceptably, associated with this artist. Then, in 1971, Boskovits attributed our picture to Orcagna[6] and compared it to his signed *Annunciation* in the Landau-Finlay collection, Florence.[7] However, his view of the stylistic links between these two pictures is unpersuasive, and the argument is further undermined by his erroneous explanation that the face of the Madonna in our picture has been distorted by restoration. A convincing attribution for our picture still remains to be found. Indeed, at present, it is not apparently possible to identify any other picture which is clearly by the same hand. It is almost certainly by a Tuscan artist, active *c.* 1350 or a little later.

Coll: Said to have been bought in the 1850s by James Hope Scott for the private domestic chapel at Abbotsford.[8] By descent to Walter Maxwell Scott of Abbotsford who sold it *c.* 1938–9.

Bought from A. Welker, London, 1942.

---

1. M. Boskovits in the *Burlington Magazine* CXIII 1971 p. 248.

2. Information from Walter Maxwell Scott; letter in Gallery files dated 8 November 1946. Berenson's opinion was based on a photograph.

3. Letter from Federico Zeri, dated 19 May 1966, in Gallery files.

4. *Loc. cit.*

5. I am indebted to Klara Steinweg who provided me with an unpublished list of pictures attributed by Richard Offner to this hand.

6. *Loc. cit.*

7. *Op. cit.* 240 ff. fig. 2. Boskovits further compared our picture to a tabernacle in the St Louis City Art Museum (*op. cit.* pp. 244 ff. fig. II) which he also attributes to Orcagna; but the attribution of the St Louis picture is not secure, and Offner had listed it under the name of the Master of the San Lucchese Altarpiece (see note 5 above).

8. Information from Walter Maxwell Scott; letters in Gallery files dated 8 November 1946 and 11 November 1946.

Diego VELÁZQUEZ *1599–1660*

His full name was Diego Rodríguez de Silva y Velázquez. He was born in Seville, and his principal training there was in the Academy of Francisco Pacheco *c.* 1613–8. During this period he specialised in scenes of everyday life, placing particular emphasis on natural objects such as kitchen utensils. He visited Madrid in 1622 and returned there the following year; by October 1623 he was attached to the Court of Philip IV, for whom he painted numerous portraits. He first visited Italy in 1629–31 and returned in 1649–51. He died in Madrid.

180 An Old Woman Cooking Eggs

Canvas: 100.5 × 119.5

Cleaned in 1957. X-rayed. In very good condition, apart from some wear in the background, and some paint loss at the edges of the painting, especially along the bottom, affecting the inscribed date, the brass bowl at the left and the green paint of the jar at the right. Cleaning revealed, at the bottom right, the clear remains of the date *16.8* which, in view of the picture's style (for which see below), must therefore be 1618; the figures are framed between two dots of paint.[1] Plesters has suggested, from the evidence of the X-rays, that the canvas Velázquez used for our picture was cut from the same roll as other early works, including the *Kitchen Scene with Christ in the House of Martha and Mary* dated 1618, the *S. John on the Island of Patmos* and the *Immaculate Conception*, all in the National Gallery, London, and the *Water Carrier of Seville* at Apsley House, London; the canvas is characterised by a relatively open weave.[2] The canvas may have been reduced by 1 cm. on all sides. An X-ray detail shows an alteration in the drapery on the woman's extended arm and there are further alterations; in the woman's other sleeve, in the basket at centre top, in the background at top right corner, in the area of the woman's knees and at the boy's collar.

Our picture is one of a group of kitchen scenes (*bodegones*) of horizontal format and with prominent still life and half-length figures, completed during the artist's Sevillian period, and probably all from the years *c.* 1618–20. It has often been suggested that these *bodegones* were inspired by North European prototypes, and in particular by engravings after Pieter Aertsen's work,[3] but as Young has pointed out,[4] Spanish sixteenth-century literature was also firmly dedicated to naturalism of this kind.[5] In particular there is a detailed description of a woman cooking eggs for a young boy in Matheo Alemán's *Guzman de Alfarache*.[6]

The model for the old woman in our picture, who was certainly painted from life, is probably the same as that for the old woman in the *Kitchen Scene with Christ in the House of Martha and Mary*, in the National Gallery, London (Inv. 1375) which is also dated 1618.[7] A pestle and mortar like those in our picture also occur in this painting as well as in the *Two Men at Table* at Apsley House. The model for the boy in our picture is probably the same as for the boy in the *Water Carrier* at Apsley House.

Justi[8] and Beruete[9] have both suggested that our picture might be a kitchen scene described by Palomino de Castro y Velasco in his *Museo Pictórico* 1724; but Du Gué Trapier has pointed out major discrepancies between this description and our picture, and rightly disputed the suggested connection.[10] Another version of our picture of uncertain date, but not apparently autograph, was in the collection of Girou de Buzareingues, Paris., in 1870, when it was photographed by Godet, and listed as by Velázquez.[11]

Coll: Very probably the picture attributed to Velázquez in his '1st manner' of 'A woman poaching eggs, and a servant boy with a melon and a bottle of wine. Various utensils in foreground', in the John Woollett sale 8 May 1813 (45) bought Samuel Peach, catalogued as 'Imported from Spain by Le Brun'.[12] Peach's sale (Elgood & Sons) 23 April 1863 (239), bought 'Smith', presumably the London dealers John Smith and Son, from whom it was acquired by (Sir) J. C. Robinson,[13] and almost immediately afterwards passed into the collection of (Sir) Francis Cook. Robinson mistakenly recorded that the picture came from a Bradford collection.[14] Lent by Francis Cook to the *Exhibition of Works of the Old Masters* R.A., London 1873 (92), to the *Exhibition of Spanish Art*, New Gallery, London, 1895–6 (135) and to the *Exhibition of the works of Spanish Painters*, Guildhall, London, 1901 (102). Passed by inheritance in 1901 to Sir Frederick Cook who lent it to the *National Loan Exhibition*, Grafton Galleries, London 1909–10 (32) and to the *Exhibition of Spanish Old Masters*, Grafton Galleries, 1913–14 (47). *Cook Collection Catalogue* 1915 III (499). Passed by inheritance in 1920 to Sir Herbert Cook who lent it to the B.F.A.C. Winter exhibition 1936–37 (22). Passed by inheritance in 1939 to Sir Francis Cook and the Trustees of the Cook Collection who lent it to Toledo Museum of Art (Ohio) 1944–5, and to the *Exhibition of Spanish Paintings*, Arts Council, London 1946 (23). On extended loan to the Fitzwilliam Museum, Cambridge, 1947–55.

Bought from Sir Francis Cook and the Trustees of the Cook Collection in 1955.

---

1. See D. Baxandall in the *Burlington Magazine* XCIX 1957 pp. 156 f. fig. 21, where the inscription is reproduced.

2. See N. Maclaren, revised by A. Braham *National Gallery Catalogue, The Spanish School* London 1970 p. 124 note 1.

3. See also F. Hawcroft in the *Burlington Magazine* XCIX 1957 pp. 95 f. note 7, who points out that the Dutch artist Cornelis Engelszen painted pictures derived in composition from those of Aertsen and Beuckelaer, and that there are similarities in both figures and still life between the works of Engelszen and some of the early *bodegones* by Velázquez. He compares the young boy in our picture and in the *Water Carrier* at Apsley House with the young boy found in a *Supper at Emmaus* by Engelszen, reproduced in the *Burlington Magazine* XCVII 1955 p. 361 fig. 36.

4. E. Young in the *Connoisseur* April 1979, p. 295.

5. Note in Gallery files by Keith Andrews. See also R. Spear *Caravaggio and his followers* Cleveland Museum of Art, Cleveland 1971 p. 19.

6. Matheo Alémán *The Rogue*, or *The Life of Guzmán de Alfarache* translated by James Mabbe 1623 (ed. London 1924 I pp. 98–9).

7. See note 2 above.

8. C. Justi *Diego Velázquez and his Times* London 1889 pp. 72.

9. A. de Beruete *Velázquez* London 1906 pp. 9 f. pl. V.

10. E. du Gué Trapier *Velázquez* New York 1948 p. 64.

11. Photo in Bibliothèque Nationale, Paris, S. N. R. Godet. This information was kindly communicated by Juliet Bareau and Enriqueta Frankfort (letter in Gallery files 14 November 1988).

12. See W. H. J. Weale's notebook (C.4 p. 18) in the V. and A., London (press mark 88 EE 48). There is no apparent basis for a statement by J. A. Gaya Nuño (*La Pintura española fuera de España* Madrid 1958 p. 341 no. 3050) that our picture was acquired in Spain by David Wilkie.

13. Information from Julia I. Armstrong, The Getty Art History Information Program (letter in Gallery files, 5 September 1991). Samuel Peach (c.1762–1832) died without a direct heir and the collection was presumably sold by his grand-nephew, Henry Keighly-Peach. These facts contradict Robinson's recollection (*Burlington Magazine* X 1906 p. 177 and note 14 below), followed in the 1978 edition of this catalogue, that Smith had sold the picture to a collector in Bradford and then bought it back.

14. J. C. Robinson in the *Burlington Magazine* X 1906 pp. 177–8. See also a letter from Neil Maclaren, dated 23 May 1955, in the Gallery files. He quotes from a copy of a letter of 1912 from Robinson to Sir Herbert Cook, sent to him by S. C. Kaimes Smith, Keeper of the Cook Collection. The relevant passage of Robinson's letter is as follows: 'This *as far as I recollect* is the history of the Velázquez ... I heard of it from a Bond Street picture dealer who had sold the picture some years before to a collector at *Bradford*. I determined to look after it, and persuaded your grandfather to go with me down to the sale, and we carried it off for a very small sum to our great contentment ...' Kaines Smith further informed Maclaren that the Bradford sale took place in 1863 and that the picture was not bought at the sale by either Robinson or Cook, but that Robinson bought it a few days later. Robinson's evidently incorrect recollections could be explained by his considerable age – he was eighty-eight in 1912.

After Diego VELÁZQUEZ

625   Philip IV of Spain (1605–65)

Canvas: 51.1 × 46

The absence of swagging threads, pulled towards the nails along the right and bottom edges, suggests that the picture may have been reduced on these two sides. The top and left edges appear to be unaffected. The paint surface is slightly worn throughout.

Philip IV succeeded to the Spanish throne in 1621. He married first Isabella de Bourbon (1615) and secondly Mariana of Austria (1649).

Acquired as by Mazo but subsequently catalogued under the name of Velázquez. It is a reduced copy, possibly from as early as the seventeenth century, of the picture by Velázquez in the National Gallery, London (Inv. 745).[1] About twenty further variants and derivatives of the London picture are known.[2] In our picture the shoulder braid and the badge of the Order of the Golden Fleece, visible in the London portrait, are missing; these features might have been lost if and when the right and bottom edges of our picture were cut down.

Our picture is said to have been paired with a bust portrait of Queen Mariana while it was in the Vega-Inclán collection, Madrid;[3] other copies of the London portrait of Philip IV (Inv. 745) which are now in Geneva and in the Academia de San Fernando, Madrid, also have companion bust portraits of Mariana.[4] No autograph version of these studio portraits of Mariana is known, and there is no evidence that Velázquez ever intended that the original portrait of Philip IV, now in London, should be paired with a portrait of the Queen.

Coll: Marqués de la Vega-Inclán collection, Madrid, from whom it was acquired by the Spanish Art Gallery, London.[5]

Bought from the Spanish Art Gallery 1923.

---

1. N. Maclaren, revised by A. Braham *National Gallery Catalogue, The Spanish School* London 1970 pp. 108 ff. Canvas 64.1 × 53.7 cm.

2. See Maclaren, revised by Braham, *op. cit.* p. 110.

3. See A. L. Mayer *Velázquez, a Catalogue Raisonné of the Pictures and Drawings* London 1936 p. 117 no 494, for the portrait of Mariana. Mayer did not list our picture. The information that our picture was originally in the collection of the Marqués de la Vega-Inclán, Madrid, and that it was paired there with Mayer no 494, originates from Tomás Harris (Letter in Gallery files from Neil Maclaren, dated 16 May 1949).

4. See Maclaren revised by Braham *op. cit.* p. 109.

5. Information from Tomás Harris; see note 3 above.

VENETIAN sixteenth-century

690   An Archer

Wood: 53.5 × 41.5

Cleaned by De Wild in 1937. X-rayed. The left and right-hand edges of the original panel are bordered by pinewood fillets *c.* 1 cm. wide. The original background of the picture is scarcely visible; the present paint surface in this area is almost all restored. The area occupied by the figure is also very badly rubbed and cracked, and there are serious paint losses around his nose and mouth, and along the line of an old vertical crack affecting his ear and nose. The best preserved area is the man's hand, and even here the damage and wear are sufficient to impede reliable assessment of the picture's original quality.

Acquired under an attribution to Giorgione. In 1913 Venturi attributed it to Cariani,[1] in 1932 and 1936 Berenson gave it tentatively to Calisto Piazza da Lodi, while in the same year Arslan proposed Francesco Torbido.[2] A tentative attribution to Torbido was followed by Viana in 1933[3] and by Morassi in 1942.[4] In the meantime Richter had described it as a copy after a lost Giorgione.[5] More recently Berenson (1963) has listed it as a 'Giorgionesque' painting and Pignatti has given it to a follower of Giorgione.[6] Ballarin believes it to be by Giorgione himself.[7] On the other hand, Mariacher has recently revived the old attribution to Cariani.[8] The variety of these attributions clearly reflects the current uncertainty as to who might have executed our picture. None of the suggested attributions can be sustained solely on the basis of the stylistic comparisons which have been offered, due to the poor condition of our picture.

Garas has made a more convincing attempt to justify the association of our picture with the name of Giorgione,[9] on the basis of a description by Ridolfi in 1648[10] of a picture attributed to Giorgione in the van Voert [sic] collection, Antwerp,[11] representing a man with his hand reflected in his armour. The possibility that our picture is connected with a Giorgione prototype of this kind cannot be excluded; but Garas' attempt to trace the subsequent provenance[12] of the picture seen by Ridolfi did not lead to the discovery of any positive evidence to link it directly with ours.[13]

All that can be safely said is that our picture appears to originate from the sixteenth century, and, to judge from its appearance, it was very probably painted in Venice by an artist from the circle of Giorgione.

Mary, Lady Ruthven bequest 1885.

---

1. L. Venturi *Giorgione e il Giorgionismo* Milan 1913 p. 235.

2. W. Arslan in *Bolletino della Società Letteraria di Verona* November 1932 p. 6 note 1.

3. D. Viana *Francesco Torbido* Verona 1933 p. 33 pl. 4.

4. A Morassi *Giorgione* Milan 1942 p. 217.

5. G. Richter *Giorgio da Castelfranco called Giorgione* Chicago 1937 p. 216 no. 19.

6. T. Pignatti *Giorgione* Venice nd. p. 146.

7. Letter from Alessandro Ballarin, dated 6 October 1977, in the Gallery files. See further A. Ballarin in *Giorgione Atti del Convegno Internazionale di Studi* Venice 1979 p. 247 note 41.

8. G. Mariacher *Giovanni Cariani* in *I Pittori Bergamaschi Il Cinquecento* Bergamo 1975 p. 295 no. 81. See further R. Pallucchini and F. Rossi *Giovanni Cariani* Bergamo 1983 p. 352 no V31.

9. C. Garas in *Bulletin du Musée Hongrois des Beaux-Arts* Budapest 1964, No. 25 pp. 51 ff. fig. 39.

10. C. Ridolfi *Le Maraviglie dell'Arte* 1648 (ed. von Hadeln, Berlin 1914–24 I p. 106).

11. For van Voert one should probably read van Veerle; cf. von Hadeln's footnote 3 to Ridolfi (see note 10 above) and Garas *op. cit.* pp. 54 ff.

12. However Garas (*op. cit.* pp. 56–7 and note 12) did point out that the van Veerle collection picture could well be identical to item 14 in a 1682 inventory of the pictures belonging to a Portuguese collector, Diego Duarte, in Antwerp, which is described as follows: *Een Mans konterfeytsel half lijf in't harnas met de hant gehantschoent op't harnas.*

13. Nor is there apparently sufficient evidence to identify our picture with a Giorgione in the Grimani collection, Venice, described there by Vasari (ed. Milanesi 1906 IV p. 91) which Garas (*op. cit.* p. 54) claims can be recognised as one of the pictures later seen by Ridolfi in the van Voert or van Veerle collection, Antwerp.

VENETIAN sixteenth-century

704   ## Scholar with Inkstand

Canvas: 89 × 109.5

Cleaned 1976. There is a seam in the canvas, which runs vertically 27 cm. from the left-hand edge. Although the paint surface has suffered from minor losses and repaints in most areas, the principal features of the figure, with the exception of his right hand, are not seriously affected.

On the left is a pile of books, two of which are inscribed [P]LATO and [HIP]POCRATES; the book on the table is inscribed along its spine ... ACCEVS. Acquired as by Bassano and hitherto catalogued under the name of Jacopo Bassano. The only portrait which can be securely attributed to Jacopo is a signed picture of a *Bearded Man with Open Book and Letter* (see Fig. 3), which first came to light in the Kress Collection, New York, in 1950 and which is now in Memphis.[1] Prior to this discovery, a number of portraits (cf. our no.3 above) had been attributed to Jacopo Bassano by various writers such as Berenson (1894, 1932, 1936, 1957), Venturi,[2] Arslan[3] and Zampetti.[4] Our picture, however, shows no close stylistic connection with either the signed picture in Memphis or the group of attributed works, and its attribution to Jacopo Bassano was rightly rejected by Arslan in 1960.[5] In design our picture is perhaps closer to a *Portrait of a Man*, signed by Leandro Bassano, and now in Dresden,[6] but the handling of our picture is not characteristic of Leandro's style. It is apparently the work of a relatively minor sixteenth-century artist who had a knowledge of Venetian portraiture and who was probably himself working in Venice; but, in view of the rather dry manner in which it is painted, the possibility that it is by an artist of Flemish or German origin should not be excluded.

Mary, Lady Ruthven bequest 1885.

1. See W. E. Suida *Paintings and Sculpture from the Kress Collection* Washington 1951 p. 124 no. 52 illus. See also F. Rusk Shapley *Paintings from the Samuel H. Kress Collection, Italian Schools XVI-XVIII century* London 1973 p. 45 no. K. 1793 fig. 82. The picture which is now in the Brooks Memorial Art Gallery, Memphis (Inv. 61.208), is on canvas 76.2 × 65.4 cm. It is signed *Jac. a Ponte Bassanensis F. in Venetiis.*

2. See A. Venturi *Storia dell'Arte Italiana* Milan 1929 IX Part IV pp. 1115 f.

3. See E. Arslan I *Bassano* Milan 1960 I pp. 161ff.

4. See P. Zampetti *Jacopo Bassano* Exhibition Catalogue, Palazzo Ducale, Venice 1957 pp. 212 ff.

5. Arslan *op. cit.* I p. 338.

6. Canvas 92 × 107 cm. Reproduced Arslan *op. cit.* II pl. 328. See also H. Posse *Die Staatliche Gemäldegalerie zu Dresden* Dresden/Berlin 1929 p. 139 no. 283.

Paolo VERONESE *probably born in 1528 died 1588*

Paolo Caliari, called Veronese after his native city of Verona. By 1555 he had settled in Venice and begun work on the decorations in the church of S. Sebastiano. He quickly achieved recognition as one of the leading Venetian artists, together with Tintoretto who was his main rival. The chronology of his work is difficult to establish because of his relatively slow development. After his death, his busy studio was taken over by his sons, Carlo and Gabriele.

339   Mars and Venus

Canvas: 165.2 × 126.5

Cleaned 1951. X-rayed (Fig. 62). There is no reason to suppose the canvas has been cut down on the right and at the bottom in spite of a statement to this effect in the 1957 Catalogue. X-rays show that the figure of Venus, with the exception of her right leg, was painted over a light underpainting to give luminosity to her flesh. In contrast, the rest of the picture is on a dark ground which contributes to the sunken appearance of Venus's right leg and accounts for the darkening of the sky and the background. The paint surface is somewhat worn, particularly in the shadows. The pattern painted on Venus's drapery was originally dark green and has discoloured, but there is no physical evidence to suggest it has been superimposed at a later date, although this possibility was raised in the 1957 *Catalogue*, largely on the basis of comparison with a reproductive print by Simone Cantarini (Bartsch XIX 32).

Acquired as by Paolo Veronese and subsequently catalogued as an autograph work by him. The design was apparently a popular one and in addition to Cantarini's etching, described above, there is a studio replica at Frankfurt;[1] a version in the Residenz-Museum, Munich;[2] and a closely related version of no more than studio quality, which was engraved by Henriquez and Cathelin when in the Orléans collection and which is now in the Musée Condé, Chantilly. In this version Mars is bare-headed and two doves are introduced at the bottom left.[3]

A sheet of preparatory studies, in pen and ink and wash and squared in black chalk, for a *Venus and Cupid with a Mirror*, now in the British Museum where it is convincingly attributed to Paolo Veronese[4] (Fig. 63), shows a clear compositional connection with the figures of Venus and Cupid in our picture,[5] but it was not necessarily originally made for this purpose, and the figure of Mars in our picture is absent from the drawing.[6]

There is no firm evidence on which to date our picture, but it seems likely, as Pallucchini[7] and Pignatti[8] have already suggested, that it is a late work dating from the late 1570s or the 1580s. To judge from the relatively dull quality of the handling, which fails to approach the standard of the quite different design of *Mars and Venus* now in the Metropolitan Museum, New York, which may be some five or ten years earlier,[9] our picture was probably produced by Paolo Veronese with some studio assistance. Rearick believes it to be 'a shop derivative by Carletto.'[10]

A suggestion by Von Hadeln that our picture might be the *Mars and Venus* by Paolo Veronese painted for Rudolf II and described by Borghini and Ridolfi is incorrect;[11] Zeri has shown that Rudolf's picture was dismembered, and he has published a fragment of it, as well as a copy of the original composition.[12] More recently Pignatti has suggested that our picture might be identified as a *Mars and Venus* by Paolo Veronese, recorded in the Lelio Boscoli collection, Parma, in 1690.[13]

Coll: The earliest certain record of our picture is when it belonged to Sampson Gideon (d. 1767) at Belvedere House, Kent.[14] By descent to his son Lord Eardley, and then by inheritance, with Belvedere House, through Lord Saye and Sele, to Sir Culling Eardley; exhibited B.I., London, June 1828 (47), lent by Lord Saye and Sele. Bought for the R.I., Edinburgh, from Belvedere House in 1859.[15]

Royal Institution 1859.

---

1. Inv. 893. Canvas 167 × 128 cm. Reproduced in T. Pignatti *Veronese, L'Opera Completa* Venice 1976 I p. 150 no. 253 and II pl. 588. This version shows the same drapery patterns as our no. 339.

2. Canvas: 127 × 91 cms. See A. Feulner *Katalog der Gemälde im Residenz-Museum München und im Schloss Nymphenburg* Munich 1924, p. 90, no. 431.

3. See *Galerie du Palais Royal gravée* II Paris 1808. See also Pignatti (*op. cit.* I p. 150 no. 254 and II pl. 589) who believes it to be probably an autograph work by Paolo Veronese.

4. Inv. 1951–11–10–79. Pen and ink and wash 172 × 127 mm. Also reproduced by Pignatti *op. cit.* II pl. 587 and by R. Cocke in *Pantheon* XXXV (2) 1977 p. 122 fig. 6. The attribution to Paolo Veronese has the support of John Gere (letter in Gallery files dated 20 October 1976).

5. The connection with our picture was first recognised by Yonna Yapou, and was first reported in the *Shorter Catalogue* 1970 p. 101. Cf. also R. Cocke in *Pantheon* XXXV (2)1977, p. 124; and R. Cocke *Veronese Drawings A Catalogue Raisonné* London 1984, no. 106.

6. Cocke *op. cit.* p. 124.

7. R. Pallucchini *Paolo Veronese* Padua (dispense univ.) 1963–4 (unpublished). I am indebted to Terisio Pignatti for this reference.

8. *Op. cit.* I p. 150 no. 253.

9. See F. Zeri and E. Gardner *Italian Paintings. A Catalogue of the Collection of the Metropolitan Museum of Art, Venetian School* New York 1973 p. 84 pl. 97 (Inv. 10.189).

10. See R. Rearick *The Art of Paolo Veronese 1528–1588* Exhibition Catalogue, National Gallery of Art, Washington 1988 pp. 136–7 no. 70.

11. See C. Ridolfi *Le Maraviglie dell'Arte* 1648 (ed. von Hadeln, Berlin 1914–24 I p. 335 note 1). But see Schweikhart's subsequent revision of D. von Hadeln *Paolo Veronese Aus dem Nachlass des Verfassers herausgegeben vom Kunsthistorischen Institut in Florenz* Ed. G. Schweikhart, Florence 1978, p. 130 no. 82 where Borghini's original error concerning the provenance is acknowledged and our picture is described as autograph and dated *c.* 1580.

12. F. Zeri in *Paragone* 117 1959 pp. 43 ff. tav. 28 and 29.

13. See Pignatti *op. cit.* I p. 150 no. 253. For the 1690 inventory see G. Campori *Raccolta di cataloghi ed inventarii inediti* Modena 1870 p. 384 where the picture in question is described as follows: ... *Marte, Vener con un Amorino a piedi e un cagnolo, il Marte armato, Venere nuda, con drappo attorno lavorato con fogliami e paese, di mano di Paolo Veronese.*

14. See R. Dodsley *London and its environs* 1761 I p. 274 and T. Martyn *The English Connoisseur* Dublin 1767 p. 9.

15. See further *Pictures for Scotland* pp. 33–4.

1139 S. Anthony Abbot as Patron of a Kneeling Donor

Canvas: 198.5 × 117.8.

Cleaned 1958. X-rayed (details from top left and bottom right only). A fragment cut from the lower left-hand side of an altarpiece; only the left-hand edge is original. Extensive paint losses along the right-hand side may have taken place when the original picture was dismembered and attempts were made to obscure and to paint out what remained of the arm and wing of a S. Michael and the dragon. These features were uncovered in 1958. There are further damages along the left-hand edge and along the line of a vertical seam in the canvas which bisects the nose of S. Anthony Abbot. Otherwise the paint surface is in quite good condition. A painted-out head, immediately behind and to the left of S. Anthony Abbot, probably represents an earlier idea for this figure. There are also minor *pentimenti* around the outstretched left hand of the donor.

The Saint wears a dark silver-grey *mozzetta* edged with scarlet piping, with a white T on his right shoulder; an unusual version of the habit of the Order of S. Anthony. The order of Antonites was principally concerned with the care of those suffering from contagious diseases.

One of three surviving fragments of a large arched altarpiece (around 4.5 metres high. See Fig. 64 for a reconstruction) which showed, above, the *Dead Christ with Angels* (now in the National Gallery of Canada, Ottawa, no. 3336),[1] at the right another donor with his patron, S. Jerome, (now Dulwich College Art Gallery no. 270),[2] and, mostly in a missing strip of c. 60 cm. in the centre, a *S. Michael and the Dragon*. The right arm of S. Michael and the left leg of the dragon can be seen on the right of our picture. S. Michael's left hand can be seen on the left of the Dulwich fragment. There is no basis for the statement in the 1914 *Catalogue*, subsequently repeated by Ingersoll-Smouse, that the missing central section with S. Michael was at Castle Howard in Yorkshire.[3] On the contrary, it is clear that this figure was sacrificed when the altarpiece was cut up, possibly as a result of damage. It had already been cut up by 1795 if the Dulwich fragment is to be identified with lot 108 in the Desenfans sale on 28 February 1795.[4] Our fragment can be traced back to 1815 (see under *Coll.* below) and was in the Duke of Sutherland collection by 1836.[5] Our fragment was again slightly cut down at the top and bottom in 1913, before it was acquired by the Gallery.[6]

Von Hadeln has convincingly suggested that this altarpiece may be identified as a *Pietà* formerly in the Petrobelli Chapel in the Church of S. Francesco at Lendinara, Rovigo,[7] recorded by Pietro Brandolese, in 1795, as a picture which had only recently disappeared.[8] Brandolese also notes a copy in the Church of the Rosary at Lendinara which he describes in more detail, confirming Von Hadeln's identification of the Dulwich, Edinburgh and Ottawa fragments. The only discrepancy is in his reference to a figure of S. John the Baptist next to the *Santo Vescovo* (S. Anthony Abbot) in the copy, since this saint is not present in our fragment from the original altarpiece.[9] Brandolese notes that the Lendinara *Pietà* had been attributed to Paolo Veronese by Bartoli (in a manuscript note, presumably made in connection with his guide-book to Rovigo, published in 1793), but he himself expressed reservations and pointed out that Carlo Ridolfi had ignored the picture in his *Maraviglie dell' Arte* Venice 1648.

Our picture entered the collection as by Paolo Veronese and this attribution has been accepted by Ingersoll-Smouse in 1926,[10] by Osmond in 1927,[11] by Fiocco in 1928,[12] and by Berenson (1932, 1936 and 1963), followed by Marini in 1968[13] and Pignatti in 1976.[14] It was overlooked by Venturi who did however include the Ottawa and Dulwich fragments in his list of Paolo Veronese's works.[15] On the other hand Pallucchini and Crosato Larcher have expressed doubts as to whether the altarpiece to which our fragment belonged was executed wholly by Paolo Veronese. Pallucchini in 1963 suggested it was a collaborative effort by both Paolo Veronese and Carletto Caliari.[16] Then in 1968 Crosato Larcher argued that the Edinburgh and Dulwich fragments should be attributed specifically to Carletto Caliari, on the basis of stylistic comparison with Carletto's picture of *S. Nicola del Lido*, now at the Cini Foundation in Venice; but she did not rule out the possibility that the Ottawa fragment was from the hand of Paolo Veronese.[17] The stylistic evidence for associating the altarpiece to which our picture belongs with Carletto Caliari is not very strong. It seems more likely that the picture was designed by Paolo Veronese, and executed by him with as much studio assistance as one might reasonably expect in such a large work.

Like many of Paolo Veronese's works it cannot be dated with any precision on stylistic grounds. Bartoli believed it to have been painted in 1565, the date recorded on a frieze above the altar in the Petrobelli Chapel in S. Francesco. Modern critics, responding to the fragments outside their original context, have all preferred a much later date.

Coll: Our fragment was in the W. Comyns sale, Christie's 6 May 1815 (61). In the Duke of Sutherland's collection at York House by 1836 when recorded by Passavant,[18] and subsequently recorded there by Waagen in 1854.[19] Duke of Sutherland sale, Christie's 11 July 1913 (94).

Bought from Thos. Agnew's, London, 1913.

---

1. M. Laskin and M. Pantazzi ed. *Catalogue of the National Gallery of Canada, Ottawa, European and American Painting, Sculpture and Decorative Arts 1300–1800* Ottawa 1987, pp. 293–5. no. 3336 fig. 47. Oil on canvas: 216 × 243 cms. The canvas, which is in poor condition, has apparently been cut slightly on both sides. See also T. Pignatti *Veronese L' Opera Completa* Venice 1976 I p. 166, no. 336 and II pl. 708.

2. P. Murray *The Dulwich Picture Gallery* London pp. 134–5 . Oil on canvas: 230.2 × 125.6 cms. See Pignatti *op. cit.* I p. 16 no. 337 and II pl. 709 .

3. F. Ingersoll-Smouse in *Gazette des Beaux-Arts* XIV 1926 II pp. 21 ff.

4. Noel Desenfans sale by Skinner and Dyke 28 February 1795 (108) as *A Cardinal Blessing the Founder of Lorretto* [*sic*] . For this identification see the 1957 *Catalogue* p.287.

5. Passavant 1836 I p. 142: 'Paul Veronese. A Bishop with the figure of a man kneeling beside him; a pendant to the one in Dulwich College'.

6. At the Duke of Sutherland sale in 1913 (see under *Coll.* above) it measured 93 × 47 in. (236 × 119 cm.).

7. D. Von Hadeln *Paolo Veronese Aus dem Nachlass des Verfassers herausgegeben vom Kunsthistorischen Institut in Florenz* Ed. G. Schweikhart, Florence 1978 p. 10 p. 130 and nos 81, 83, and 213.

8. Pietro Brandolese *Del Genio de' Lendinaresi per la Pittura e di alcune pregevoli pitture* Padua 1795, pp. 14f. I am grateful to Michael Pantazzi for providing xeroxes of this.

9. Brandolese *op. cit.* p. 15 as follows: *nostro pittore, che s'è suo lavoro convien dire superasse se stesso. Questa ci ricorda che nella parte superiore del quadro venia rappresentato il morto Rendentore sostenuto dagli Angeli: stava nel mezzo S. Michele Arcangelo comprimente Lucifero: da un lato v'era dipinto S. Girolamo, dall'altro S. Giovambattista con un altro Santo Vescovo. Di qua, e di là rimanean ginocchioni due divoti, ed orano i ritratti delle persone della Famiglia, che ordinarono la tavola. Il*

campo poi era ornato di maestosa architettura, onde ne risultava la più grandiosa, e ben ordinata rappresentazione.

10. Ingersoll-Smouse *loc. cit.*

11. P. Osmond *Paolo Veronese, His Career and Work* London 1927 p. 82.

12. G. Fiocco *Paolo Veronese* Bologna 1928 p. 19.

13. R. Marini *L'opera completa di Paolo Veronese,* Milan 1968 p. 113 no. 156B.

14. Pignatti *op. cit.* I pp. 166–67 no. 338 and II pl. 710.

15. A. Venturi *Storia dell'Arte Italiana* Milan 1929 IX Part IV pp. 950–51.

16. R. Pallucchini *Paolo Veronese* Padua (dispense univ.) 1963–64 (unpublished). I am indebted to Terisio Pignatti for this reference.

17. L. Crosato Larcher in *Arte Veneta* XII 1968 pp. 222 ff. The attribution to Carletto has received some support from Diana Gisolfi Pechukas (letter in Gallery files dated 20 September 1988).

18. Passavant *loc. cit.*

19. Waagen 1854 II p. 61.

Andrea del VERROCCHIO *c. 1435–88*

Andrea di Michele di Francesco Cioni. A Florentine goldsmith, sculptor, and painter.[1] He ran a busy workshop where, according to Vasari, his pupils or assistants included Leonardo da Vinci, Lorenzo di Credi and Pietro Perugino. He is first recorded as a painter in 1468 when he painted a standard for the Medici *Giostra* in honour of Lucretia de' Donati. Then in 1475 he painted a pennant that Giuliano de' Medici carried in a tournament in honour of Simonetta Vespucci. Both these works are now lost. In 1479 he was commissioned to paint an altarpiece for the Cathedral of Pistoia which remains *in situ*. It was not quite completed in 1485 and most critics now believe it was executed on Verrocchio's design by his pupils, principally Lorenzo di Credi to whom it was attributed by Vasari in 1568.[2] A *Baptism of Christ*, now in the Uffizi, Florence, and formerly in the monastery of San Salvi, has also been attributed to Verrocchio, although, according to Vasari, Leonardo da Vinci painted the angel, holding some clothing, in the left foreground.[3] Leonardo may also have executed parts of the landscape, and possibly the figure of Christ as well. A *Madonna and Child with Saints*, now in Budapest, which is apparently identical with a picture Vasari attributed to Verrocchio, is usually judged to be unworthy of his hand, and has been attributed to Biagio d'Antonio, although Oberhuber has recently reopened this question with the suggestion that it might after all have been painted by Verrocchio himself in the late 1450s.[4] There is also a group of undocumented pictures representing the Virgin and Child which are generally accepted as works of Verrocchio or his immediate circle; they all show close links with the design of Verrocchio's marble and terracotta relief sculptures on the same theme. A *Virgin Holding the Child*, now in the Dahlem Museum, Berlin (Inv. 104A) is probably the picture most often attributed to Verrocchio himself, although on the basis of stylistic comparison with the Uffizi *Baptism* this attribution is still not conclusive.[5] A *Virgin with Standing Child*, also in Berlin (Inv. 108), and a *Virgin and Child with Two Angels* in the National Gallery, London (Inv. 296),[6] are both usually regarded as particularly close to Verrocchio. And although some writers have attributed them both to an Umbrian follower of Verrocchio, such as the young Perugino, this view should be treated with caution inasmuch as it seems to depend largely on an unconvincing stylistic comparison with a *Virgin and Child* attributed to Perugino, *c. 1470*, in the Jacquemart-André Museum, Paris.[7] A *Virgin and Child* in the Städelsches Kunstinstitut, Frankfurt (Inv. 702) also appears to be by an artist closely associated with Verrocchio; it has been attributed by Zeri to the Master of the Gardner Annunciation subsequently identified as Pier Matteo d'Amelia.[8]

Attributed to Andrea del VERROCCHIO and workshop

338   Madonna and Child

Canvas transferred from wood: 106.7 × 76.3

Cleaned 1973–5 by John Brealey in London immediately before its acquisition by the Gallery. X-rayed at the Courtauld Institute, London, in 1960 (Figs. 65, 66 and 67). The original transfer from wood to canvas took place in Venice in 1877[9] and it was transferred a second time in Britain around 1891.[10] The original panel consisted of three planks lying vertically, to judge from the evidence of paint losses along the old joins. The right-hand plank apparently retained less of the pigment than the other two, so that the condition of the paint surface to the right of a line through the Madonna's left shoulder is noticeably worse than elsewhere. These damages have left the essential structure of the design unimpaired. The heads and hands are also relatively intact. The least well preserved areas are the Child's legs and the Madonna's drapery in the lower right corner. The canvas texture has imposed itself on the paint surface.

According to White, who witnessed the second transfer to canvas, the figure of an angel was sketched by the artist in the brown underpainting.[11]

The X-rays reveal an elaborate network of perspective lines, incised in the gesso with a sharp stylus, with the diagonals converging on a point just below the Madonna's hands. The perspective grid appears to have been worked out directly on the prepared panel, rather than transferred from a cartoon.

Fahy has pointed out that our picture represents the *Adoration of the Child all' antica*.[12] The ruins shown in the background of the picture are the remains of the Temple of Peace, a Roman basilica that was supposed to have collapsed the night Christ was born. This tradition was recorded *c.* 1275 in the *Golden Legend* of Jacobus de Voragine, Archbishop of Genoa. Throughout the Middle Ages and the Renaissance the Temple of Peace was identified with the Basilica of Constantine at the north-east corner of the Forum in Rome. Fahy believes the ruins shown in our picture evoke the basilica sufficiently to suggest that the artist had some information about the building's appearance, perhaps from drawings or second-hand reports.

The earliest record of our picture dates from 1852 when it was in the Manfrini collection, Venice. It was described there by Selvatico and Lazari as a work of Filippo Lippi,[13] an attribution which was noted by Eastlake in 1855,[14] by Zanotto in 1856,[15] and by Nicoletti in 1872.[16] Although our picture shows the very strong influence of Filippo Lippi's pictures, particularly in the design of the kneeling Madonna, its attribution to the artist can no longer be sustained and had already been questioned by the time Ruskin acquired it. A new attribution to Verrocchio, first reported by Ruskin in July 1877, may equally well have been due to Fairfax Murray, the agent who advised Ruskin and negotiated the picture's purchase for him.[17] Most of the subsequent writers to have discussed our picture, up until the time it was cleaned in 1973–5, accepted it as an important work of high quality produced in Verrocchio's workshop; they include

Bode,[18] Van Marle,[19] Berenson,[20] Dussler,[21] Dalli Regoli,[22] Rusk Shapley,[23] Ottino
Della Chiesa,[24] and Shearman.[25] Berenson expressed the view that at least parts of it
were executed by Verrocchio himself, probably around 1471–2, and Shearman has also
lent support to this idea. On the other hand, in 1960 Martini suggested it might have
been executed by the young Leonardo da Vinci in Verrocchio's workshop.[26] His opinion
was based largely on the extremely elaborate and carefully drawn perspective of the
architectural background which he compared with Leonardo da Vinci's drawing of the
Adoration of the Magi in the Uffizi, Florence.[27] Martini's suggested attribution has
attracted no fresh support, and it must be emphasised that there is no *prima facie* reason
to suppose Verrocchio incapable of constructing the geometrical perspective of our
picture. Vasari, after all, described him as an expert in perspective; and this is quite
evident from Verrocchio's relief of the *Beheading of S. John the Baptist* on the Silver
Altar, now in the Cathedral museum, Florence, as well as from the foreground of the
Pistoia altarpiece.[28]

Since our picture was cleaned, both Zeri and Fahy have independently suggested it
might be an early work by Domenico Ghirlandaio,[29] a pupil of Alesso Baldovinetti
(according to Vasari), at the period around 1470 when he was apparently closely
influenced by Verrocchio, to judge from works such as his documented fresco of the
Madonna of Mercy in the Vespucci chapel in the church of Ognissanti, Florence. Fahy
argues that in Domenico Ghirlandaio's work alone do we find an exact parallel for the
meticulous handling of paint, the handsome physical types, the doctrinal projection of
space, and the interest in antiquity which characterises our picture. He compares its
perspective construction with that of Domenico Ghirlandaio's fresco of the *Last Supper*
at Passignano, a documented work of 1476. And he indicates that the pilasters in the
background of our picture can be seen in Ghirlandaio's early frescoes at Brozzi, Cercina
and Passignano, as well as in his *Adoration of the Shepherds* in S. Trinità, Florence;
while counterparts for the barrel vault are to be found in Ghirlandaio's frescoes in Santa
Maria Novella, Florence.

Fahy associates our picture with four other undocumented pictures representing the
Virgin and Child, and all apparently dating from *c.* 1470. Of these, one is in the National
Gallery, Washington (Fig. 68), where it is catalogued on stylistic evidence as the work of
Domenico Ghirlandaio.[30] Another (Fig. 69), in the Louvre, Paris (Inv. 1367A), was
attributed to Domenico Ghirlandaio by Berenson in 1933.[31] A third, in the monastery at
Camaldoli (Fig. 70), bears a traditional attribution to Domenico Ghirlandaio which
received further support in 1974–5 when it was exhibited under this name in Arezzo.[32]
A picture (Fig. 71), now in the Metropolitan Museum, New York (Inv. 14.40.647), was
catalogued as workshop of Verrocchio by Zeri, who nevertheless himself drew attention
to its stylistic proximity to the three pictures attributed to Domenico Ghirlandaio,
described above.[33]

The association of this group of pictures has received further support from other
scholars. Middeldorf believed our picture to be by the same hand as the *Virgin and Child*
at Camaldoli although he attributed both to Verrocchio;[34] Oberhuber believed our
picture to be by the same hand as those in the National Gallery, Washington and the
Louvre but he too favoured an attribution to Verrocchio;[35] Grossman accepted the
attribution of all these pictures to Domenico Ghirlandaio.[36]

In the absence of documentation, it may well prove impossible to determine with any certainty whether these pictures are by Verrocchio or by the young Domenico Ghirlandaio at a time when he was closely associated with Verrocchio. In these circumstances it seems best to leave our picture under the name of Verrocchio and workshop, in the belief that whoever painted it, and the other small pictures which have been associated with it, was certainly an artist who formed his style under Verrocchio's spell.[37]

Coll: Manfrini collection, Venice, by 1852, as Filippo Lippi.[38] Manfrini collection sale catalogue 1856 (356) still as Filippo Lippi.[39] Bought by John Ruskin from the Manfrini collection through the agency of Charles Fairfax Murray in 1877, and exhibited in his S. George's Museum at Walkley; transferred 1890 to the Ruskin Museum at Meersbrook Park, Sheffield.[40] Deposited by the Trustees of the Guild of S. George in the Graves Art Gallery, Sheffield, from *c.* 1952–73; lent to the *Exhibition of Italian Art from the thirteenth to the seventeenth century* City of Birmingham Museum and Art Gallery 1955 (114), and to the exhibition *Italian Art and Britain* R.A., London 1960 (318).

Bought with help from the National Art Collections Fund and the Pilgrim Trust from the Trustees of the Guild of S. George 1975.

---

1. For biographical details see M. Davies *National Gallery Catalogue, The Earlier Italian Schools* London 1961 pp. 553–4; and G. Passavant *Andrea del Verrocchio als Maler* Düsseldorf 1959.

2. See Passavant *op. cit.* pp. 29 ff. pl. 1.

3. See Passavant *op. cit.* pp. 58 ff. pl. 37.

4. See Passavant *op. cit.* pp. 88 ff. pl. 84; and G. Passavant *Verrocchio. Sculptures, Paintings and Drawings* London 1969 pp. 212–3. See K. Oberhuber in *Revue de l'Art* 41 1978 pp. 63 ff. My own knowledge of the Budapest picture is limited to good photographs.

5. See G. Passavant *Andrea del Verrocchio als Maler* Düsseldorf 1959 pp. 95 ff. pl. 92.

6. See Passavant *op. cit.* pp. 151–2 pl. 97, and pl. 98. See also Davies *op. cit.* pp. 554–5.

7. For the attribution of the Berlin picture to Perugino see R. Longhi in *Paragone* 33 1952 p. 42. For the attribution of the London pictures see F. Zeri in *Bolletino d'Arte* XXXVIII 1953 p. 134.

8. See F. Zeri in *Bolletino d'Arte* XXXVIII 1953 pp. 125–29. But cf. Davies *op. cit.* p. 554; and G. Passavant *Verrocchio. Sculptures, Paintings and Drawings* London 1969 p. 208 App. 31 illus. For the attribution to the young Pier Matteo d'Amelia see P. Todini in *La Pittura Umbra* 1989 I p. 284 II fig. 1062.

9. See *The Works of John Ruskin* Library Edition ed. E. Cook and A. Wedderburn London 1907 XXIX p. 165 and London 1907 XXX p. 193.

10. For a description of the transfer see W. White *The Principles of Art as illustrated by examples in the Ruskin Museum* London 1895 pp. 74 ff. This is reprinted in *The Works of John Ruskin* Library Edition ed. E. Cook and A. Wedderburn London 1907 XXX p. 193 note 3, with a photograph of the picture before the second transfer, pl. XI. White wrote as follows: 'Three years ago, it was found to again require skilled attention, the *gesso* having in parts become detached from the canvas. The only remedy in this case was the delicate operation of entirely removing the *gesso* itself, which was cautiously planed away, until the back of the paint first laid on was exposed, revealing the drawing of the additional angel, already referred to, against the drapery of the Madonna, which was painted over it. The painting was then secured to three thicknesses of canvas, and the superficial painting that had been added under previous restorations was carefully removed, thus exhibiting the original work in its integrity, as nearly as possible. The dangerous process was performed with complete success, and the work is now as originally painted, although, of course, it cannot be affirmed that the picture is precisely as it appeared when fresh from the hand of the master. There are, for instance, signs of there having been an extension of the embroidery in gold upon the hem of the robe and the dress, and also upon the edge of the thin veil which drapes the head. It is, moreover, interesting to know that at one time a nimbus of gold surrounded the head of the Madonna: but the painter himself appears to have reconsidered this point, and decided to paint it out again.' It should be noted that there is no sign of a nimbus around the Madonna's head in the X-rays of our picture.

11. See note 10 above.

12. The views of Everett Fahy, quoted in this catalogue entry, all originate from his lecture *Ruskin's Verrocchio Madonna in Edinburgh* which was first delivered at the Royal Scottish Museum, Edinburgh, on 26 October 1976. Fahy has reiterated his attribution to the young Domenico Ghirlandaio in a letter of 4 September 1988 (in Gallery files).

13. P. Selvatico and V. Lazari *Guida di Venezia e delle isole circonvicine* Venice-Milan-Verona 1852 p. 299.

14. Charles Eastlake *Notebooks* (National Gallery, London, MSS) 1855 II f. 6 v. and f. 9 v. On f. 6 v. he describes it as 'Filippo Lippi – ruined – Madonna and Child (perhaps P. Uccello)...' Eastlake noted the picture again two years later, 1857 III f. l r. as follows: 'Madonna adoring Child on ground – much injured (Child's leg) but formerly careful specimen and might be restored – about 4 ft. high about 2 ft. wide – wood – architecture and background very carefully executed. Called Lippi – probably Pesello...' I am indebted to the National Gallery for permission to publish Eastlake's notes.

15. F. Zanotto *Nuovissima Guida di Venezia* Venice 1856 p. 345.

16. G. Nicoletti *Catalogo della Pinacoteca Manfrini* Venice 1872 (MS in Biblioteca Marciana Misc. C. 11231; photocopy in the library of the National Gallery, London).

17. See *The Works of John Ruskin* Library Edition ed. E. Cook and A. Wedderburn, London 1907 XXIX p. 165.

18. W. Bode in *Jahrbuch der Königlich Preussischen Kunstsammlungen* III 1882 pp. 250–51; reprinted in *Italienische Bildhauer der Renaissance: Studien zur Geschichte der Italienischen Plastik und Malerei auf Grund der Bildwerke und Gemälde in den Königl. Museen zu Berlin* Berlin 1887 p. 132.

19. R. Van Marle *The Development of the Italian Schools of Painting* The Hague 1929 XI p. 547.

20. See B. Berenson *The Drawings of the Florentine Painters* New York 1903 p. 33; also in *Bolletino d'Arte* XXVII 1933 pp. 203–4. Also listed by Berenson in 1909, 1932, 1936 and 1963.

21. L. Dussler in Thieme-Becker XXXIV p. 295.

22. G. Dalli Regoli *Lorenzo di Credi* Cremona 1966 pp. 14 and 30 fig. 69.

23. See F. Rusk Shapley *Paintings from the Samuel H. Kress Collection, Italian Schools XIII–XV century* London 1966 p. 119. She discusses our picture together with a *Madonna Adoring the Child* at Birmingham Museum of Art, Alabama (Inv. K. 1722), which she catalogues as by a follower of Verrocchio. She also reports an earlier unpublished suggestion by Roberto Longhi that both pictures might be by the young Botticelli *c*. 1466.

24. A. Ottino Della Chiesa *L'opera completa di Leonardo pittore* Milan 1967 p. 115 no. 125.

25. J. Shearman in the *Burlington Magazine* CIX 1967 p. 127 note 24. It should be added that Shearman's view of Verrocchio also includes the *Dreyfus Madonna* in the National Gallery of Art, Washington (Inv. K.1850), and a *Virgin and Child* from the Gambier-Parry collection, which is not generally accepted as Verrocchio's work.

26. A. Martini in *Arte figurativa: antica e moderna* VIII 1960 pp. 32 ff.

27. Reproduced by Martini *op. cit.* p. 37. For a discussion of the preliminary drawing of the architecture in our picture, following X-ray examination see S. Rees Jones in the *Bulletin of the Institute of Physics* June 1950 pp. 157 ff.

28. Reproduced by G. Passavant *Verrocchio, Sculptures Paintings and Drawings* London 1969 pl. 54.

29. Letter from Federico Zeri, dated 9 September 1976, in Gallery files. For Everett Fahy's views cf. note 12 above. It should be added that the possibility of an attribution to the young Domenico Ghirlandaio had already been raised by E. K. Waterhouse in the *Burlington Magazine* XCVII 1955 p. 295.

30. See Rusk Shapley *op. cit.* p. 125 Inv. K. 2076 fig. 344.

31. B. Berenson in *Bolletino d'Arte* XXVII 1933 p. 257 fig. 20. The picture has previously been attributed to Mainardi.

32. *Arte nell' Aretino* Exhibition Catalogue, San Francesco, Arezzo 1974/75 pp. 100 ff. no. 37.

33. F. Zeri and E. Gardner *Italian Paintings, A Catalogue of the Collection of the Metropolitan Museum of Art, Florentine School* New York 1971 pp. 151–2.

34. Letters from Ulrich Middeldorf, dated 21 January 1976 and 28 September 1977.

35. K. Oberhuber in *Revue de l'Art* 1978 no. 42. pp.63 ff.

36. S. Grossman in *Städel Jahrbuch* 1979 7 pp.101 ff.

37. Cf also H. Brigstocke in *A Dealer's Record Agnew's 1967–81* London 1981 pp.24 ff.

38. See note 13 above.

39. *Catalogo dei Quadri esistenti nella Galleria Manfrini in Venezia* 1856 (photocopy in the library of the National Gallery, London).

40. Reproduced in the 1913 *Portfolio* (no. 2) of the Arundel Club for the Publication of Reproductions of Works of Art in Private Collections and Elsewhere.

VITALE DA BOLOGNA *active by 1334 died 1359–61*

Vitale d'Aimo de' Cavalli, called Vitale da Bologna. He is the first Bolognese painter with a distinctive artistic personality. His work includes the signed *Madonna dei Battuti* in the Vatican Gallery, Rome, the signed *Madonna and Child* (from S. Maria dei Denti at Mezzaratta) of 1345, now in the Davia-Bargellini Gallery, Bologna, and a *Polyptych* in S. Salvatore, Bologna, documented in 1353. He died between 4 June 1359 and 31 July 1361.

952 **Adoration of the Kings with S. Ursula and S. Catherine of Alexandria; (in the spandrels) the Annunciation**

Wood: (including original mouldings) 60.4 × 38.6

Cleaned 1977. The two bottom corners are damaged by woodworm and there is a small vertical split in the panel at the top centre. There are losses of gesso from the frame-work, especially the side pillars, and from the punched decoration at the top. The paint surface is generally in good condition. Minor paint losses affect the robe of the king at the top right, part of the halo of S. Catherine, and the right arm of the seated attendant in the centre foreground. The foliage above the heads of the horses at the bottom right appears to have been altered or repainted. The faces of the figures and the gold back-ground are slightly worn. The original painted gesso on the reverse (and edges) was uncovered during cleaning in 1977, revealing a geometric design, but with substantial losses.

The left wing of a diptych. The right wing, representing a *Pietà*, is in the collection of the Longhi Foundation, Florence.[1] Acquired and catalogued as Sienese school[2] until 1957 when it was given to Vitale da Bologna. This attribution, which is now beyond dispute, was first suggested by Berenson and was recorded as early as the 1929 *Catalogue*.[3] The attribution to Vitale da Bologna was then followed by Sandberg Vavalà in 1930,[4] by Longhi in 1934–5[5] and again in 1950,[6] and our picture was exhibited under this name in Bologna in 1950.[7]

Various dates have been suggested for our picture. In 1930 Longhi argued that it was an early work of *c.* 1325–35,[8] but by 1950 had revised this idea and proposed *c.* 1345–50 instead.[9] More recently Gnudi has proposed a more probable dating of *c.* 1353–5,[10] on the basis of stylistic comparison with the *Polyptych* in S. Salvatore, Bologna, which was commissioned in 1353.[11]

Coll: Acquired for the Fine Art Society, London, by R. Langton Douglas.[12]

Bought from the Fine Art Society, London, 1908.

---

1. See A. Boschetto *La Collezione Roberto Longhi* Florence 1971 no. 10 illus. See also note 6 below.

2. But in 1924 R. Van Marle (*The Development of the Italian Schools of Painting* The Hague 1924 IV p. 350) suggested it was a product of the school of Rimini.

3. See further Berenson 1968.

4. In *Rivista d'Arte* XII 1930 pp. 1–3 fig. 22.

5. See R. Longhi *Lavori in Valpadana: La Pittura del Trecento nell' Italia settentrionale* 1934–5 (*Opere Complete di Roberto Longhi* VI Florence 1973 p. 21).

6. In *Paragone* 5 1950 p. 9.

7. See *Mostra della Pittura Bolognese del Trecento* Bologna 1950 p. 28 no. 15.

8. See note 5 above.

9. See note 6 above.

10. C. Gnudi *Vitale da Bologna* Milan 1962 pp. 66 and 70.

11. For this picture see Gnudi *op. cit.* p. 69 tav. CII.

12. According to a letter from the Fine Art Society, dated 11 February 1908, now in the Gallery files.

Marco ZOPPO *1432–78*

Born at Cento. Assistant of Francesco Squarcione at Padua 1453–5. Also worked in Bologna, and in Venice where he died in 1478.

Attributed to Marco ZOPPO

1719 Noli Me Tangere

Wood: 33.5 × 24.5

X-rayed. The picture had already been severely overcleaned and then restored by the date of its acquisition. During the 1950s some of the repaints were removed, including a long skirt covering Christ's legs. The distant landscape has been virtually rubbed away. The only areas in sound condition are the face, hands and feet of Christ, the highlights on the Madonna's hair, and the rock forms in the immediate foreground.

Acquired as by Zoppo. The attribution was made first by Longhi,[1] and also by Berenson (1932, 1936 and 1963). It has been followed by Ruhmer,[2] and by Armstrong[3] who compares our picture in terms of style, with the signed Collegio di Spagna polyptych in San Clemente, Bologna, and tentatively suggests it might date from the mid-1460s. From the little that remains of the original paint surface, it still seems reasonable to associate our picture with Zoppo's name.

Coll: Signore Campi, Florence 1918;[1] Dr. James Simon, Berlin; Simon sale by Frederic Mueller and Cie, Amsterdam 25–26 October 1927 (51) illus.

Bought from Knoedler's, London, 1928.

1. R. Longhi *Officina Ferrarese* 1934 (*Opere Complete di Roberto Longhi* V Florence 1956 pp. 27 and 96 note 53). Longhi claimed to have first identified the picture when it was with Signore Campi in Florence as early as 1918.

2. E. Ruhmer *Marco Zoppo* Vicenza 1966 pp. 71–2 no. 59 illus.

3. L. Armstrong *The Paintings and Drawings of Marco Zoppo* (*Outstanding Dissertations in the Fine Arts*) New York/London 1976 pp. 129 and pp. 350–1 no. 5.

4. See Longhi *loc. cit.*

Francisco de ZURBARÁN *1598–1664*

Born at Fuente de Cantos. Apprenticed to Pedro Díaz de Villanueva in Seville. His earliest dated work was completed in 1616. He lived in Llerena from 1617–28 and then in 1629 settled in Seville. In 1634 he was working in Madrid and eventually returned to live there from 1658 until his death in 1664. His work shows the successive influence of Velázquez, Ribera and later of Murillo. Although there are numerous dated pictures from all periods of his career, the chronology of his other work cannot be established with any precision, due to the relatively slow development of his style.

340   The Immaculate Conception

Canvas, arched top: 255.5 × 177
Cleaned 1954. Although the picture is in good condition for a work of its size and age, there are numerous small paint losses in many areas. They particularly affect the Virgin's hair, her right eye and an area between her nose and left eye. The cupid on the left beneath the Virgin's feet is affected by extensive paint losses around the mouth and left eye, and there is a damage on S. Anne's left cheek. There are more extensive damages along the bottom edge of the canvas. Pemán has raised the possibility that the canvas might have been cut substantially along the bottom,[1] but to judge from the clearly accentuated swagging threads in the canvas, pulled towards the bottom edge, this is improbable.

The representation of the Immaculate Conception of the Virgin as an event treated historically, instead of symbolically, dates from at least the early sixteenth century but only became common at the end of that century.[2] By then the iconography had become established, more or less in its final form, by Italian artists: the Virgin is shown in the sky 'clothed with the sun, and the moon under her feet, and upon her head a crown of twelves stars' (*Revelation* XII, 1). Further emblems of the Virgin are sometimes shown in the clouds and on the earth below.

The subject of the Immaculate Conception became extremely popular in Spain, and particularly in Seville, after the publication there in 1618 of a Papal bull encouraging the cult of the Conception. Zurbarán painted the subject on numerous occasions throughout his active life. Inasmuch as the iconography of these works varies at all, it is generally in the direction of greater simplicity. In the earliest example by Zurbarán at Bilbao, which is signed and dated 1616, the Virgin is crowned with stars and stands on a full moon.[3] In three later pictures, one in Barcelona dated 1632,[4] and others at Sigüenza,[5] and in the Prado, Madrid,[6] as well as in our picture, the Virgin is shown standing on a crescent moon with her hands clasped in prayer and surrounded by symbolic emblems which are inserted into the pattern of clouds; in our picture the symbols include the temple, palm, cypress, and a tower, while in the distance there is a city (*Civitas Dei*). Here Zurbarán was influenced by an engraving of the subject by Raphael Sadeler the younger, published in Munich in 1605.[7] In these four paintings by Zurbarán, however, unlike the print, the Virgin stands on the convex part of the moon; evidently the artist had followed the instructions of Pacheco (who in his turn had been influenced by the treatise of Luis de Alcázar) where it is pointed out that if the sun and the moon meet, both points of the moon must be seen to point downwards.[8] A further painting of the subject by Zurbarán, in Seville Cathedral, also follows the same iconographic form, except for the relatively unusual insertion of a crown on the Virgin's head.[9] In other versions of the subject Zurbarán shows the Virgin with eyes raised to heaven and with her open arms outstretched; this is seen, for instance, in a picture exhibited at Colnaghi's in 1974[10] and in a picture at Budapest which is signed and dated 1661.[11] Our painting stands apart from other known versions of the subject by Zurbarán because of the inclusion of the half-length figures of S. Joachim and S. Anne. As Baticle has pointed out, the Feasts of S. Anne and S. Joachim, which had been suppressed by Pope Pius V in 1568 after the Council of Trent, were reinstated in 1584 by Pope Gregory XIII.[12]

Acquired as by Zurbarán and clearly by him, but its origins and its date have never been firmly established beyond the Galerie Espagnole in Paris in 1838. In 1950 Pemán described our picture as similar in style to a group of works painted by Zurbarán for the Carthusian Monastery at Jerez, which were later deposited in the Cadiz Museum.[13] Of the seven principal pictures in this group, only a *S. Bruno in Prayer* is still in Cadiz, together with several other pictures of individual saints and angels.[14] The sale of six other major pictures from the Jerez group is documented in 1837, and by 1838 they were in the Galerie Espagnole in Paris.[15] From the description made at the time of the sale in 1837, they can be firmly identified as the *Battle of El Sotillo* in New York,[16] the *Virgin of the Rosary with Carthusians* now in Poznán;[17] and the *Annunciation*, the *Adoration of the Shepherds* (signed and dated 1638), the *Adoration of the Magi* and the *Circumcision* (signed and dated 1639) which are now all in Grenoble.[18] After comparing the style of our picture with these pictures from Jerez, Pemán then proposed that it too might have originally belonged to the same monastery. More specifically he argued that it was probably originally placed as a pendant to the Poznán picture on a wall of the lay choir, and that the remaining pictures of the group together formed the main altar for which Pemán advanced a hypothetical reconstruction. Finally, Pemán concluded that our picture must at some later date have changed places with the New York picture, since by the time Ponz visited the monastery the New York picture was exhibited on a wall of the lay choir together with the Poznán picture.[19] However Pemán's suggestion regarding the origins of our picture are entirely speculative. It is not mentioned in the documents relating to the sale in 1837 of the six pictures from Cadiz which are now in New York, Poznán and Grenoble. Equally, there is apparently no reference to a picture of the *Immaculate Conception* by Zurbarán in any published description of the Carthusian Monastery at Jerez, whereas each of the other seven principal pictures by Zurbarán originating from the monastery is specifically mentioned in Ponz's detailed account.[20] In these circumstances Pemán's thesis should be treated with extreme caution, although it has been fully accepted by Guinard,[21] adopted with some variations by Soria[22] and further endorsed by Baticle, who draws attention to the particular devotion of the Carthusians both to the Immaculate Conception and to the cult of S. Anne.[23] Not only is there no circumstantial reason for supposing the Edinburgh picture came from Jerez, it is not even particularly close in style to the Jerez group, and does not necessarily date from the same moment c. 1639. Volmer's suggestion of a slightly later date for our picture (i.e. in the early 1640s) which was later overshadowed by Pemán's theories, deserves to be seriously reconsidered.[24]

Coll: Probably Galerie Espagnole, Louvre, Paris, 1838 (342);[25] Louis Philippe sale Christie's 7 May 1853 (143) bought Hickman; collection of Lord Elcho (later 10th Earl of Wemyss) who lent it to Manchester *Art Treasures Exhibition* 1857 (793).[26] Also recorded in Lord Elcho's collection by Waagen in 1857.[27] Bought by the R.I., Edinburgh, in 1859.[28]

Royal Institution 1859.

1. C. Pemán in *Archivo Español de Arte* XXIII 1950 pp. 218 ff.

2. See E. Mâle *L'Art Religieux après le Concile de Trente* Paris 1932 pp. 40 ff.; M. Trens *Mariá-Iconografiá de la Virgen en el arte español* Madrid 1947 pp. 96–190; and N. Maclaren, revised by A. Braham *National Gallery Catalogue, The Spanish School* London 1970 p. 78.

3. See M. Soria *The Paintings of Zurbarán* London 1953 p. 133 no. 1. pl. 1.

4. See Soria *op. cit.* p. 146 no. 59 fig. 34, as private collection, Jerez de la Frontera. See T. Frati *L'opera completa di Zurbarán* Milan 1973 p. 93 no. 95.

5. See *Exposición Zurbarán* Casón del Buen Retiro, Madrid 1964–5 p. 98 no. 4 illus. This picture was formerly at Jadraque and is now in the Diocesan Museum at Sigüenza.

6. Inv. 2992. Reproduced by Frati *op. cit.* p. 96 no. 135.

7. See Soria *op.cit.* p. 146 fig. 35.

8. F. Pacheco *Arte de la Pintura* Seville 1649 pp. 481–84.

9. See Soria *op. cit.* p. 154 no. 88 fig. 58. Here Zurbarán has perhaps followed earlier pictures of the subject by Luis Pascal (cited by Pacheco *loc. cit.*) by Pacheco himself (reproduced by Trens *op. cit.* p. 176 fig. 101) and by Roelas (reproduced by P. Guinard *Zurbarán et les peintres espagnols de la vie monastique* Paris 1960 p. 209).

10. See E. Young in *Archivo Español de Arte* XLV 1972 pp. 161–6, where he suggests a date around 1628–9.

11. See Soria *op. cit.* p. 188 no. 222 pl. 100.

12. J. Baticle *Zurbarán* Exhibition Catalogue (English Edition) Metropolitan Museum New York 1987, pp. 198–200, no. 33. See further O. Delenda in *Gazette des Beaux-Arts* CXI April 1988, pp. 243 ff, fig. 9.

13. Pemàn *loc. cit.*

14. See Soria *op. cit.* pp. 163–4, nos. 124–32 and pp. 168 f no. 141 fig. 96.

15. For the history and documentation of the disposal of the Cadiz pictures see E. Romero de Torres in *Boletín de la Comisión Provincial de Monumentos de Cádiz* 1908 pp. 98 ff. and E. Tormo in *Cultura Española* 13 February 1909 pp. 29 ff.

16. See Soria *op. cit.* p. 164 f. no. 133 pl. 62.

17. See Soria *op. cit.* p. 165 no. 134 fig. 92.

18. See Soria *op. cit.* p. 166 nos. 137–40 pls. 69–72 and figs. 94 and 95.

19. A Ponz *Viage de España* Madrid 1792 XVII Carta 6 pp. 276 ff. See also J. A. Ceán Bermúdez *Diccionario Histórico de los Profesores de las Bellas Artes en España* Madrid 1800 VI p. 51.

20. *Loc. cit.*

21. *Op. cit.* pp. 198 ff. and p. 210 no. 11 illus.

22. *Op. cit.* p. 168 no. 143.

23. Baticle *loc. cit.* (see note 12 above).

24. H. Vollmer in Thieme-Becke XXXVI p. 602.

25. Cf. J. Baticle *La Galerie Espagnole de Louis-Phillipe au Louvre 1838–1848* Paris 1981 pp. 219–20, no. 342.

26. For Lord Elcho see Colin Thompson *Pictures from Gosford House* Edinburgh 1957 p. 7.

27. Waagen 1857 p. 64.

28. According to a letter from J. Skene to the Rt. Hon. B. F. Primrose, dated 4 August 1859 (R.I. Letter Book deposited in the Scottish Record Office) the sale had already taken place by that date. The sale is also reported in the *Daily Scotsman* 13 September 1859. A statement in the 1957 *Catalogue* p. 307 that the picture was presented to the R.I. by Lord Elcho is incorrect.

NUMERICAL INDEX OF PAINTINGS
IN THE PERMANENT COLLECTION

The present numerical sequence was started in the 1919 *Catalogue*. Before that date the numbers were changed according to the sequence of pictures exhibited on the walls of the Gallery. Up to no. 331 the list follows an alphabetical sequence by artists, based on the attributions current in 1919; all these pictures were already in the collection when the National Gallery of Scotland building was opened in 1859. Thereafter, the list generally follows the order of accession, starting from the year 1859 onwards.

3	Bassano	109	Pietro da Cortona
4	Bassano	110	Raphael
7	Ricci	339	Veronese
9	Bonifazio Veronese	340	Zurbarán
10	Bordon	459	Carducho
17	Canaletto	600	Rosa
18	Cambiaso	600A	Rosa
19	Emilian	622	Rosa
20	Borgianni	638	Giulio Romano
21	Neapolitan	645	Italian
29	Mola	646	Lorenzo di Credi
30	Furini	689	Tintoretto
31	Furini	690	Venetian
32	Garofalo	704	Venetian
35	Giorgione	812	Italian
39	Guercino	828	Guardi
40	Guercino	829	Guardi
42	Cantarini	910	Italian
48	Borgianni	952	Vitale da Bologna
55	Paggi	953	Gozzoli
60	Lombard	1021	Pérez
63	Procaccini	1023	Matteo di Giovanni
70	Reschi	1030	Rosselli
76	Scorza	1139	Veronese
77	Scorza	1189	Fortuny
79	Sirani	1190	Cima da Conegliano
83	Novelli	1210	Castagno
84	Neapolitan	1250	Pesellino
85	Italian	1498	Guardi
91	Tiepolo	1499	Guardi
92	Tiepolo	1511	Bassano
96	Tintoretto	1513	Serodine
97	Tintoretto	1528	Amedei
98	Tintoretto	1535	Ferrarese
99	Tintoretto	1536	Botticelli
100	Bassano	1538	Sellaio
103	Titian	1539A, B	Master of the San Lucchese Altarpiece
104	Titian		
105	Polidoro da Lanciano	1540A, B	Master of 1419

LIST OF ATTRIBUTIONS
CHANGED SINCE THE 1957 CATALOGUE

Old attribution	Inventory number	New attribution
Gerolamo Bassano, ascribed	1635	studio of Jacopo BASSANO
Jacopo Bassano, ascribed	704	VENETIAN sixteenth-century
Ludovico Carracci, ascribed	21	NEAPOLITAN second quarter seventeenth-century
Fiorenzo di Lorenzo, ascribed	1745	FERRARESE C. 1500
Florentine, mid-fourteenth-century	1539 A, B	MASTER OF THE SAN LUCCHESE ALTARPIECE
Florentine, c. 1420-5	1540 A, B	MASTER OF 1419
Florentine, mid-fifteenth-century	1528	Giuliano AMEDEI
Florentine, fifteenth-century	1974	workshop of APOLLONIO DI GIOVANNI
Florentine, fifteenth-century	1975	MASTER OF THE ADIMARI CASSONE
Guercino, ascribed	29	follower of Pier Francesco MOLA
Guercino, after	39	GUERCINO
Italian	110	after RAPHAEL
Italian, seventeenth-century	19	EMILIAN seventeenth-century
Jacopo di Cione, workshop, ascribed	1958	TUSCAN mid-fourteenth-century
Alessandro Longhi, manner of	1638	ITALIAN eighteenth-century
Raphael, studio	638	GIULIO ROMANO and workshop
Guido Reni, ascribed	42	Simone CANTARINI
Jusepe de Ribera, follower	83	Pietro NOVELLI
Jusepe de Ribera, manner	84	NEAPOLITAN second half of seventeenth-century
Jusepe de Ribera, manner	812	ITALIAN C. 1630
Sebastiano and Marco Ricci, ascribed	7	attributed to Marco RICCI
Rossello di Jacopo Franchi, ascribed	1738	workshop of Giovanni TOSCANI
Leonardo Scaletti, ascribed	1634	EMILIAN late fifteenth-century
Johann Schönfeld	85	ITALIAN seventeenth-century
Spanish, fifteenth-century	1021	attributed to Gonzalo PÉREZ
Venetian, eighteenth-century	910	ITALIAN eighteenth- or nineteenth-century
Venetian, eighteenth-century	2014	follower of CANALETTO
Venetian, eighteenth-century	2120	Francesco MONTI

PICTURES CATALOGUED AS ITALIAN OR SPANISH
IN THE 1957 CATALOGUE
BUT EXCLUDED FROM THE PRESENT CATALOGUE

Old attribution	Inventory number
GRIMALDI, ascribed	38
ITALIAN, sixteenth-century	56
ITALIAN	108
MURILLO, ascribed	432
TAVELLA	88

LIST OF ATTRIBUTIONS
CHANGED SINCE THE 1978 EDITION

Old attribution	Inventory number	New attribution
Apollonio di Giovanni, follower of	1940	APOLLONIO DI GIOVANNI
Fillippino Lippi, circle of	2099	circle of BOTTICELLI
Pietro da Cortona, after, or by a follower of	109	ITALIAN, late seventeenth-century

COPIES AFTER ITALIAN PICTURES,
NOT INCLUDED IN THE PRESENT CATALOGUE

Inv. no.	Copy after		Artist to whom attributed
66	After Raphael in the Vatican Gallery, Rome	*The Transfiguration*	G. URQUHART
43	After Guido Reni in Brera Gallery, Milan	*The Apostles Peter and Paul*	S. WILLIAMS
106	After Titian in the Louvre, Paris	*The Entombment*	T. DUNCAN
128	After Paolo Veronese in the Louvre, Paris	*The Marriage at Cana*	T. DUNCAN

INDEX OF COLLECTORS

ILLUSTRATIONS, INCLUDING COMPARATIVE FIGURES

[Pl. 1] Attributed to Giuliano Amedei
The Death of S. Ephraim [1528]

[Pl. 2] Apollonio di Giovanni
Triumphs of Love and Chastity [1940]

[Pl. 3] Workshop of APOLLONIO DI GIOVANNI
The Rape of the Sabines [1974]

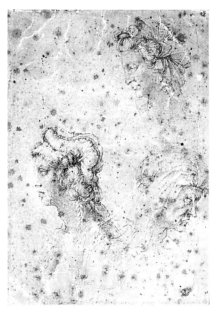

[Fig. 1] BACCHIACCA
Gathering of Manna
Wood: 112 x 95
National Gallery of Art, Washington

[Fig. 2] MICHELANGELO
Study of Three Heads
Black chalk: 34 x 23
Uffizi, Florence

[Pl. 4] BACCHIACCA
Moses Striking the Rock [2291]

[Pl. 5] Jacopo BASSANO
Adoration of the Kings [100]

[Pl. 6] Traditionally attributed to
Jacopo BASSANO
Portrait of a Gentleman [3]

[Fig. 3] Jacopo BASSANO
Bearded Man with Open Book and Letter
Canvas: 76.2 x 65.4
Brooks Memorial Art Gallery, Memphis

[Pl. 7] Studio of Jacopo BASSANO
Christ Driving the Moneychangers from the Temple [4]

[Pl. 8] Studio of Jacopo BASSANO
Adoration of the Shepherds [1511]

[Pl. 9] Studio of Jacopo BASSANO
Madonna and Child
with S. John and a Donor [1635]

[Pl. 10] After Jacopo BASSANO
S. Francis Kneeling
before the Virgin and Child [1636]

[Pl. 11] Pompeo BATONI
Portrait of Princess Cecilia Mahony Giustiniani (1741-89) [2369]

[Pl. 12] After Giovanni BELLINI
The Feast of the Gods [458]

[Pl. 13] Studio of Bonifazio Veronese
The Last Supper [9]

[Pl. 14] Paris Bordon
A Venetian Woman at her Toilet [10]

[Pl. 16] After Orazio Borgianni
S. Christopher [20]

[Pl. 15] Orazio Borgianni
S. Christopher [48]

[Pl. 17] Workshop of Botticelli
The Virgin and S. John Adoring the Infant Christ [1536]

[Pl. 18]
Circle of Botticelli
S. John the Baptist [2099]

[Pl. 19] After Botticelli
Portrait of a Youth [1792]

[Pl. 20] After, or by a follower of, Bronzino
*Portrait of Garzia
or Giovanni de' Medici* [1943]

[Pl. 21] Workshop of Bernardino Butinone
Christ Disputing with the Doctors [1746]

[Pl. 22] Luca CAMBIASO
Holy Family with the Young S. John [18]

[Pl. 23] Follower of CANALETTO
The Grand Canal, Venice [17]

[Pl. 24] Follower of CANALETTO
Grand Canal: S. Lucia and the Church of the Scalzi, Venice [2014]

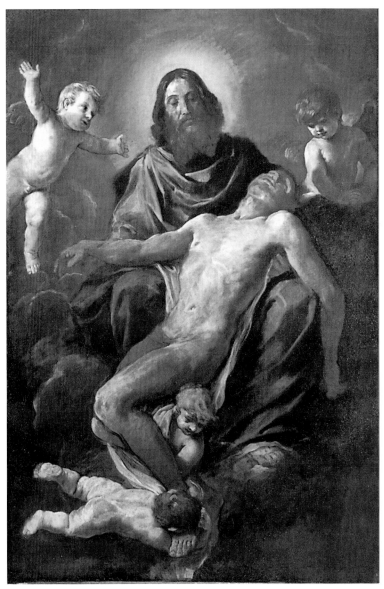

[Pl. 25] Simone CANTARINI
The Holy Trinity [42]

[Fig. 4] Simone CANTARINI
The Transfiguration
Canvas: (no measurements available)
Palazzo della Cancelleria, Rome

[Fig. 5] Simone CANTARINI
The Transfiguration
Canvas: 380 x 197
Brera Gallery, Milan

[Fig. 6] Simone CANTARINI
Detail (head of Christ)
from *The Transfiguration*
Palazzo della Cancelleria, Rome

[Fig. 7] Simone CANTARINI
Detail (head of God the Father)
from *The Holy Trinity*
National Gallery of Scotland

[Pl. 26] Vicente CARDUCHO
Dream of S. Hugh, Bishop of Grenoble [459]

[Pl. 27] Giovanni Busi called CARIANI
S. Agatha [2494]

[Pl. 28] Attributed to a close follower of Andrea del CASTAGNO
The Last Supper [1210]

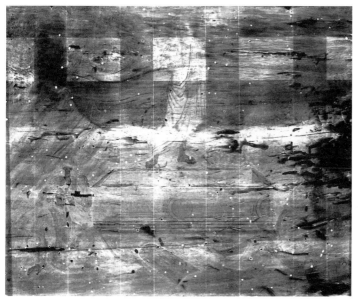

[Fig. 8, *opposite*] Andrea del CASTAGNO, follower of
X-ray of *The Last Supper*
Wood: 29 x 36.2
National Gallery of Scotland

[Fig. 9, *top*] Andrea del CASTAGNO, follower of
X-ray of *The Crucifixion*
Wood: 28.5 x 35
National Gallery, London

[Fig. 10, *above*] Andrea del CASTAGNO, follower of
X-ray of *The Resurrection*
Wood: 28.5 x 33.7
Frick Collection, New York

[Pl. 29] Vincenzo CATENA
Portrait of a Venetian Lady [1675]

[Pl. 30] Giovanni Battista CRESPI (Il Cerano)
Head of S. Francis in Ecstasy [2129]

[Pl. 31] CIMA DA CONEGLIANO
The Virgin and Child with S. Andrew and S. Peter [1190]

[Pl. 32] Bernardo DADDI
A Triptych: The Crucifixion [1904]

[Fig. 11] Bernardo DADDI
The Crucifixion (wing of triptych)
Wood 62 x 17
Courtauld Institute Galleries,
University of London

[Pl. 33] DOMENICHINO
The Adoration of the Shepherds [2313]

[Fig. 12]   [Fig. 13]   [Fig. 14]

[Fig. 15]

[Fig. 12] DOMENICHINO
Study for S. Joseph
Black and white chalk: 385 x 224 mm
Royal Library, Windsor Castle
(reproduced by gracious permission
of Her Majesty the Queen)

[Fig. 13] DOMENICHINO
A Standing Male Nude
Black and white chalk: 385 x 224 mm
Royal Library, Windsor Castle
(reproduced by gracious permission
of Her Majesty the Queen)

[Fig. 14] Annibale CARRACCI
Study of a Boy
Black and white chalk: 353 x 230 mm
Royal Library, Windsor Castle
(reproduced by gracious permission
of Her Majesty the Queen)

[Fig. 15] Giovanni LANFRANCO
Adoration of the Shepherds (detail)
Duke of Northumberland,
Alnwick Castle

[Pl. 34] EMILIAN late fifteenth-century
Madonna and Child with S. Francis,
S. Jerome and Two Angels [1634]

[Pl. 35] EMILIAN seventeenth-century
S. Peter Delivered [19]

[Pl. 36] FERRARESE late fifteenth-century
Madonna and Child with Two Angels [1535]

[Pl. 37] Ferrarese? around 1500
S. Francis Receiving the Stigmata [1745]

[Pl. 38] Florentine fifteenth-century
Madonna and Child [Loan]

[Pl. 39] Mariano Fortuny
Le Brindis de l'Espada
(The Bull-Fighter's Salute) [1189]

[Pl. 40] Francesco FURINI
S. Sebastian [30]

[Pl. 41] Francesco FURINI
Poetry [31]

[Pl. 42] GAROFALO
Christ Driving the Money-Changers from the Temple [32]

[Pl. 43] After, or by an imitator of, GIORGIONE
Portrait of a Man holding a Recorder [35]

[Pl. 44] Attributed to GIULIO ROMANO
and workshop
*Two Heads from the Massacre
of the Innocents* [638]

[Pl. 45] GIULIO ROMANO
The Holy Family with the Infant S. John [2398]

[Pl. 46] Francisco de GOYA
El Médico (*The Doctor*) [1628]

[Pl. 47] Style of Benozzo GOZZOLI
Christ on the Road to Calvary [953]

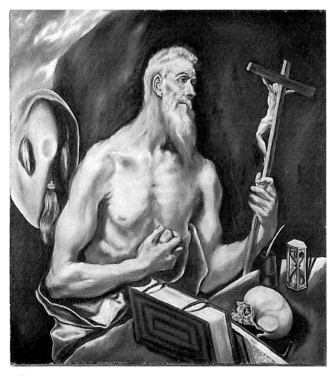

[Pl. 48] EL GRECO
S. Jerome in Penitence [1873]

[Pl. 49] EL GRECO
The Saviour of the World [2160]

[Pl. 50] EL GRECO
Allegory ('Fábula') [2491]

[Fig. 16] EL GRECO
Allegory
Canvas: 49.8 x 64.1
Stanley Moss Collection, New York

[Fig. 17] EL GRECO
Allegory
Canvas: 71 x 92
Earl of Harewood Collection

[Pl. 51] Francesco GUARDI
Santa Maria della Salute, Venice [1498]

[Pl. 52] Francesco GUARDI
San Giorgio Maggiore, Venice [1499]

[Pl. 53] Francesco GUARDI
Piazza San Marco, Venice [2370]

[Pl. 54] In the style of GUARDI
A View in Italy [828]

[Pl. 55] In the style of GUARDI
A View in Italy [829]

[Pl. 56] GUERCINO
S. Peter Penitent [39]

[Pl. 57] GUERCINO
The Madonna and Child with the Young S. John [40]

[Pl. 58] ITALIAN early sixteenth-century
Madonna and Child with the Young S. John [645]

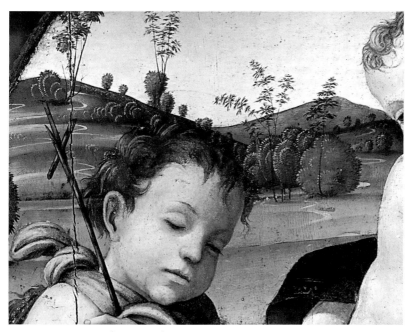

[Fig. 18] ITALIAN early sixteenth-century
Detail (landscape) from *Madonna and Child with the Young S. John*
National Gallery of Scotland

[Fig. 19] ITALIAN early sixteenth-century
Detail (landscape) from the *Preaching of S. John the Baptist*
Metropolitan Museum of Art, New York

[Pl. 59] ITALIAN seventeenth-century
Battlefield - Trumpeters Sounding a Recall [85]

[Pl. 60] ITALIAN late seventeenth-century
Portrait of a Prelate [109]

[Pl. 61] ITALIAN c. 1630
A Hermit Saint doing Penance [812]

[Pl. 62] ITALIAN eighteenth-century
Portrait of a Man [1638]

[Pl. 63] ITALIAN eighteenth- or nineteenth-century
A City Square [910]

[Pl. 64] After Leonardo da Vinci
Madonna of the Yarnwinder [2270]

[Pl. 65] Filippino Lippi
The Nativity, with Two Angels [1758]

[Pl. 66] LOMBARD late sixteenth- or early seventeenth-century
Christ on the Mount of Olives [60]

[Pl. 67] Follower of LORENZO DI CREDI
Holy Family [646]

[Pl. 68] Lorenzo Monaco and workshop
Madonna and Child [2271]

[Pl. 69] Lorenzo LOTTO
Virgin and Child with SS. Peter, Jerome, Clare (?) and Francis [2418]

[Pl. 70] Attributed to MARMITTA
The Scourging of Christ [1673]

[Fig. 20] Francesco MARMITTA
Crucifixion (Della Rovere Missal)
Museo Civico, Turin

[Fig. 21] Francesco MARMITTA
Virgin and Child
with S. Benedict and S. Quentin
Wood: 220 x 138 cm
Musée du Louvre, Paris

[Pl. 71] MASTER OF THE ADIMARI CASSONE
Triumph of a Roman General [1975]

[Pl. 72] MASTER OF THE S. LUCCHESE ALTARPIECE
A Baptism [1539A]

[Pl. 73] MASTER OF THE S. LUCCHESE ALTARPIECE
A Martyrdom [1539B]

[Pl. 74] MASTER OF 1419
The Stigmatization of S. Francis [1540A]

[Pl. 75] MASTER OF 1419
S. Anthony Abbot Exorcising a Woman Possessed by the Devil [1540B]

[Fig. 22]
MASTER OF 1419
S. Julian Polyptych
Museo Civico,
San Gimignano

[Pl. 76] Matteo di Giovanni
Madonna and Child with S. Sebastian, S. Francis and Angels [1023]

[Pl. 77] Attributed to a follower of Pier Francesco MOLA
S. Jerome [29]

[Pl. 78] Francesco MONTI
Rebecca at the Well [2120]

[Pl. 79] Giovanni Battista MORONI
Portrait of Giovanni Bressani [2347]

[Fig. 23] ARSENSIO
Portrait of Giovanni Bressani
Medal: diameter, 53 mm
Accademia Carrara, Bergamo

[Pl. 80] Pietro NOVELLI
'A Mathematician' [83]

[Pl. 81] NEAPOLITAN second quarter of the seventeenth century
Cain Killing Abel [21]

[Fig. 24] NEAPOLITAN
second quarter of
the seventeenth century
Detail (figure of Abel) from
Cain Killing Abel
National Gallery of Scotland

[Fig. 25] NEAPOLITAN
second quarter of
the seventeenth century
Detail (figure of Abel) from
Cain fleeing from the Body of Abel
Corsini Collection, Florence

[Pl. 82] NEAPOLITAN
second half of the seventeenth century
The Martyrdom of S. Sebastian [84]

[Pl. 83] Giovanni Battista PAGGI
Rest on the Flight into Egypt [55]

[Pl. 84] Attributed to Gonzalo Pérez
S. Michael Killing the Dragon [1021]

[Pl. 85] Pietro PERUGINO
Four Male Figures [1805]

[Pl. 86] Nineteenth-century imitator of Pesellino
Madonna and Child with the Young S. John [1250]

[Pl. 87] Style of Piero di Cosimo
Two Censing Angels Holding a Crown [1633]

[Pl. 88] Attributed to Pietro da Cortona
Landscape with Mary Magdalen [2378]

[Pl. 89] Giovanni Battista PITTONI
The Apotheosis of S. Jerome
with S. Peter of Alcantara
and an Unidentified Franciscan [223]

[Fig. 26] Photomontage reconstruction
of original setting
of Pittoni's S. Jerome altarpiece
in S. Maria dei Miracoli, Venice

[Pl. 90] POLIDORO DA LANCIANO
Holy Family [105]

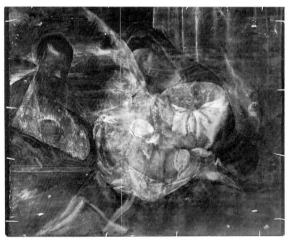

[Fig. 27] POLIDORO DA LANCIANO
X-ray of the *Holy Family*

[Pl. 91] POLIDORO DA LANCIANO
Madonna and Sleeping Child [1931]

[Pl. 92] POPPI (Francesco Morandini)
The Golden Age [2268]

[Fig. 28] Giorgio VASARI
The Golden Age
Pen and ink: 420 x 282 mm
Musée du Louvre, Paris

[Pl. 93] Giulio Cesare PROCACCINI
Cupid [63]

[Pl. 94] Giulio Cesare PROCACCINI
The Raising of the Cross [2276]

[Pl. 95] RAPHAEL
Holy Family with a Palm Tree [Loan]

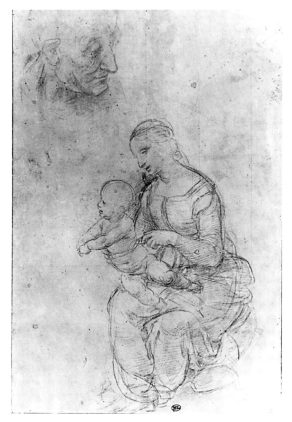

[Fig. 29, *above left*] RAPHAEL
Holy Family with a Palm Tree
(before cleaning)
[Loan]

[Fig. 30, *above right*] RAPHAEL
X-ray of the
Holy Family with a Palm Tree

[Fig. 31, *left*] RAPHAEL
Study for the
Holy Family with a Palm Tree
Metalpoint: 225 x 152 mm
Musée du Louvre, Paris

[Pl. 96] RAPHAEL
The Bridgewater Madonna [Loan]

[Fig. 32] RAPHAEL
X-ray of *The Bridgewater Madonna*

[Fig. 33] RAPHAEL
Madonna and Child
Pen and ink: 250 x 194 mm
Devonshire Collection, Chatsworth
(reproduced by permission of
the Trustees of the Chatsworth Settlement)

[Fig. 34] RAPHAEL
Study for *The Bridgewater Madonna*
Pen and ink: 254 x 184 mm
British Museum, London

[Fig. 35] RAPHAEL
Study for *The Bridgewater Madonna*
Black lead, pen and ink: 256 x 184 mm
Albertina, Vienna

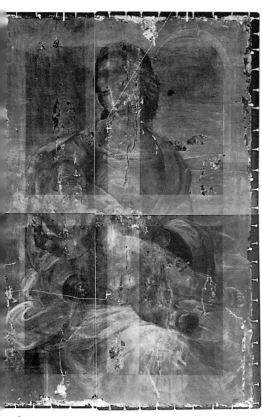

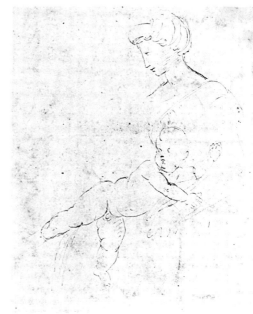

[. 32]   [Fig. 33]

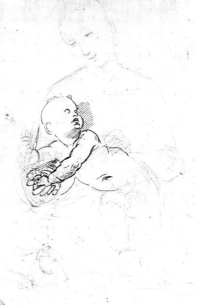

. 34]   [Fig. 35]

[Fig. 36]

[Fig. 36] RAPHAEL
Study for *The Bridgewater Madonna*
Pen and ink: 249 x 271 mm
Uffizi, Florence

[Fig. 37] RAPHAEL
Studies for an *Infant Christ*
Metalpoint on pink prepared surface:
168 x 119 mm
British Museum, London

[Fig. 38] RAPHAEL
Studies for an *Infant Christ*
Metalpoint on pink prepared surface:
167 x 119 mm
Musée des Beaux-Arts, Lille

[Fig. 37]

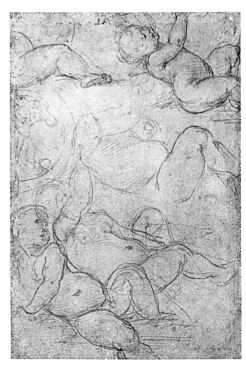

[Fig. 38]

[Fig. 39] NICOLAS DE LARMESSIN
Engraving after Raphael's
Bridgewater Madonna

[Fig. 40] J. HOULANGER
Engraving after Raphael's
Bridgewater Madonna

[Pl. 97] Raphael
Madonna del Passeggio [Loan]

[Pl. 98] After RAPHAEL
Madonna with the Veil [Loan]

[Pl. 99] After RAPHAEL
S. Peter [110]

[Pl. 100] After RAPHAEL
*The Madonna and Child
with S. John* [1854]

[Pl. 101] Guido RENI
Moses with Pharaoh's Crown [2375]

[Pl. 102] Pandolfo RESCHI
A Battle [70]

[Pl. 103] Attributed to Marco RICCI
Landscape with Monks [7]

[Pl. 104] After Salvator ROSA
A Figure in Armour [600]

[Pl. 105] After Salvator ROSA
A Figure in Armour [600A]

[Pl. 106] After Salvator ROSA
River Scene with Figures [622]

[Pl. 107] Cosimo ROSSELLI
S. Catherine of Siena as the Spiritual Mother
of the Second and Third Orders of S. Dominic [1030]

[Pl. 108] Workshop of Sano di Pietro
Coronation of the Virgin [1565]

[Pl. 109] Andrea del SARTO
Portrait of Domenico di Jacopo
di Matteo Becuccio, Bicchieraio [2297]

[Fig. 41] Andrea del SARTO
Domenico di Jacopo di Matteo Becuccio
Wood, circular, diameter 11
Art Institute, Chicago

[Pl. 110] Sinibaldo SCORZA
Landscape with the Story of Philemon and Baucis [76]

[Pl. 111] Sinibaldo SCORZA
Landscape with the Story of Latona and the Peasants [77]

[Pl. 112] Jacopo del SELLAIO
Christ as the Man of Sorrows, with S. Raphael and the Young Tobias, and S. Sebastian [1941]

[Pl. 113] Attributed to Jacopo del SELLAIO
Triumphal Procession; Reception and Coronation of a Prince or Victor [1538]

[Pl. 114] Giovanni SERODINE
The Tribute Money [1513]

[Pl. 115] Elisabetta SIRANI
The Child S. John in the Wilderness [79]

[Pl. 116] Pietro TESTA
Adoration of the Shepherds [2325]

[Fig. 42] Pietro TESTA
X-ray (detail) of *Adoration of the Shepherds*

[Pl. 117] Attributed to Pietro TESTA
The Triumph of Painting [2326]

[Fig. 43] Pietro TESTA
Triumph of Painting (Bartsch XX 35)
Etching: 47.2 x 71.8

[Pl. 118] Giovanni Battista TIEPOLO
The Meeting of Antony and Cleopatra [91]

[Fig. 44] Giovanni Battista TIEPOLO
The Meeting of Antony and Cleopatra
Fresco decoration
Palazzo Labia, Venice

[Fig. 45] Giovanni Battista TIEPOLO
The Meeting of Antony and Cleopatra
Canvas: 45 x 65.5
Wrightsman Collection, New York

[Pl. 119] Giovanni Battista TIEPOLO
The Finding of Moses [92]

[Fig. 46] Giovanni Battista TIEPOLO
The Finding of Moses, with a Halberdier
Reconstruction photograph, showing the original appearance
of a picture now divided between the National Gallery of Scotland
(left-hand section) and a private collection, Turin.
The complete picture was on canvas and measured *c.* 205 x 475.

[Pl. 120] TINTORETTO
Portrait of a Venetian [Loan]

[Pl. 121] TINTORETTO
Male Head [689]

[Fig. 47] TINTORETTO
X-ray (detail of top half) of
*A Venetian Family presented
to the Madonna by S. Lawrence
and a Bishop Saint*

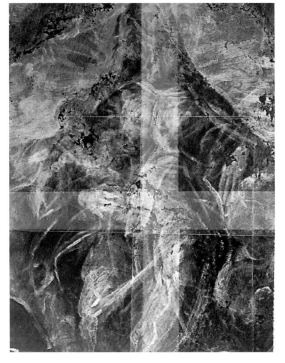

[Pl. 122] TINTORETTO
A Venetian Family presented to the Madonna
by S. Lawrence and a Bishop Saint [2161]

[Pl. 123] TINTORETTO
The Deposition of Christ [2419]

[Fig. 48] TINTORETTO
X-ray (detail) of the *Deposition of Christ*
See also Figs. 49-51

[Fig. 49]   [Fig. 50]

[Fig. 49] J. MATHAM
Engraving (dated 1594)
after Tintoretto's
Deposition of Christ

[Fig. 50] Copy after TINTORETTO
Deposition of Christ
Pen and wash and black chalk:
406 x 257 mm
Walker Art Gallery, Liverpool

[Fig. 51] Photomontage showing
Matham's engraving inserted
into the altar frame of the Dandolo
Chapel, San Francesco della Vigna,
to indicate the probable original
setting of Tintoretto's *Deposition*.

[Fig. 51]

[Pl. 124] Studio of TINTORETTO
Portrait of a Man [99]

[Pl. 125] Follower of TINTORETTO
Summer [96]

[Pl. 126] Follower of TINTORETTO
Spring [97]

[Pl. 127] Follower of TINTORETTO
Winter [98]

[Pl. 128] TITIAN
The Holy Family with S. John the Baptist [Loan]

[Fig. 52] TITIAN
X-ray (detail of the Child, head and arms of the Virgin, S. Joseph) of
The Holy Family with S. John the Baptist

[Fig. 53] V. LEFEBRE
Engraving after Titian:
Holy Family with S. Dorothy and S. Jerome

[Pl. 129] TITIAN
The Three Ages of Man [Loan]

[Fig. 54] TITIAN
X-ray of *The Three Ages of Man*

[Fig. 55] V. LEFEBRE
Engraving after Titian: design related to Titian's *Three Ages of Man*

[Pl. 130] TITIAN
Venus Anadyomene [Loan]

[Fig. 56] ANTONIO LOMBARDO
Venus Anadyomene
Marble: height 40.6
Victoria & Albert Museum, London

[Pl. 131] TITIAN
Diana and Actaeon [Loan]

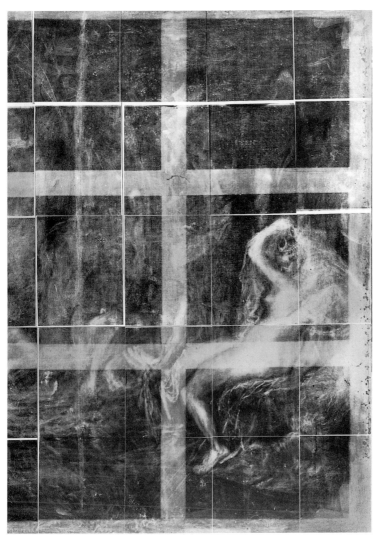

[Fig. 57] TITIAN
X-ray (detail of right-hand side) of *Diana and Actaeon*

[Pl. 132] TITIAN
Diana and Callisto [Loan]

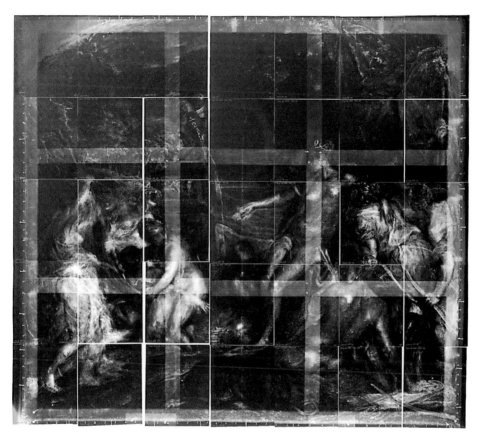

[Fig. 58] TITIAN
X-ray of *Diana and Callisto*
See also Figs. 59-61

[Fig. 59] TITIAN
Diana and Callisto
Canvas: 183 x 200
Kunsthistorisches Museum, Vienna

[Fig. 60] TITIAN
X-ray (detail of left-hand side) of
Diana and Callisto
Kunsthistorisches Museum, Vienna

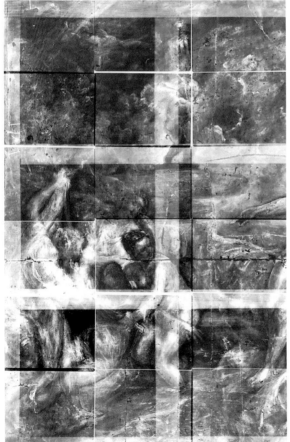

[Fig. 61] C. CORT
Engraving (about 1565) after *Diana and Callisto*

[Pl. 133] After TITIAN
Bacchanal: the Andrians [103]

[Pl. 134] Imitator of TITIAN
Portrait of a Man [104]

[Pl. 135] Workshop of Giovanni Toscani
Cassone, with Scenes from Boccaccio's Decameron [1738]

[Pl. 136] TUSCAN mid-fourteenth-century
A Triptych: The Madonna enthroned
Left wing: *The Adoration of the Kings*
Right wing: *The Crucifixion* [1958]

[Pl. 137] Diego VELÁZQUEZ
An Old Woman Cooking Eggs [2180]

[Pl. 138] After Diego Velázquez
Philip IV of Spain (1605-1665) [1625]

[Pl. 139] Venetian sixteenth-century
An Archer [690]

[Pl. 140] VENETIAN sixteenth-century
Scholar with Inkstand [704]

[Pl. 141] Paolo VERONESE
Mars and Venus [339]

[Fig. 62] Paolo VERONESE
X-ray of *Mars and Venus*

[Fig. 63] Paolo VERONESE
Venus and Cupid
Pen and ink and wash:
172 x 127 mm
British Museum, London

[Pl. 142] Paolo Veronese
S. Anthony Abbot as Patron of a Kneeling Donor [1139]

[Fig. 64] Reconstruction of Veronese's Lendinara altarpiece,
showing the Edinburgh, Dulwich and Ottawa fragments

[Pl. 143] Attributed to Andrea del Verrocchio and workshop
Madonna and Child [2338]

[Fig. 65] Andrea del Verrocchio and workshop
X-ray detail (showing perspective construction,
with vanishing point beneath Madonna's hands)
of the *Madonna and Child.*
See also Figs. 66-71

[Fig. 66]
Andrea del VERROCCHIO and workshop
X-ray detail
(showing the pavement on the left)
of the *Madonna and Child*

[Fig. 67]
Andrea del VERROCCHIO and workshop
X-ray detail
(showing the architecture, top left)
of the *Madonna and Child*

[Fig. 68] Domenico Ghirlandaio
Madonna and Child
Transferred from wood to masonite: 73.4 x 50.8
National Gallery of Art, Washington

[Fig. 69] Domenico Ghirlandaio
Madonna and Child
Wood: 78.7 x 55.5
Musée du Louvre, Paris

[Fig. 70] Domenico Ghirlandaio
Madonna and Child
Wood: 54 x 87
Monastery, Camaldoli

[Fig. 71] Workshop of Verrocchio
Madonna and Child
Transferred from wood to canvas: 66 x 48.2
Metropolitan Museum of Art, New York

[Pl. 144] Vitale da Bologna
Adoration of the Kings with S. Ursula and S. Catherine of Alexandria,
(in the spandrels) *the Annunciation* [952]

[Pl. 145] Attributed to Marco ZOPPO
Noli Me Tangere [1719]

[Pl. 146] Francisco de ZURBARÁN
The Immaculate Conception [340]